Our Knowledge of the Growth of Knowledge

PETER MUNZ

Our Knowledge of the Growth of Knowledge

Popper or Wittgenstein?

ROUTLEDGE & KEGAN PAUL
London, Boston, Melbourne and Henley

First published in 1985
by Routledge & Kegan Paul plc

14 Leicester Square, London WC2H 7PH, England

9 Park Street, Boston, Mass. 02108, USA

464 St Kilda Road, Melbourne,
Victoria 3004, Australia and

Broadway House, Newtown Road,
Henley on Thames, Oxon RG9 1EN, England

Set in Baskerville
by Hope Services Ltd, Abingdon
and printed in Great Britain
by Billings and Sons Ltd,
Worcester

Library of Congress Cataloging in Publication Data

Munz, Peter, 1921–

Our knowledge of the growth of knowledge
Includes index.
1. Knowledge, Theory of. 2. Popper, Karl Raimund, Sir, 1902– . 3 Wittgenstein,
Ludwig, 1889–1951.
I. Title
BD161.M86 1985 121 85–1730

British Library CIP data also available

ISBN 0-7102-0460-4

FOR JACOB
UT TEMPORIS DILIGAT FUGAM

Contents

Preface

This book is an attempt to explore some special consequences of one of the greatest changes which have come over our view of the world. Until not so very long ago we believed that nature was steady and unchanging, without a history; and that human culture had a history but that that history was not part of the steady existence of nature but more like an ephemeral dance performed on nature's stage. In our new view of the world which has firmly established itself in the course of the twentieth century, nature and history have come together. Nature herself, we have come to see, has a history and human history is inserted into it. Thus, there must be some kind of link between the historicity of nature and the historicity of man. The history of nature influences the history of man; and the history of man, in the shape of man's knowledge of nature, in turn, reflects upon the history of nature. If there still are two 'cultures' the extension of historicity has made their practitioners realise that they have a lot in common.

Unfortunately, the clarity of this vision tends to be clouded when we expect too much from our knowledge of history. It is one thing to be aware of the historicity of nature and of man. But it does not follow that we can be equally certain of the actual course of these histories. On the contrary, historical knowledge is subject to the same doubts and uncertainties as all knowledge and cannot be used to establish any final view about the growth of knowledge, let alone firm thoughts about a lack of growth or about the finality of the relativism of all knowledge.

In writing this book I was very much the beady-eyed historian who seeks to explain the limitations of historical knowledge and the conditions it is subject to. Bearing those limitations in mind, I am arguing in favour of a philosophy of knowledge which, while encompassing the historicity both of nature and of man, does not depend on historical knowledge alone. Again, writing as a historian I have little interest in conceptual analysis. The form of discourse I employ is not coercive, but explanatory in Robert Nozick's sense. But unlike Nozick I do not believe that any explanation can be self-explanatory. On the contrary: in explaining I have to have constant recourse to a theory in terms of which any explanation holds good. In this case, the theory in question is the theory of evolution and for the purposes of this book, that theory is itself not a subject to be explained. However, lest the reader think that in saying that all explanations are relative to a theory I am subscribing to Richard Rorty's view that all truths and meanings are relative to a speech community or a tradition of rhetoric, I wish to state that I hold the opposite view. In saying that explanations are never absolute but always in terms of something else, I mean that whatever they are relative to must, in turn and on a different occasion, be open to criticism and be explained.

Not counting the Introduction, the book falls into three parts. In the first part (chapters 1 and 2) I try to explain the historicity of our knowledge and specify the conditions to which our knowledge of all historicity is subject. The second part (chapters 3, 4 and 5) is devoted to a critique of widespread contemporary attempts to cull too much from our knowledge of history. In the third part (chapters 6 and 7) I return to the main theme by developing Karl Popper's evolutionary philosophy of knowledge and by sketching the major transformations of thought which become possible and desirable when one takes historicity seriously.

The shape of my argument is almost wholly dependent on the fact that I was a student of Karl Popper in Christchurch, New Zealand (1940–4) and of Wittgenstein in Cambridge (1946–8). At the time these early influences were the result of accidents: I had come to Christchurch as a refugee from the Second World War, and to Cambridge to study medieval history. There was no plan to learn from either Popper or Wittgenstein and it took me several decades to discover how this educational accident came to be turned into a fundamental and meaningful philosophical experience. I have since recorded this extraordinary accident in a paper on 'Transformation in Philosophy through the Teaching Methods of Wittgenstein and Popper' (*Proceedings of the Tenth International Conference on the Unity of the Sciences,* New York, 1982, vol. 2, pp. 1235–65).

In writing the present book which spans so many disciplines – history and sociology, the history of science, philosophy, biology and physics as well as the philosophy of science and of knowledge – I have relied on the help of a large number of friends and colleagues who, though they do not all share all of my views, have given me generous support and encouragement, both moral and substantial. First of all I owe an immense debt to W.W. Bartley III (Stanford) and to Gerard Radnitzky (Trier) and Anthony O'Hear (University of Surrey), who provided much more than mere inspiration; and Peter Webster (Wellington, NZ) whose personal interest in the progress of the book has been invaluable. Gerhard Vollmer (Giessen), Eric Geiringer (Wellington) and Georg Süssman (Munich) have been my mentors in both biology and physics; I ought here also mention my colleague David Beaglehole, Professor of Physics at the Victoria University of Wellington, who was always happy to explain physics to me but kept adding sceptically: 'Your trouble is that you read too many books.' Eduard Bonsel (Harlem), Bob Tristram (Wellington), Peter Wilson (Otago University, Dunedin), Anthony Flew (Reading and York Universities), Colin Davis (Wellington) and John Blackmore (Vienna) have all read the first draft of the book and made valuable criticisms and comments. For more generalised sympathetic encouragement I want to thank Paul and Eva Hoffmann in Tübingen, Ian Jarvie and Jagdhish Hattiangadi of York University (Canada) and Hans Albert in Heidelberg. Last, not least, I wish to thank Eugene Kamenka (Canberra) for a fruitful comment of ten years ago. 'If you believe,' he said to me in his inimitably avuncular way, 'that universals are nothing but thoughts, you have a thing coming to you!' It did. I am equally grateful to Paul Levinson (New York) for first encouraging me to put down on paper my thoughts on the evolutionary fruitfulness of dogmatism. Without this initial invitation, work on this book would never have been started.

I owe a great debt to the Fritz Thyssen Stiftung of Köln (Germany) for their generous assistance over a number of years; and to the various Research and Publication Funds of my own university. Finally, I wish to thank Barbro MacNamara for her impeccable library skills, and Gwen Wright and Gloria Biggs for the patience and skill with which they have typed draft after draft.

Department of History
Victoria University
Wellington, New Zealand
May 1984

Introduction

Towards the end of October 1946 I had the good fortune to be present at a confrontation in Cambridge which marked a water-shed in the history of modern philosophy. The Cambridge University Moral Sciences Club had invited Karl Popper to speak. As was customary in that club, the secretary had written to Popper and invited him to produce a philosophical puzzle. I recollect vividly the evening on which a major philosophical disagreement found its dramatic expression. The meeting was held in Braithwaite's room in King's College. Apart from the usual crowd of undergraduates, there was present quite a selection of important people. There was Wittgenstein himself and Bertrand Russell, Braithwaite and Stephen Toulmin and Norman Malcolm and Geach and probably other eminent philosophers whom I cannot now recall. At that time the *Philosophical Investigations* had not yet been published and although Wittgenstein had been playing language games in his weekly seminars which he held in his room in Whewell's Court of Trinity College, his position was not widely known outside Cambridge and his general fame was the fame of the *Tractatus*. As to Popper, the *Logic of Scientific Discovery* had not yet been translated into English though his claim to have solved the problem of induction was widely known. His fame, however, at that time, rested on *The Open Society and its Enemies*. Neither *Objective Knowledge* nor his many papers on Darwinian evolution had yet been written, and had possibly not even been thought of. Nevertheless, the evening's events were symbolic and, in hindsight, prophetic.

After Popper's declaration that he did not believe in puzzle-solving and his affirmation that there were genuine philosophical problems, Wittgenstein started to challenge him to name a 'philosophical' problem. I cannot now recall the precise sequence of events, but after Popper tried to name one or two philosophical problems and Wittgenstein kept countering by saying that he did not know what he could 'mean' by his statements, the drama occurred. Popper was sitting on one side of the fireplace, and Wittgenstein on the other. Both were facing the audience. In the middle, in a big armchair, facing the fireplace with his back to the audience, there was Bertrand Russell. Suddenly Wittgenstein, who had been playing and fidgeting with the poker in the fire, took the red-hot poker out of the fire and gesticulated with it angrily in front of Popper's face. Thereupon, Russell – who so far had not spoken a word – took the pipe out of his mouth and said very firmly in his high-pitched, somewhat scratchy voice: 'Wittgenstein, put down that poker at once!' Wittgenstein complied and soon after got up and walked out, slamming the door.

Looking back now after nearly forty years, one can see the real significance of that incident. It prefigured the clash of philosophical opinions which has developed ever since the gradual decline of Positivism has turned into a rout.

During the first half of this century – from the triumph of Einstein's Special Theory of Relativity to Ayer's *Language, Truth and Logic* – it seemed not only as if Logical Positivism had at long last solved the problem of knowledge, but that it had solved it in such a way that its solution had come to stay. 'I am, therefore, of the opinion that the problems have in essentials been finally solved,' said Wittgenstein in the last paragraph of his Preface to the *Tractatus*. Not that Einstein was a Logical Positivist; but to many people his way of dealing with, for instance, simultaneity appeared as the ultimate vindication of Positivism. The meaning of 'simultaneity', he said, is determined by the methods we use to measure the phenomenon.[1] Since there is no communication faster than light and since the transmission of light is not instantaneous, there can be no such phenomenon as absolute simultaneity. In some sense, all subsequent elaborations of Logical Positivism right down to Ayer's *Language, Truth and Logic* were refinements and explications of this strategy. Einstein's apparent Positivism had been a more finely balanced mesh of theoretical and observational forms than anything one could have learnt from Ayer, and it was this fine mesh which came to be known as the 'Received View of Knowledge'.

Positivism, Logical or other, was a philosophy which said that there is nothing for philosophy to do. Science will and can tell us what we want to know and truth is the sum total of sentences about the sum total of facts (or events, depending on one's jargon). In this way, Positivism claimed to contain two certainties. First, the certainty that all philosophical problems were scientific ones; and second, the certainty that the first certainty could be known with certainty. Such Positivism applied to the philosophy of science became known — and this is telling — as the 'Received View'.[2] The only thing left — and this was a problem which not even Positivism could solve — was the problem whether what we know through science was a presentation of reality or a representation of reality, i.e. whether it was an ultimate, an irrevocable, appearance or whether it was the real thing itself.

However, there was one thing which Positivism had overlooked. It had not taken the full measure of the theoretical component in every theory. This matter was dimly foreshadowed by the awkward (awkward to Positivists) fact that the general theories of science could not exhaustively be verified by, or reduced to, a limited number of particular propositions. Positivists always managed to get around this awkwardness either by believing in the logical validity of induction or by maintaining that general laws are merely time-saving summations (Mach's phrase) or inference tickets (Ryle's phrase); a further alternative was to maintain that they were not to be taken literally. But behind this limited problem there lurked the larger one: the problem that all theories not only went beyond a finite number of observations but also contained theoretical terms which were incapable of verification and which kept changing their meanings as they crept up in different theories, terms like 'force', 'energy', 'field' and such like.

These skeletons could be conveniently locked in a cupboard and could not detract from the enormous value of Locke's dogma that the proper way to gain information about the world is to look at the world, to watch it and to rely entirely on observation. In order to find out what the world really was like one had to observe it and to use all of one's observations; the philosopher's role, it was held, was to make sure that one used nothing but one's observation. In this way one could not fail and this recommendation was, therefore, at the same time a philosophy the truth of which was itself without fail.

But thought is the slave of life and life, time's fool. As the century went by, Positivism as well as Logical or Empirical Positivism seemed less and less attractive. There were open rejections and recantations by its main practitioners.[3] It was not only that Einstein himself renounced what many had taken to be the philosophical principles behind the Special Theory of Relativity. In the 1920s, when Heisenberg once defended his Positivistic interpretation of Quantum Mechanics by pointing out that he was simply using Einstein's own method as it had been practised in the Special Theory, Einstein replied: 'Yes, that may be true, but it is nonsense all the same!'[4] For one thing, the absolute constance of the velocity of light on which the 'Positivism' of the Special Theory of Relativity depended, was itself, after all, a 'theory'.

These and similar uncertainties, all went back right to the eighteenth century. The presence of a large and uncertain theoretical component in knowledge had already been noticed in the eighteenth century when people admired Newton for very different and quite incompatible reasons. Some seized on the mathematics and the mechanisms of motion. Others, on the work of 'forces'; and to others again, though they were hard put to explain with precision what they meant, Newton was simply a synonym for knowledge. All these ambiguities go back to Newton himself and are illustrated by the conceptual differences between the *Principia* and the *Opticks*.[5] Even more striking than Einstein's rejection of Positivism, was the manner in which Wittgenstein turned against his own *Tractatus*, which had positively been the most classical and elegant statement of Positivism: the world consists of facts and knowledge of the world in propositions which picture these facts. Wittgenstein not only rejected his own early work but refused to discuss the rejection. No finality could have been more final.

Equally telling and equally signal was the failure of Positivism to account for the growth of knowledge such as it came to be experienced during the twentieth century. To be sure, Positivism had been able to explain the growth of knowledge as accumulation and as increasing generalisation, and could even account for the dropping of false theories. But it could neither predict nor, after the event, account for the shift from Newtonian Mechanics to General Relativity. When it showed itself that growth was neither by accumulation nor by the abandonment of 'false' theories but proceeded in a more subtle manner, Positivism proved inadequate. Positivism, moreover, could not explain how in the philosophy of science itself there were occurring two different and competing moves away from the Positivistic philosophy of science. One move was towards Wittgenstein's philosophy of the closed circles of language games and towards Kuhn's theory of paradigms. The other move was towards Popper's evolutionary epistemology and the injection of Darwinism into philosophy. During the twentieth century we have thus witnessed not only a growth of knowledge which Positivism could not account for, but also the emergence of meta-scientific theories which Positivism could not envisage. Knowledge itself and knowledge of knowledge was increasing in a way not allowed for by Positivism. Positivism could envisage only the idea that knowledge was the sum total of propositions about the sum total of events. In this sense, Positivism was not so much a philosophy of knowledge as a simple ontology. Once it had shown itself that that simple ontology was untenable, Positivism, so to speak, had deconstructed itself.

The fate of Positivism was, last not least, sealed by the realisation that not even the basic assumption which had at first recommended Positivism, could stand up to reflection. The rock-bottom of every Positivist argument had always been the notion that we gain knowledge by letting the world act causally on our bodies. The more we sit back and the less we do, the better we will experience and take in the effects of these causal actions. This view is untenable as soon as one realises that every observation (i.e. the effect of such causal action) is theory-laden. In its most elementary sense, this objection to Positivism is valid because it shows that Positivism is a contradiction in terms. Positivists assert that sentences are true *because* they reflect or describe or express sensations *caused* by our body's causal proximity to whatever causes the sensation. In such Positivism it was assumed that one knew for certain and without shadow of doubt what causes what. In reality, one can have such knowledge of what causes what only by virtue of a theory about what causes what. If that theory happens to be false, the observation statement in question ceases to be *caused* and hence, though alleged to be based on observation, is in fact not so based. If one suspects that the theory in question may be false, the observation statement in question will not strike one as having been *caused*.

During the second half of this century, the rejection of Positivism has given rise to two competing models of thought. There is, first, the recommendation that if the knowledge we have cannot be justified by an appeal to the instruments we use, to protocol statements, to observations, to sense-data; and if we cannot have elementary propositions which picture elementary facts, we can justify the knowledge we have only by showing that we have the knowledge we have because it is based on the prevailing norms or speech habits of a given community of speakers.

There is, second, the dawn of Evolutionary Epistemology[6] which seeks to explain that the knowledge we have is, even when it is highly abstract knowledge, part of or an extension of the adaptive evolutionary process which began many million years ago when living cells first emerged. This process began and has continued through random mutations and selective retentions of some mutations. These adaptations never 'represent' the environment; and the selections are not justified but only tolerated by the environment. Evolutionary Epistemology treats knowledge as non-representational and unjustified.

The first model is not really an alternative to the idea that knowledge, to be knowledge, ought to be justified. In this model, we find merely a new method of justification. In Positivism, knowledge was supposed to be justified because it was based on some kind of indubitable experience or observation. In the new model, knowledge is still considered to be justified. The difference is that it is no longer considered justified because it is built on indubitable sensory or experiential certainty but, being propositional, it is justified by the speech habits of the community in which it is cherished. With this adherence to justification as the ultimate *sine qua non,* the new model is much less new than one might think. Such newness as it has, however, is confined to the ensuing relativism. Where Logical Positivism considered knowledge that was justified by protocol statements or similar devices to be absolutely justified, the new model considers knowledge which conforms to the speech habits of a community to be justified relative to that community. Not much of a net gain!

There remains, then, for serious consideration, only the alternative represented by Evolutionary Epistemology. Here the shift away from all varieties of Positivism is really significant. Evolutionary Epistemology explains that there is progress in the growth of knowledge, but does not assess such progress as increase in the accuracy of depiction or as an increase in certainty. It measures this progress in terms of an increase in universality and abstraction and presents the startling conclusion that we have knowledge of reality even though we cannot represent or depict reality.

The shift away from Positivism was necessitated by the realisation that there was a gap between knowledge and observation and that the former could not be reduced exhaustively to the latter. Two possibilities presented themselves for closing that gap. The first possibility was a turn towards sociology; the second, a turn towards biology. When the simple constraint believed to have been exercised by observation turned out to be insufficient and possibly illusory, some people started to look towards sociology for an explanation as to how knowledge *was* constrained. Admitting that knowledge was not arbitrary phantasy, they looked for social explanations. One can discern three stages in this sociologising of knowledge. First, there was Durkheim, who had argued that our power or faculty to make abstractions is derived from the fact that we are members of social groups. In such membership we learn to abstract and follow rules. Since our knowledge is not what observation compels us to believe, it is what our existence as social beings compels us to believe. Next, there came Wittgenstein, who, after rejecting his *Tractatus*'s Positivism, explained our knowledge as determined by the rules the society we are members of has laid down. He said that the issue was either Positivism or his later philosophy about 'rule-following'.[7] There is a subtle though vital difference between Durkheim and Wittgenstein. To the former, we merely learn the forms of having knowledge from our membership of a social group. Wittgenstein declared, on the other hand, that 'having knowledge' is the same as 'following rules' and that rule-following must of necessity be a social phenomenon. There cannot be, he argued, a situation in which one is following a 'private rule' or using a 'private language'.[8] The third stage in the sociologisation of knowledge came with the suggestion that our knowledge is really a form of ideology and that its content is directly determined not by our observation of the world, but by our experience of society. This sociology of knowledge has appeared in many different forms ever since Marx and one could consider Mary Douglas as its most articulate contemporary advocate.[9] In any of these varieties, the attempt to bridge the gap between observation and knowledge by sociology is a form of narcissism. It makes us think that knowledge is not a relation between knower and known, but a narcissistic reflection of our own image in our society or of our society in us.

Having detected the narcissistic element in the sociologisation of knowledge, we should take a close look at the other possibility – that is, at the possibility of bridging the gap with the help of our knowledge of biology. Biology suggests that our power for abstraction and our faculty of having expectations is the result of natural selection, that our cognitive apparatus is adaptive, and that the whole of our knowledge consists of theories which are embodied (i.e. organisms) proposals or disembodied (i.e. conscious theories) proposals made to the environment.

It is tempting to describe these alternative models of knowledge as paradigm shifts. The old paradigm , the paradigm of Positivism is fast disappearing below the horizon. We are left with two competing alternatives: the paradigm of the epistemic authority of speech communities; and the paradigm of Evolutionary Epistemology. During recent years it has been very fashionable to look upon such paradigm shifts as arbitrary events determined, if at all, by accidental or extraneous circumstances. It is vitally important, however, to realise that there is nothing arbitrary in these paradigm shifts. The demise of the old paradigm did not take place because its practitioners died – as Kuhn, the inventor of the 'paradigm' paradigm, would have us believe. The decision which of the two new competing paradigms should prevail cannot be left to an irrational accident as the inventors of the 'paradigm' paradigm would like us to expect. If these shifts and the ensuing competition were arbitrary or seemingly accidental, one would have to have recourse to a sociological, i.e. philosophically irrational, explanation.

The truth, however, is that the old Positivism lost its hold because it lost an argument and that argument would have been lost even if the upholders of Positivism were still alive. Wittgenstein's biography is a case in point. He gave up the *Tractatus* not because he died. He gave it up because he was very much alive and, being alive, realised that it was an untenable argument. Einstein's remark to Heisenberg is even more telling. Einstein said that he had not believed in Positivism even when he seemed to have been practising it.

The argument was lost largely by default. At the heart of the Positivist case stood the conviction that sense experience and observation are either an infallible guide to knowledge or a crucial test of knowledge or some other kind of ultimate criterion. It was taken for granted that sense experience, at any rate, was vastly superior to all other sources of information. This contention does, however, not go without saying and does not appear strong in the absence of a biological perspective which could ground the contention in evolution and the adaptiveness of whatever has evolved. Moreover, Positivists were to a man neglectful of the physiology of perception which, again, has to be viewed in an evolutionary and biological perspective. But once this is done, everything appears very different from the way envisaged by Positivism.

Positivists viewed the world as the sum total of events and the knower as an external observer. In the event, the findings of both physics and biology have shown us that that view is naive in the extreme. All observations are made by means which are themselves an integral part of what is to be observed. The nervous system consists of molecules and so do stimuli that impinge on it. When a physicist is noticing a hadron, he does so with the help of protons, or whatever, in a cloud chamber or a reactor which itself consists of hadrons and photons and protons. There can be no question of knowledge as something that appears to an external observer, but merely of knowledge as a vastly intricate pattern of self-reference and ever-widening self-reference. This is very different from the view of the old Idealists who took the observer very much into account. But they saw him either as a perturber of what was observed or as the manufacturer of what was observed. In the new perspective we have picked up from physics and biology, the observer is neither perturber nor manufacturer. He is himself part of the system.

There have been countless professors of Positivism and a small number of explicit advocates. But the efforts to justify the advocacy can be counted on the fingers of the hand and then they turn out to be flawed. Wittgenstein in his *Tractatus* never went to the heart of the matter; Mach in his many writings, though he turned handsprings, ended up with positions which were equivocal. Sometimes he was no better than an Idealist, even though he argued that sense experiences gave us *more* than sense experiences. And sometimes he was such an extreme Positivist that he discounted not only absolute space (which other people were discounting for different reasons, anyway), but also atoms which most other people, preferring truth to Positivism's purity, were quite comfortable with.

Mach was not alone in his agonies. In Britain there was a long line of argument which stretched from Russell's worries about *sensa* to Ayer's *Foundations* (1940) and the concern with the privacy of sense-data and the publicity of the material world. Nobody, it seems, stopped to think about the biological basis of perception and the phenomenon of adaptation. Everybody seemed content with the idea that mankind had evolved to the point of Enlightenment at which one simply *knew* that observation was a good guideline and infinitely better than any other source of information. 'We should consider ourselves lucky to have eyes to *see* the light,' everybody was saying, 'and not frivolously throw such a gift to the winds and give credence to intuition, authority, tradition or reason.' It never occurred to anybody that there was a very good reason, given the existence of light, why he had eyes and an equally good reason why we should prefer the testimony of our eyes to that of authority or revelation. Instead, all people worried about was whether what they *saw* was what there *was* or whether it was an appearance and if an appearance, whether there was a reality behind it and if so, whether that reality was likely to be significantly different, etc., etc. The thought that the presence of the eye was guarantee of the presence of light, that light had selected organisms with eyes for survival, and that that may be reason why we should go by our eyes rather than by revelation never seems to have crossed anybody's mind!

The heart of the matter is that Positivism could not present a proper reasoned case, but was simply a view people found themselves left with when most other views had been eliminated. How had this come about?

In the age of Voltaire, more and more people were impressed by science. Voltaire himself was a sort of catastrophist. He believed that there were not only bad catastrophes, but also sometimes good catastrophes. He counts four: Pericles' Athens, Augustus' Rome, Medici Florence and the Age of Louis XIV. But this was a very unhistorical and unpersuasive view. The Enlightenment, in other words, was lacking a historical explanation. Finally, the historical explanation came in the shape of the theory that mankind was evolving from barbarism to religion to science. In this view, science was simply the last Enlightenment stage and, being the last, the best stage. And if people thought that the stage of science meant the elimination of both superstition and religion, they concluded that science meant knowledge based on sense observation undisturbed and undistorted by superstition and religion. Thus, Positivism was justified not philosophically but historically – the end product of man's evolution.

This view of history provides a historical explanation of the Enlightenment and in this sense was clearly superior to Voltaire's catastrophism. But in so far as it was historicist, it suffered from the drawback from which all historicism suffered. However this may be, we can now see that Positivism recommended itself not philosophically but as a *fait accompli* achieved by what was alleged to be an iron law of historical development. Historicism and Positivism, in other words, were dependent on each other. That by itself would not be so bad. What was really intolerable was that neither historicism nor Positivism had any support from any other source. Hence, the doubts which arose were neither vague nor marginal. They concerned a substantial issue and were due to rational scrutiny.

The shift away from Positivism was not an irrational shift, but had a lot to do with the fact that the historicist law of development which had recommended Positivism as the last and most enlightened stage in the development of mankind became more and more implausible. There were few other arguments which Positivists could fall back upon. The two shifts to sociologising and to biology, too, were not irrational. The sociologisers and speech-community philosophers in moving away from Positivism, did not abandon the idea that all knowledge, to be worthy of its name, has to be justified. In shifting, they have done no more than to produce a new kind of justification. There is nothing irrational in this move. The other shift, the shift towards Evolutionary Epistemology, too, is a perfectly intelligible shift. It is explicable in terms of the development of modern biology. This move recommends itself not on the ground of sociological factors or other irrelevant considerations, but because it is plausible in terms of the growth of knowledge itself.

As we are all agreed that there has been a move away from all forms of Positivism, how should we describe the issue which is at the heart of the debate between the move towards sociologising and towards biology? The best way to grasp the issue is to see that it centres upon one's conception of knowledge. On one side, the sociologisers are saying that knowledge can no longer be seen as a relation between a knower and a known, a subject and an object. Once it had become clear, they are arguing, that knowledge is not a relation between a mental substance ('mind', or whatever) and the outside world consisting of material events and *other* minds to which we gained access via their bodies, i.e. via material events, knowledge had to be seen as something other than a relation between an 'inner' and an 'outer' world. One had to look upon it more like a state of mind, or, preferably, just as a state.

In this sense, it was something one shared with one's friends or with the tribe or community one lived in. It could be looked upon as something one says in one's family circle. This alternative to the view that knowledge is a relation between an 'inner' and an 'outer' world was eventually formalised by Wittgenstein and has entered the history of philosophy as the playing of language games. There is, however, another possibility. One can continue to consider knowledge to be a relation between a knower and something that is known. One merely ceases to identify the knower with a subjective, mental, inner-consciousness and the known with the rest of the outside world.

For the development of an Evolutionary Epistemology, the works of Karl Popper and the ideas of Donald Campbell are seminal. I mean this literally: Popper has put his ideas into a number of works which can be studied and discussed. Donald Campbell has been very reticent and has presented his ideas in a number of specialised papers, some of which purport to be nothing but commentaries on the work of Popper.[10] It seems to me that Donald Campbell has been too modest. It is perfectly true that the general outlines of Evolutionary Epistemology have been worked out by Popper. But Donald Campbell has in his own modest and self-effacing way brought these ideas into sharp focus by inventing two fundamental expressions: 'hypothetical realism', to describe the kind of realism which biological evolution entitles us to believe in; and 'random mutation and selective retention', to describe the acquisition and growth of knowledge about that real world.

Although Karl Popper is now an old man and has been working and writing for nearly half a century, the real significance of his work is only just beginning to emerge. Its real significance consists in his view that we can have knowledge about the world even though this knowledge is not induced by, or induced from, that world. The truth of that knowledge or its verisimilitude is not dependent on, or justified by, the method we have used to gain it – be it sensory observation, protocol statements or induction. His basic proposition is that there is information about the world that can be generated in our mind (or whatever it is that has knowledge) without any actual transfer of anything. The mind generates the information and the world selects that information which is suitable without causing that information by mechanical or spiritual transfer. With this bold contention, Popper has obviated the need to worry how sense experience or other forms of induction make knowledge possible. At the same time, the general thrust of this thought links up with Darwinism.[11]

The staggering insight of Charles Darwin was that evolution proceeds by natural selection. This means that the environment designs the shapes and the behaviour of living matter by a process of elimination. In Darwinism there is no teleology, no goal, no instruction. The relentless elimination of non-fitting organisms produces better results than any design or plan could have produced. This insight is directed against traditional religion in that it states that there was no design of God; and it is equally directed against the view that we learn or that any organisms learn because they pick up instructions from the environment. Thus, the idea of natural selection is not only directed against religion and theology, but also against the Baconian tradition which had insisted that we learn because we are instructed or that we learn because we accumulate information and observations. Darwin's idea was that all organisms learn because those that behave as if they had not learnt are eliminated. Those that survive look as if they had listened to instruction and learnt their lesson. But in reality, they have not learnt. They are left over because the countless organisms which were not a fit to their environment have been removed.

I am concentrating on one single feature in Darwin's thought; throughout this book, when I speak of Darwinism, I am thinking of this feature. Darwinism has undergone many changes since Darwin. Since this book is concerned with philosophy and not with biology – or rather, only with biology in so far as it sheds light on philosophy – it is immaterial for the present argument whether one takes one's stand with the 'New Synthesis' or in what sense one considers oneself to be a neo-Darwinian. By all standards, the formula that evolution proceeds by mutation and selection is obsolete because it cannot explain appropriately the nature of the evolutionary response.[12] In continuing to speak of 'random mutation and selective retention' I am not proposing a commitment to any particular biological theory or to any special version of neo-Darwinism. I am merely thinking of the formula as a philosophically valid explanation of the growth of knowledge by means other than the accumulation of observations and the reliance on induction. Especially the term 'mutation' should not be construed in its biological sense; rather, it should be taken to refer to the spontaneous or chance emergence of something new and of something which is not induced by the pressures of the environment. Philosophically speaking, I mean by 'Darwinism' the view that the target of selection is 'the new'. Biologists are currently debating what precisely 'the new' consists of,[13] but from a philosophical point of view the outcome of this debate is irrelevant.

In Darwin's days, the argument against religion was in the foreground. Since then, we have seen that Darwin's argument was only one of many arguments against religion and Darwin has taken his place among many secularisers of human thought and knowledge. In the present century, the anti-Baconian aspects of Darwin have come to the fore and have become much more important than the anti-religious features of his thought. The battle against dogmatic religious knowledge has been won, with Darwin's help and the help of a great many other people. But the battle against Baconian method, against induction and against the view that we learn by picking up instructions and that the knowledge we have gained is justified in so far as, and no further than, we have picked up correct instructions, is far from won. It is in this battle against Bacon and against induction and against the belief that knowledge has to be 'justified' by induction or by sense experience that Popper has joined forces with Darwin.

There is a real parallel here between Darwin and Popper. It has always been impossible to show how 'learning' from nature might have worked. Acquired characteristics, no matter what the nature of the mechanism of acquisition, are not hereditary and cannot have played a part in evolution. Darwin himself, because of his ignorance of molecular biology, was a little doubtful on this point. However, the discovery of DNA and the Central Dogma that DNA can instruct the proteins of which organisms consist but not the other way round, have clinched this matter – at least for the time being. As a result, this aspect of Darwinism which said that organisms learn without instruction, so to speak (i.e. without actually learning when 'learning' means 'picking up and retaining information'), has moved into the centre of the stage. In the Baconian tradition, one ought to be able to account for the process of acquisition and accumulation of observations. But it is notoriously difficult to account for this acquisition. At least since Hume we have known that inductive reasoning cannot be justified, for no finite amount of observations (and that is all we can ever have) can ever justify a general law. Since then, we have also painfully understood that no knowledge can be reduced to the sense-data that were supposed to justify it, or be explained as the result of the protocol statements on which it claimed to be based, or be exhaustively justified in terms of any 'experience'.

The Central Dogma about the *asymmetry* between DNA and proteins has its parallel in the conclusion that no knowledge can be *justified* by observations, by sense experience or sense-data. Organisms do not evolve by picking up instruction from the outside world; and human beings do not gain knowledge by picking up and accumulating instructions from the outside world, either. Darwin's theory of natural selection as the motor of evolution finds its complement in Popper's theory that we do not gain knowledge by induction but propose theories to the environment and make the environment falsify most of these theories by our own critical selection for retention of those theories which the environment fails to falsify. Popper's immense contribution to our knowledge of knowledge lies in his extension of Darwinian evolution to knowledge in general. We know, or we are here, because of the relentless elimination of all those pieces of knowledge or organisms which are not a fit to the environment. Popperian acquisition of knowledge, like Darwinian evolution, is a negative process of elimination.

With Darwinism and especially with the link of Darwinism to philosophy as envisaged by Karl Popper, there has come a new conception of rationality. Ever since Plato we have been used to think of rationality as the condition in which we manage to control our passions with the help of reason. Closely allied with this Platonic rationality there was the rationality of Aristotle, who taught that essence precedes existence and that we can determine truth by the exercise of our rationality. Our reason, he said, teaches us that we are non-feathered bipeds and provided we follow the dictates of reason we will learn to live up to the demands of our essence as non-feathered bipeds. The view that essence precedes existence and that we know our essence by reason and ought to model our existence accordingly, held sway until Shakespeare, who forcefully drew our attention to a more realistic appraisal of rationality: 'Thought is the slave of life,' he proclaimed, 'and life, time's fool.' Eventually, Hume produced a large number of sceptical arguments with regard to reason and assigned it so lowly a place that it could never hope to discover 'essences'. Close on his heels there came the Romantics, who devalued rationality and contrasted it unfavourably with the voice of the heart which spoke most purely through the mouth of a child or through the mouth of those few adults who had managed to survive attempts made to educate and civilise them. Given Hume's scepticism in regard to reason, there was a lot to be said for the Romantics. Finally, the reassessment of rationality was capped by Jean-Paul Sartre in our own century with his firm declaration that the entire Platonic–Aristotelian tradition had been wrong: existence, he said, echoing Shakespeare, was prior to essence. 'Thought is the slave of life'! Reason, in this view, is at best a rationalisation after the event.

Conventional histories of philosophy never mention Darwin in this context – but they should. The great importance of Darwin for the history of our conception of rationality lies in the fact that he showed that there was a very un-Baconian, though perfectly rational, way in which organisms learn and in which knowledge is acquired. For Bacon, rationality consists in avoiding mistakes. Mistakes are avoided, he wrote in Aphorism XXVI of Book 1 of the *Novum Organum*, as long as correct observation is heaped upon correct observation and by feeling one's way from observation to observation. By not straying from such rationality (which he called 'the interpretation of nature'), one must arrive at the truth through the avoidance of error. For Darwin (and this has become more strikingly obvious since our improved understanding of genetics and of the role of DNA),[14] rationality consists, on the contrary, in making mistakes, in comparing mistakes, and in the retention of those errors of replication that are the most adaptive fits to the environment. Darwin has introduced us to the idea that rationality does not consist in the avoidance of error, but in the occurrence of error and the elimination of error by natural selection. When we proceed from organisms as theories to theories proper, we can say that rationality consists in making bold guesses and conjectures (as Popper would say) and then subjecting them to ruthless criticism. In this view of rationality, the path of reason is not a secure path which leads from certainty to certainty; rather, it is a wild display of the imagination, the products of which are scrutinised by criticism. Bacon had maintained (Aphorism XIX) that it is rational to derive axioms from the senses and particulars, and then rise by a gradual and unbroken ascent. Darwin's and Popper's rationality consists not in finding the right method, but in following no method other than chance and in subjecting the chance proposals to criticism and refutation. The rational man, in this view, is not the man who controls his imagination, but the man who subjects the products of his imagination to criticism. Rationality, here, consists in making mistakes and in selecting the lesser mistakes for temporary retention: the rational man learns from his errors. This is a very novel view of rationality.[15] For in the traditional view, rationality used to consist in the ability to avoid mistakes. The novel view is superior to the old view. For in the old view, in order to avoid mistakes, one had to know the goal and one had to know the road that would lead to that goal. The old view of rationality, in other words, was teleological. When teleology was dropped from philosophy, most philosophers thought, as Sartre for example did, that one would also have to abandon rationality. With Darwin and Popper, we can now see that this is not the case: the method of conjectures and refutations is a rational method without teleology.

The present book is an application and explication of Popperian Darwinism. It is based on the insight that Darwin's theory of evolution and Popper's theory of knowledge have a common denominator. Though Popper is mentioned frequently and quoted critically or uncritically in almost every conceivable context, there is only one good introduction to his thought. But even Anthony O'Hear's book[16] ignores Popper's evolutionism and the changes in Popper's own thought which have been brought about by his growing acknowledgment of biological evolution in general, and his affinity with the work of Konrad Lorenz. There is no sharp break in Popper's thought: the ideas he developed in the 1960s and 1970s have grown out of his early solution of the problem of induction. Though there is nothing to compare with the radical break we find in the thought of Wittgenstein, Popper's extension of his early concept of falsifiability to natural and critical selection is vitally important. The early philosophy of falsification which made him famous would, by itself, never have made possible an Evolutionary Epistemology. The present book is an attempt to fill this gap and to show that the most important part of Popper's philosophy is his advance towards biology and evolution. None of the books which have appeared about Popper make this clear. This book is written in the hope that this advance can be illuminated.

The book's underlying theme, which will come up in chapter after chapter, is the theory that since the disappearance of Positivism there are two choices in front of us. There is the move towards a sociologising philosophy, as represented by Wittgenstein; or the move towards a biology-oriented philosophy, as represented by Popper. If so far we have been prevented from seeing clearly that the proposals of these two philosophers – both Viennese and both domiciled in Britain – represent the two hearts of the matter, it is because we have allowed ourselves to be distracted by side-issues.

As far as Popper is concerned, everybody knows that he dealt decisively with the problem of induction and that he has taken a liberal stance in politics so that he has become suspect to all Marxists, radicals and other Utopians. But this is where the matter is usually allowed to rest. Not long ago, an eminent American philosopher told me that he could not understand why people kept talking about Popper, for Popper, he said, was after all a very minor philosopher who, many decades ago, had some quibbles with Carnap over induction and verification.

As far as Wittgenstein is concerned, his real importance is obscured by the opposite effect. Wittgenstein, unlike Popper, has become a cult figure and a culture hero. Nobody quite knows what he taught or stood for. All books on philosophy, the social sciences, literature and psychology use his eminently quotable epigrams and *bons mots*, whether they make sense or not. There is many a philosopher who claims he is doing the same sort of thing Wittgenstein was doing without being able to say what that sort of thing actually was.

All these matters are comparatively trivial and probably accidental and obscure the central issue. The central opposition and its importance comes out when one recalls that Wittgenstein maintained that whatever we are doing or saying, we are playing a language game and that the truth and the meaning of everything we are saying is relative to such a particular language game. Popper, on the other hand, maintains that the growth of knowledge has been continuous 'from the amoeba to Einstein', and that the truth and meaning of whatever has been said is not relative to any particular phase in that continuity – or, if it is, each phase can be compared to what went before and to what came after. The two positions can be summed up in the following way. Wittgenstein says that everything is absolutely relative; and Popper, that everything is relatively absolute. With a little reflection one sees that the two positions between them exhaust the possibilities before us after the fall of Positivism, that they are mutually incompatible and directly contradictory. Wittgenstein's position is an anti-historical and anti-evolutionary position *par excellence.* There have been changes, he is saying. Not everybody plays the same game. But every game ever played is a law unto itself and a final arbiter of its own rules. Thus, with Wittgenstein, we are back with Linnaeus and the eighteenth-century belief that every species is final and was created once and for all, as well as with Ranke and the nineteenth-century belief that all societies are 'equidistant from God'. Popper's position, by contrast, is evolutionary and historical. There are changes, he is saying. But the changes are related to each other and some are for better and some are for worse. The following chapters should be seen as an explanation of the meaning of this fundamental confrontation.

Chapter 1

The Historicity of Knowledge

The Dynamics of Alternatives

Everybody agrees that knowledge has grown and that it was not just there, one fine day. Knowledge is therefore a historical phenomenon, something that happens and changes as time passes. But there are two different ways in which one can see that growth, and there is no agreement at all as to which of these two ways is the right one. One can, first, take it that the relationship between the passage of time and the growth of knowledge is more or less random; or, one can take it that the relationship between the passage of time and the growth of knowledge is not random.

The first view is the view of Positivism in any of its many varieties. For Positivists, the advent of knowledge itself is the product of history. After millennia of superstition, be it theological or metaphysical, the Enlightenment brought rational knowledge. Once enlightenment has brought about knowledge, the growth of knowledge ceases to have a history. In the view of Positivism, when people make mistakes about knowledge, the mistaken view is simply discarded. It is true that there is a history of science in the sense that there is a saga of discarded ideas. But this history is itself only of anecdotal interest, a mere curiosity. It is not itself part of the enterprise of growing knowledge. The history of science, in this view, is irrelevant to science.

For all those people to whom Positivism is not a valid account of the origin and growth of knowledge, the matter is not so simple. Old-fashioned empiricists or Baconians or Positivists believed that a theory is the sum total of its verifications and had to be discarded as soon as these verifications failed. To these people, the history of science is co-extensive with the sequence of true theories. This kind of history writes itself and is, at the same time, both banal and redundant. To people who believe that theories are held until they are falsified, the history of theory-holding becomes more interesting and more relevant. For they have to ask themselves why some theories were held in the first place, i.e. before they were falsified; and what, at some stage or other, prevented or precluded their falsification.

But people who hold that some theories are held even after they have been falsified, and that some theories prove, up to a point, immune to falsifying instances, will see that the history of science is not only interesting but moves into the centre of the stage. For they must ask themselves why some theories are comparatively immune from falsification or even observation and why they continue to be held; why they are considered immune; and why and when such immunity may cease.

As we have advanced slowly and gradually from naive Positivism to a view of knowledge which states that there is valid knowledge, even though it cannot be exhaustively accounted for in observational terms, the preoccupation with the history of science has grown. But there is more to the growing preoccupation with the historicity of science than the move away from Positivism. In earlier days and precisely when philosophers like John Locke first sought to account for the genesis of knowledge, they thought to account for it by using physics as their model. Early physics was very much a push-me-pull-you affair, a universe in which masses moved in response to a stimulus. In this kind of universe, knowledge came to be thought of as something like energy transfer. A body emitted light; the light hit the retina; the retina sent messages to the mind; and so, the mind ended up by having knowledge of the source of the light. The quality and veracity of knowledge was considered to be proportional to the purity of the energy transfer. In essence, knowledge was considered to be the effect the known object had on the mind of the knower. The known caused knowledge, or induced knowledge, in the mind of the knower.

We know today that this account of knowledge on the model of physics is only partially correct. To be sure, there is always a certain amount of energy transfer. But once the energy reaches the nervous system of the knower, the process becomes infinitely complex and interpretative. Feedback starts to operate inside the nervous system and what emerges in the end as 'knowledge' bears very little resemblance to the 'object' which can be said to have caused the initial energy transfer. Rather, we now know that the acquisition of knowledge can be understood much better when we use a model from biology instead. Biological evolution does not proceed by energy transfer and the emergence of new organisms is not induced or constrained by the environment. On the contrary, the initiative lies inside the organisms. They make proposals to the environment and the environment selects those proposals which are viable. Similarly, we can think of knowledge as a theory about the world and evaluate the theory, in order to distinguish true theories from false theories, by trial-and-error pattern matching.[1] The biological model is a better guide to the acquisition and growth of knowledge than the physical model and, for that matter, even knowledge about the physical universe must be seen to have been acquired on the biological model.

In this way, we can see that the knowledge we have is not something that is determined or constrained by the world we have knowledge of. If one starts with that idea, one will immediately recognise the historicity of all knowledge because one must see that correct or true or viable knowledge comes in sets of alternatives. Just as there is more than one solution to a watery environment – there are fish, amoebas, crabs, reptiles, etc. – so one can see that one can, for example, describe the planetary system by Newtonian Mechanics or by Einstein's General Theory of Relativity. When there are alternatives, the succession of alternative views constitutes the historical dimension of knowledge. Some alternatives are earlier than others, some presuppose others, and even discarded ones – such as the phlogiston theory or the theories of alchemy – must be seen as having their limited uses for very limited observations. They are not so many 'errors', but partial successes.

As soon as one understands that knowledge is not a representation of the world and a blow-by-blow account of the world in all its details, one recognises that the choice between Ptolemy and Copernicus is not as easy as it sounds. One can use Ptolemy in order to account for the movement of the earth around the sun. Ptolemy's system is extremely cumbersome, but provided one does not expect it to explain why apples fall to the ground as well, it has its uses. In other words, it is discarded because of its cumbersomeness and because of its lack of universality, but not because it is directly found not to be a true representation of the way things are. When one sees Ptolemy and Copernicus as alternatives, one begins to study science in its historical dimension. The reason why Ptolemy came to be discarded and Copernicus accepted is part of scientific knowledge because that reason is not simply a matter of substituting the true for the false. It is a matter of comparing alternatives.

When Herbert Butterfield introduced the history of science into academic education in his lectures at Cambridge University and published his famous book in 1949, he was a great pioneer. However, he was still living in the age of innocence. The history of science, to him, was educationally important and had to be studied because science was and is a force in culture. But there is nothing in that book which would have surprised or disturbed Positivists like Carnap or Mach, or made any reader suspect that the history of science is actually part of science. The discovery of the historical dimension of science is comparatively recent. It was brought home to people only with the demise of the old belief that knowledge was simply truth about the world; that false knowledge gradually was discarded; and that, provided the world itself did not change, the truth about it could not change. Whitehead's famous epigram that a science which hesitates to forget its founders is lost, is a perfect expression of this old view of knowledge in which the more true simply supersedes the less true and the false. But the moment it was recognised that such certainty in regard of representational truth and accuracy of detailed depiction was inapplicable to knowledge, criteria other than pure truth pushed themselves forward. When one has to weigh and compare theories according to the consensus they command, according to their differential explanatory power, their verisimilitude, their relevance, their coherence and their correspondence with each other, the history of science becomes the history of alternative theories and moves into the centre of the stage. With every one of these new criteria of knowledge, past knowledge was never completely discarded; rather, it remained relevant or, at least, remained as an evolutionary preparation for a later theory. In this view of the history of knowledge, even the ancient belief in the rationality of God can be seen as a necessary step in the evolution of mathematical reasoning about nature.

On the old view, the history of science was irrelevant. Phlogiston, Ptolemy, alchemy, the ether, absolute space, etc., were all so many errors of judgment and of perception. They found their place with the devil, with the three-tiered universe of biblical imagination and with the immortality of the soul in the long history of superstition. The problem that was of real interest to contemporary philosophers was the distinction between reality and appearance and the degree of veracity to be attributed to those theories which scientists had pronounced to be true. Was there a reality *behind* the appearance described by those theories? Were those theories all we knew or all that existed? If the world was in reality the way Plato had described it in his *Timaeus,* why did it appear the way Aristotle had described it in his *De Anima*? In other words, philosophers used to weigh and compare theories. But they did not see them as alternative accounts of the world. They took one theory to be a description of the world as it really was; and another as a description of the world as it appeared. The question they worried about was the question of which was which.

The realisation that phlogiston and Ptolemy, ether and alchemy were actually based on quite a lot of correct observation, even though they could not be exhaustively accounted for by observation, and that neither Relativity nor Quanta – let alone quarks and quasars – could be exhaustively reduced to observation statements, brought a change. It began to dawn on philosophers that the heart of the problem was not: What is appearance and what is reality? Instead, it became: How is one to see the succession of alternative theories and how can one distinguish between them? At the moment in which the debate about appearance and reality was replaced by a debate about alternative theories, the history of science became part of science.

The Germans have given a special word to the historicity of science: *Theoriendynamik* – the dynamics of theories. With the conception that knowledge has a historical dimension and that the theories knowledge consists of have a dynamism and succeed one another, even though they are all theories about the same world, one can abandon the older idea that different theories are different 'appearances' or different portraits of reality. Hence, now that we can think of the dynamics of theories, we need no longer worry whether an appearance is an appearance of reality or whether, as has at times been argued, it is reality itself; and if an appearance of reality, whether it is a deceptive appearance even though, as an appearance it is true as a theory; or, if not deceptive, whether the reality behind it is inferred or 'real'. Instead we can now see that the real problem is, first, to determine the nature of the dynamics, i.e. to see how one can explain the succession of theories, weigh alternative theories and explain their succession by showing that the more 'rational' theories keep on stealing a march on the less 'rational' ones; second, to determine the meaning of 'rational' in this context; third, whether alternative theories *can* be compared and whether the history of the sequence of alternatives is random or not, i.e., whether it is a story in which one damned thing happened after another.

On this view of knowledge as the sum of alternative solutions, knowledge has a history. But on such a view, that history has no direction. Alternatives come and go and are substituted for one another. In order to grasp that that history of substitutions and exchanges has a genuine historicity, one has to remind oneself of another feature of knowledge. One has to understand knowledge as knowledge of universals or of universal regularities. We count as knowledge only information about universal regularities, even though that knowledge need not be about absolutely unlimited universalities. Knowledge or information about simple 'here and now' details and unique perceptions is not knowledge. One might even question whether knowledge as 'here and now' is even possible.

Not even particular statements are descriptions of nature. Any particular statement, in so far as it employs words (or concepts), is making use of words which transcend particular phenomena. For this reason, not even a concrete particular statement can be descriptive and its validity cannot be judged in terms of its degree of pictorial accuracy or in terms of its power to 'represent' or mirror. Not even historical knowledge is descriptive or representational, no matter how particular the several sentences of which it consists are. In any case, it does not represent the time-span in which the events have happened in the way a mirror mirrors or a picture depicts. It selects; and the most one can say is that the events which have taken place do not contradict certain parts of the time-span.

Since knowledge is always knowledge of regularities and has therefore to be couched in terms of universal laws, it follows that knowledge cannot be representational. Knowledge is neither a map nor a mirror nor a portrait. Once this is admitted, we can again see the historical element in knowledge. If knowledge is knowledge of general laws, then the growth of knowledge is not just an accumulation of detailed and particular observations, but a growth of the universality of the general laws. We speak of progress, when the particular facts explained by a general law can be explained by a new general law which explains not only the particular facts already explained, but also other particular facts which had not been explained by an old general law. Knowledge of regularities cannot be representational because a universal law does not represent anything we can observe. At best, we can observe only a limited number of instances. A general law asserts something about regularities and therefore cannot represent what we can observe. With this argument we can eliminate from consideration all those thorny problems which occupied Positivists in general and Mach in particular. Mach was deeply concerned to distinguish between presentationalism, of which he approved, and representationalism, of which he disapproved. The former was the idea that the world is presented directly to consciousness and that the appearances *are* the external world and that observation of particular instances *is* real knowledge. Statements of regularities, he said, are merely shorthand devices to sum up myriads of direct observations. Representationalism, on the other hand, was the idea that the external world is *not* directly presented to consciousness and that appearances are something mental and that the external world is something one can reliably infer from these appearances. If one takes this view, there is no reason, he said, why one should imagine that any inference of this kind is 'reliable'. Since we cannot consider either presentationalism or representationalism as knowledge, the whole question as to which of these two views is the correct one is without interest.

The Faculty of Abstraction

All but the most rabid empiricists are aware that there is a large component in our knowledge which is *a priori*. We are presumed to be able to learn a language and we are capable of *expectations*. Some people even believe that we have innate ideas with a specific content, though this is more open to doubt. If we had no expectations *before* we have experience, we could never make comparisons between experiences and distinguish similar experiences from dissimilar experiences. If one is looking, for example, at a circle and cannot form the expectation that there are other circles like it, one will look at other circles without being able to recognise them as circles. For without the expectation that 'circulateness' is a regular occurrence, one will look at the next circle with completely innocent and fresh eyes and thus allow oneself to be diverted by all the differences, no matter how minute, between the first circle and the second circle; and would conclude, very reasonably, that they are not really alike. Hence, our very ability to make comparisons and distinctions and to classify experiences under headings, depends on our ability to have expectations of certain regularities.

As I have said, there is really no doubt about this matter. Even those rabid empiricists who believe that the mind is a bucket and that everything, even our expectations, are poured into it, accept that we have expectations of regularities. They would merely add that these expectations have to be 'learnt'.

There is, however, considerable doubt and large areas of disagreement as to the source of these *a priori* faculties, as well as in regard to the question of whether there really are regularities in nature to correspond to our expectations of regularities. Let us discuss these two separate questions in turn, starting with the question of whether there is anything in nature which corresponds to our expectations.

At one end of the scale there are people like Sir Arthur Eddington, who could not get himself to deny the *a priori* component but who considered it entirely subjective. In his view, the *a priori* component in knowledge – which he recognised, for example, in the General Theory of Relativity – vitiated its veracity because he considered it to be 'wholly subjective'[2] and something which one should hope would eventually be eliminated. Obviously, he did not believe that it corresponded to anything in nature. Next, we find philosophers like Husserl and Frege, who invoked *a priori* concepts or categories in order to escape from the subjective clutches of psychologism. Unlike Eddington, they held firmly to *a priori* categories – but not because they were sure that they corresponded to anything in nature. They thought that they were a good ploy to avoid the extremes of subjectivity. Next are those neo-Positivists who, having given up the attempt to reduce *a priori* expectations to observational experiences, argue that observational phenomena have the properties they would have *if* they were embedded in a world in which there really are regularities, even though, literally, they are not so embedded – or, at least, can never be shown to be so embedded.

Then we come to Kant. Kant was quite certain that there are *a priori* categories and forms of understanding. However, he was also certain that they could not correspond to nature as it is in itself. They are in our minds and in nature as experienced by our minds. Next, we come to Plato. Plato postulated that the mere fact that we have knowledge of ephemeral, particular events is proof that we must have *a priori* knowledge of expectations. They must, he argued, be in nature; for if they were not, we would have no knowledge of nature. This argument looks potent, but is circular. For the nature he said we have knowledge of is precisely the sort of nature one cannot have knowledge of unless one has *a priori* knowledge of certain expectations. On this interpretation of Plato, he too is one of those philosophers who are not so sure that the regularities we seem to have expectations of are really embedded in nature.

When we turn our attention to society rather than to nature, we are immediately struck by the fact that there are regularities. But these regularities are manmade and artificial. They consist in legal norms, in positive legal enactments, in customs and conventions. Nobody has ever denied that they are real and that they exist, whether we watch them or not. But then, they are different kinds of regularities and not the sort of regularities Kant, Plato and Eddington were thinking of. They are obviously there only because we put them there. 'Being a member of a society' *means* that we have certain expectations about the behaviour of other members of that society and about our own likely behaviour.

Finally, at the opposite end of the spectrum there are those philosophers who believe dogmatically that regularities are embedded in nature. However, the only reason they can produce for this belief is the belief that God made nature to have regularities. For example, they say, we can use mathematics to describe the world because God Himself was a mathematician.

It now turns out that we can look towards biology to settle the dispute and to assure us that there are regularities in nature and that the *a priori* expectations we have of them are not only justified, but also that their presence in our minds or nervous system – whichever one prefers – can be explained by the theory of evolution by natural selection.

When we are thinking about the biology of evolution we must assume that there are regularities in nature. Without such regularities there could be no adaptation by natural selection. Every organism which is adapted is adapted to the *regularities* in its environment. It makes no sense to say that it is adapted to the infinitely random vagaries of all possible details and particulars of its environment. To be adapted to all possible variations and individual particularities would not only require a store of information which would transcend the storage capacity of even the most complex organism, let alone of individual cells. It would also make adaptation impossible because it would reduce it to successful learning; or, alternatively, it would require us to think that any organism is infinitely adaptable and could adapt itself to any environment whatsoever.

> The blind, fixed avoidance response of a Paramecium incorporates only a single element of information about the objects blocking its path; namely, that there is at that point an insurmountable obstacle to locomotor progression.[3]

Infusoria, for example, by means of their phobic and topic responses, seek an environment

> containing *inter alia*, a particular concentration of H-ions. The commonest acid found in nature is carbonic acid, the highest concentration of which is found in waters in which paramecia flourish, especially in the vicinity of rotting vegetable matter, because the bacteria that live on this matter give off carbon dioxide. This relationship is so dependable, and the occurrence of other acids, let alone toxic ones, is so rare, that the parmecium manages admirably with one single item of information, which put into words would say that a certain acid concentration signifies the presence of a mass of bacteria on which to feed.[4]

To quote Konrad Lorenz again:

> The mechanism which enables so many animals to develop conditioned responses is an adaptation to the physical fact of energy-transformation. Preparatory or avoidance response to the

> conditioned stimulus preceding the biologically relevant one is only adaptive (in terms of species-survival) when the two stimuli occur in sequence with reliable regularity. This is only the case when both are links in the same causal chain. The mechanism of the conditioned response takes in only one piece of information about this relationship – that the effect follows the cause in time. And this 'cognitive feat' is of tremendous survival value! In addition, it is actually a correct piece of information, since it remains quite true even when viewed from the higher level of human causalistic thought.[5]

We can see from these examples that evolution by natural selection and adaptation would not be possible, let alone conceivable, *unless* we were able to assume that there really are regularities in nature. The organisms which have the right expectations about them are 'adapted' and get selected. Those that do not have the approximately correct expectations, cannot be selected for survival. They are too unadapted. From the single-cell organisms upwards to the presence of *Homo sapiens* we can be sure that the process of evolution has been possible because there are regularities in nature.

Now that the question about the presence of regularities in nature has been settled by biology – we would not be here, in other words, if there were no regularities – we can turn to the next question: How has it come about that we know about these regularities and have expectations about them? Obviously, the answer that we learn about them by observation must, by the nature of the case, be ruled out. These expectations, wherever they come from, cannot come *a posteriori*. The whole reasoning behind the doctrine that our knowledge of regularities is *post rem* is not only false, but actually absurd. There is first a logical consideration which leads to this conclusion. No matter how many observations any organism is capable of, the number of conceivable observations must always be limited. One can therefore not get knowledge of real regularities from a limited number of observations. Even myriads of observations can at best only be summed up as 'so many' observations of a regularity. There can be no knowledge that the regularity will occur tomorrow and that we are entitled to 'expect' it to occur. Next, there is a psychological consideration which leads to the same conclusion. Without an expectation, we could not even look for a regularity or recognise one if it occurred. Suppose we observed the sun rise once.

Unless we were able to have an expectation of a regular repetition of that sunrise, we would not be able to recognise the second event as a sunrise. The first day it would appear red; the next day it would seem golden; the third day the sun might be hidden by a cloud. Unless we expected the sun to rise, we would be bound to be misled by these particular differences into thinking that whatever was happening on the horizon was *not* a repetition of the first event. Unless we had an expectation, we could not make the necessary abstraction and dismiss the differences in accidental colouring as irrelevant.

Having thus dismissed the possibility that expectations of regularities are lodged in our minds *a posteriori* because they are *post rem*, we are nevertheless left with a bewildering array of explanations as to how such *a priori* knowledge got into the mind. One of the obstacles to a settlement of this question comes from the fact that philosophers have concentrated on the mind of *Homo sapiens* and have always overlooked the fact that cognition is not specifically human, but part of the entire evolutionary process.

Aristotle reasoned that *a priori* knowledge of universals, i.e. expectations, must be something spiritual. Particular observations, he said, are observations of physical phenomena. Since no sum of particular observations can amount to an expectation of regularities, our expectation of such regularities must be 'spiritual'.[6] Next we come to the view that we have no expectations at all and that what we designate as our *a priori* expectation of the regularity of occurrences is *flatus vocis*. This view is partly based on the false idea that all there is, is a 'here and now' of particular occurrences. If this idea were viable, we would not have evolved to be here to have this idea. Partly, this idea is based on the notion that there well may be regularities but that, by the nature of the case, we can have no knowledge of regularities. This notion is not as absurd as it may seem, for it is indeed very mysterious that we have *a priori* expectations – at least, it is mysterious as long as one avoids looking at biology.

Plato thought of abating the mystery by claiming that we gain knowledge of *a priori* expectations before we are born, when our soul is not yet encased in a body. In this unembodied state, he argued, the soul is capable of looking at these regularities and of taking them in. Though birth and incarnation cause the soul to suffer a certain clouding of these expectations, they can be polished up by careful memory-work. As against Plato, Kant believed that we simply happen to have them when we are alive.

Whitehead believed that our expectations, justified or not, derive from a historical accident. He argued that in the early days of Western culture people believed in an omnipotent God who had made the universe and regulated it according to immutable laws. This notion is most probably false. But, he continued, we have become so used to the idea that there are immutable regularities that we have been able to turn an ancient superstition to good account. We have given up the idea that God made the world; but we have retained the notion that there are regularities in the world. And so, science was born out of religion.[7] Our religious past, he maintained, endowed us with an instinctual habit of thought about regularities and order. In this way, Whitehead would really explain our *a priori* knowledge as a historical accident. Consider, in contrast, the position of knowledge in ancient China. Here, too, myth taught that there was an order and that there were regularities both in nature and in society. Everything in the universe, according to this myth, was in spontaneous harmony. This harmony was such that there were no specific laws or regularities. Hence, educated Chinese in the eighteenth century, confronted through the arrival of the Jesuits by knowledge of European science and its contention that nature was regulated by general laws, dismissed such science as a form of naivety inspired or conditioned by an anthropocentric presumption that there were regularities. For this reason, science could not take roots in Chinese culture.[8] If Needham and Whitehead are right, the whole question as to the presence of *a priori* expectations in our knowledge is a cultural accident. In the West, we were just lucky that we had inherited a science-promoting myth; in China, on the other hand, people were just unlucky in that the myth they had inherited was not science promoting or philocognitive, even though, as Needham is the best to inform us, they obtained quite a lot of knowledge in a different way.

If Whitehead explained our *a priori* knowledge as a lucky historical accident, we also find a number of sociological explanations which see it less as an accident and more as a product of our cultural evolution. Ever since Durkheim, many people have believed that it was through religious belief that man realised that the material world could not be apprehended solely through sense-data. The first step towards the power of abstraction came when man realised that a clan and its totemic emblem, though very different in terms of sense-data, partook of the same essence. From that moment on, both religious and scientific thinking have sought to translate the realities of direct observation into an intelligible language. This idea has been taken up by countless investigators. For example, we find that Alfred Sohn-Rethel as recently as 1970 attempted to explain the power of abstraction as the result of the market economy. When people had to exchange the products of their labour for their 'equivalents' in the marketplace, they were forced to abstract, for the products of their labour were, as their observation told them, different from the goods or services they exchanged them for.[9] Even more recently, Eric Gans has presented another sociological theory about the origin of language in general and the origin of designating particular objects by general words. In this process, we can see the emergence of abstract thinking and generalisation. In very primitive tribes thousands of years ago, people had inchoate desires of aggression which were displayed in violent sacrifices. Then there came a moment of crisis when members of the tribe, desiring to seize the victim's remains, were suddenly held in check by the realisation that in this free-for-all sacrifice, every member might be the next victim. Thus there begins a communal holding back which, in turn, becomes a source for reciprocal awareness through which actual and generalised violence becomes mediated violence. The most effective instrument of mediation is the growth of language – the realisation that objects can be designated and that one word can stand for a variety of events. Thus, violence is abated and contained and men learn to grasp the significance of universal words, i.e. of speech acts which cover more than one particular instance.[10]

It does not really matter whether one finds these or other Durkheim-derived theories attractive or plausible. What matters is the cogency of the attempt to explain the presence of *a priori* knowledge, of expectations and of our ability to abstract. Plato had a mythical explanation; Kant had no explanation at all. Whitehead considered it a matter of luck. From Durkheim on, we have been invited to look towards cultural evolution and the history of social structures for an explanation.

At the present time, when one is taking the work of Konrad Lorenz, Egon Brunswik and Donald Campell into consideration, one can observe that a paradigm shift is taking place. We are now invited to abandon these sociological explanations and consider biological explanations instead. The research programme seems to be changing. But lest we prejudge the issue, I would like to point out that the change is taking place according to perfectly rational criteria. The change is not taking place because the sociological research programme is ceasing to yield fruits, as Imre Lakatos would have it. On the contrary. Though there is a change, the old sociological programme is yielding ever new fruits – as the abundance of sociological literature on the subject and the whole pursuit of the sociology of knowledge proves. Nor is there an impending shift because, as Kuhn would have it, the older generation of sociologists is dying out. On the contrary. The number of younger people engaging in the sociology of knowledge is far greater than the number of sociologists of the older generation. The change is coming because the biological explanation is wider than the sociological explanation. Everything that was explained by the sociological explanation, from Durkheim on, can be explained by the biological derivation of *a priori* expectation. Moreover, the biological explanation also covers a vast array of phenomena in biology and evolution and links the presence of expectations in the human mind or nervous system to the ability for abstraction one finds in infusoria or in the primitive tick, an insect parasitic on dogs, sheep and cattle. The new biological theory of the origin of our power to abstract and our ability to have expectations is, therefore, a genuine progress.

Curiously enough, Plato's and Kant's view are compatible with the new biological paradigm. In the new paradigm, we find that *a priori* expectations are indeed present at birth. Where Kant did not and could not have given an explanation, and where Plato gave a mythical explanation by postulating that the soul had pre-existed its encasement in a body, the biological explanation shows that the presence of *a priori* expectations comes through evolution. There are regularities in nature and those cells which are adapted, in the sense that they behave as if they expected the regularities in their environment, have a better chance of survival than those which don't. In this sense, through the process of natural selection and heredity, the ability to have expectations of regularities is phylogenetically *a posteriori*. Organisms 'learn' from the environment. However, they do not learn as individuals but as species, because only those that are adapted to expecting the regularities survive and have offspring. This process makes the *a priori* expectation of regularities ontogenetically *a priori*. Every individual organism is born with the appropriate expectation. In this way, the regularities which exist in nature are eventually transferred to the organisms which survive by natural selection and the order of nature becomes the nature of order. With the evolution of sexual reproduction, the process of incorporation of *a priori* expectations is vastly speeded up. Sexual reproduction presupposes kinship recognition and this means that individuals must be able to abstract sufficiently from the amorphous mass of stimuli they encounter: they must be capable of distinguishing the members of their own species with which they can mate successfully from all other individuals, animal or material. Hence, with sexual reproduction, there is a special premium on the ability to abstract and generalise. In this process, phylogenetic and ontogenetic experience are combined and thus we can explain what has puzzled empiricists and rationalists for centuries. The rationalists held fast to the idea that we have *a priori* expectations, but could not explain why. The empiricists held fast to the idea that we learn from observations, but could not explain why. In the biological model of the growth of knowledge, these two processes of cognition are beautifully meshed. The biologist has taught philosophers of all persuasions that experience and *a priori* expectations derive from different layers of the evolution of organisms and that phylogeny and ontogeny are meshed to make up adaptation. The old empiricist, of course, has to accept that learning is not induction or ingestion, but the selective elimination of those organisms which have not happened to have the right responses. Similarly, the old rationalist has to accept that while it is true, as he contended, that there is *a priori* knowledge in every individual, that knowledge is not absolutely innate but the result of phylogenetic experience, i.e. phylogenetically *a posteriori*: it appears, therefore, as ontogenetically *a priori*.[11]

However, the expression 'phylogenetically *a posteriori*' is, strictly speaking, misleading. There can be no suggestion of earlier organisms gathering painfully, by inductive accumulation, experiences of regularities. All that is meant is that expectations of regularities evolve together with the species. Organisms which have poor or no expectations are eliminated and, in this way, as the species evolves so do the expectations of regularities. In every species, the correct expectations have become adapted because all organisms with incorrect expectations or without expectations have been eliminated as a result of their reproduction rate being slower than that of the organisms with more fitting expectations. We ought, therefore, simply to speak of 'phylogenetic experience' rather than of expectations which are 'phylogenetically *a posteriori*'.

When one thinks of knowledge as knowledge of regularities, one recognises the *a priori* element which enables one to make abstractions so that one recognises similarities and differences in particular observations and classifies them and considers them relevant or irrelevant to one's expectations, as the case may be. Knowledge, therefore, is essentially in the shape of general laws, i.e. in the shape of statements about regularity. It is true that there is other knowledge. For example, our knowledge of the constitution of the atmosphere as a ratio between oxygen and nitrogen is not the knowlege of general laws. But it would be impossible to achieve the knowledge of that ratio if we were not able to pick out oxygen and nitrogen by their respective regularities in the first place. Similarly, we have knowledge that something is the planet Venus without necessarily knowing general laws about the planet Venus. But we could not identify a certain star as a planet if we could not know of the regularities pertaining to planets. Therefore, though much knowledge is not couched in terms of general laws, it must always be derived from knowledge couched in terms of general laws.

If one meant by knowledge the mere accumulation of particular and unrelated pieces of information, the passage of time would be connected with such accumulation in a banal and trivial sense only – that is, in the sense that it takes time to accumulate particular pieces of information. Knowledge, in brief, is not a dictionary – though one could not even compile a dictionary without the ability to abstract and recognise similarities and differences and disregard what one judges to be accidental or insignificant details. Genuine knowledge is knowledge of the regularities. Every organism, even the most simple and most primitive amoebic cell, has an inbuilt ability in its rudimentary nervous system (or in what takes its place) to register information about regularities. By contrast, the ability to become consciously aware of individual characteristics and particular instances requires a well-developed nervous system and, in the end, a finely attuned sense of discrimination. The ability to pick out particular instances as such is of no great value for survival and is probably, even as far as purely theoretical knowledge is concerned, of very limited interest. The faculty which really matters is the almost Platonic faculty to pick out particular instances and *recognise* those instances they are similar to and to discriminate whether these similarities are of consequence or not. Such sorting out depends on an expectation of regularities; for only if one knows beforehand what to expect can one form a judgment as to which similarities are significant. A fly has certain similarities with an aeroplane; but it would be of little interest to study flies and aeroplanes unless one had a theory about aerodynamics which one wanted to test and examine. By contrast, if one had a theory about passenger transport, the similarities between flies and aeroplanes would become negligible.

We are here concerned with the power to make abstractions, i.e. to recognise differences and similarities. This ability depends on the ability to disregard irrelevant details, that is, to be able to abstract from individual observations and experience. We could not do so if we did not have expectations of similarities and differences. Certain experiences might tell us that flies are very small aeroplanes. Abstraction tells us that this is not so. We could not abstract unless we expected differences and kept on looking for them. Without this ability to abstract and disregard irrelevant details in the environment, the paramecium could not have survived; or rather, those paramecia which were lacking in this ability to have expectations of similarities, are not here to tell the tale. The power to abstract and to behave ratiomorphously (Egon Brunswik's term) is the result of evolution and the basic form of adaptation to the environment. In conscious human beings this remarkable ability is highly developed. But even here, 'long before one can formulate reasons for it, one often notices that a particular complex of events appears interesting or fascinating. Only after a while does one begin to suspect that there is something regular about them.'[12] One can document this observation from the biographies of great scientists. 'What precisely is thinking?' Einstein wrote.[13] 'When at the reception of sense impressions, memory pictures emerge, this is not yet "thinking". And when such pictures form series, each member of which calls forth another, this too is not yet "thinking". When, however, a certain picture turns up in many such series then – precisely through such return – it becomes an ordering element for such series, in that it connects series which in themselves are unconnected. Such an element becomes an instrument, a concept.' I. Bernard Cohen described Newton's 'style' in a slightly different way. Newton, Cohen writes, displayed his style in an alternation of two phases of investigation. In the first phase, he deduced the mathematical consequences of an imaginative construct which was founded on a simplified and idealised natural system. Next, he compared the deductions with observations of nature and somewhat altered the initial construct accordingly, and then deduced again the mathematical consequences, and so on.[14] Phase one begins usually with nature simplified and idealised, i.e. with expectations of regularities and the omission of details.[15] One can see the same process at work in a completely different description of Newton's mind. Frank E. Manuel, relates how Newton, in early childhood deprived of his beloved mother, kept longing for her and was powerfully drawn to distant persons. Since this yearning never found expression in sexuality, it could have 'achieved sublime expression in an intellectual construct whose configuration was akin to the original emotion.'[16] There might well have been a relationship between this longing and a later intellectual structure in which a sort of an impulse to attraction is a key term descriptive of a force. The picture of attraction at a distance turned up again and again. Newton, therefore, disregarded the details so that he could make the attraction to his distant mother and the attraction of the planets to the sun similar, in spite of obvious differences in almost all details.

The Increase in Universality

We count as knowledge only knowledge of universal regularities. We have explained how we can think of such knowledge without imagining that it is built up laboriously from the summation of particular observations. We can now detect that knowledge of universal regularities embodies the notion of progress or, more precisely, embodies automatically the idea that the growth of knowledge is unilinear in the direction of progress.

Progress consists in the formulation of theories which are more and more universal, so that with the help of one theory we can understand or explain phenomena which used to be separate and for the understanding of which we used to need two or three different theories. Progress in this sense is a matter of increasing depth, not of an increase in reclaimed land. 'I suggest,' Popper writes, 'that whenever in the empirical sciences a new theory of a higher level of universality successfully explains some older theory *by correcting it*, then this is a sure sign that the new theory has penetrated deeper than the older ones.'[17] Progress in the sense of an increase in depth means that Newton was a progress over Galileo and Kepler; and Einstein, a progress over Newton. The DNA theory of molecular biology is a progress over Mendelism.[18]

The demand for the greatest possible universality of general laws is not a demand for a virtuoso performance or a form of misguided monism which requires all knowledge to be deducible from one single formula. The demand follows directly from the notion of radical criticism. It would be perfectly feasible to rephrase any expectation of regularities, even the meanest one, as a general law. 'When diaphragms contract, lungs will fill with air.' The knowledge expressed in this general law is very elementary. It explains why lungs fill with air. But it then leaves something else unexplained, i.e. the general law about lungs and diaphragms. Why, we may ask, do lungs fill with air when the diaphragm contracts? Critical judgment must seek to explain, and the best explanation is to obviate the unexplained general law by producing another general law of higher universality which enables us to deduce the correlation between lung-filling and diaphragm-contraction. If we can deduce this correlation as well as many other things from the new general law, we will call it more universal than the law which merely correlated lung-filling and diaphragm-contraction. Thus, the move towards higher universality and the preference for laws of higher universality derive directly from the criticism that the initial general law did not explain much and stood, in turn, in need of an explanation. The more general laws are subsumed under fewer laws of greater universality, or the more different phenomena can be explained from fewer general laws of high universality, the less is there left to be explained. In this fashion, knowledge grows by the universalisation of knowledge. As general laws of high universality make general laws of low universality superfluous, our ignorance decreases when fewer and fewer low-universality laws remain to be explained.

The growth of knowledge is therefore not a growth in pictorial or representational accuracy, but a decrease in the kind of knowledge which stands itself in need of further explanation.

For an old-fashioned or traditional empiricist, 'progress' will mean a transition to a theory that provides more empirical tests for its basic assumptions, and this means that progress consists in greater accuracy and more justification. A little reflection will show that this notion of progress is unimportant or even misleading. All knowledge enables one to make predictions about the future. But it is possible to measure the quality of one's knowledge and the quality of one's predictions by two different standards – one sensible, and the other absurd. Let us look at the absurd one first. One can measure the quality of knowledge by the accuracy of its predictions. Imagine weather forecasts in New Zealand. New Zealand consists of islands surrounded by the Pacific Ocean; when the forecasters and meteorologists are following their knowledge, their forecasts show a very high degree of incorrectness. This derives from the geographical situation of the country, which makes accurate prediction almost impossible. Suppose that somebody in New Zealand forecasts the weather by tossing a coin. It is likely that his predictions will have a higher degree of accuracy than the predictions based on meteorological knowledge. If one measured the quality of 'knowledge' by the accuracy of the predictions it yields, one would in New Zealand have to prefer the coin-tossing method to the meteorological method.[19]

The other standard of measuring the quality of knowledge is not based on the accuracy of the predictions one can make, but on the smallness of the number of laws one needs in order to make predictions. The fewer general laws needed, the better the knowledge. One can see that it is more sensible to speak of progress when one has to use fewer general theories. Such progress consists then in an increase in explanatory power. If one speaks of progress if there is an increase in the accuracy of one's predictions, one would often have to consider a theory such as coin-tossing for weather prediction to be a progress over meteorological knowledge – which clearly would be an absurdity. If knowledge is always knowledge of general laws, and if knowledge grows by the formulation of more and more universal laws, knowledge cannot be representational. Every statement of regularities always transcends the finite observations we can make. No general law, whatever its degree of universality, can be said to depict or represent a state of affairs.

Newton's breakthrough is a special instance of this contention. Newton did not just observe nature and did not just produce mathematical principles; but he produced *mathematical principles of nature*. Nothing in nature was described accurately by these mathematical principles and the old question whether nature has to be mathematical to be described by Newton's or anybody else's mathematical principles does not arise. The growth of science takes place by the increasing universality of theories. Theories are supplanted by theories which have *greater* universality, and it is in this that the growth of knowledge consists. Theories are never, or hardly ever, supplanted by theories which have a comparable range in universality. The growth, in this sense, is guided by the purely rational consideration that a more universal theory is preferable to a less universal theory. Consider as an example the case of optical phenomena. When some of these phenomena could not be explained by Newton's particle theory of light, one had the choice of giving up Newton's particles or Newton's optics. The choice was made in favour of Maxwell's conception of light and against the idea that light is particles because at that time Maxwell's conception of light as waves was a more unifying and universal theory than the theory that light consisted of particles. The so-called paradigm shifts do not take place at random. A paradigm is not dropped because it happens to explain x, y and z instead of a, b and c. The substitution is more likely to take place when the new paradigm has a greater universality and explains not just x, y and z, but also w, x, y and z. As is well known, Kuhn has argued that there is no progress in paradigm shifts. But he is able to maintain this argument only because he never compares paradigms according to their range and their explanatory power. As soon as one takes the universality of paradigms into consideration, one can see that there is usually a rational ground for the shift and that the shift is in the direction of greater universality.

Or consider the history of the nature of heat. The caloric theory of heat had been able to explain all sorts of things, but it received its death-blow from the understanding of the atomic nature of matter. The kinetic theory of gases as developed by Boltzmann and Maxwell linked phenomena of heat to molecules in continual motion. Here, we find that progress is made because there was a shift towards a paradigm of greater universality.

If progress is a growth in universality, we must presume that greater universality is greater truth. Truth itself is not the factor which provides the momentum, for it would be very hard to define truth as anything other than accuracy of individual or particular observations. If one presumes that the momentum in the growth of knowledge is furnished by a desire for the achievement of truth, one will remain ineluctably bound to deriving knowledge from knowledge of particular observations rather than from knowledge of regularities. Nevertheless, truth does come into the matter because when we explain four phenomena rather than two by one single theory, we must presume that we can do so because the theory which explains four rather than two phenomena has greater truth. So while truth is not itself a guiding principle, it is a value which is ultimately linked to universality. Our preference for greater universality follows from our insight that knowledge has to be knowledge of universals and not just detailed information about myriads of particular instances. Knowledge enables us to *deduce* detailed information. Hence, the more universal knowledge is, the greater the amount of detailed information we can deduce from it. The progress in the growth of knowledge is therefore not an intentional move towards greater truth, but we presume that greater truth is an unintended outcome of that growth.

In broad terms, the growth of knowledge is very similar to evolution itself. Evolution takes place because natural selection makes use of materials which had evolved earlier and which had been put at its disposal.[20] Helium develops from hydrogen and lungs from gills –never the other way round – and such development is an irreversible process. In knowledge there is a similar irreversible process when planetary motion and the temperatures of gases are explained by one single theory when before there had been two different theories. Progress is ascertained when a new theory explains old observations *as well as* new observations. A new theory which explains only new observations, leaving old observations *un*explained, would have very little to commend itself and would certainly not be considered improved knowledge.

Progress in Knowledge and in Art

Knowledge differs from all other human pursuits and institutions by virtue of its progressiveness. In all other pursuits – such as art, literature, morals and social institutions – there are changes, but no progress. If one sees progress in any of these pursuits it derives from the extraneous declaration that there is a value in some forms of art and not in others, or in some social institutions and not in others. If one does not set up such a heteronomous goal for art, literature, morals and social institutions, one cannot discern progress in the changes they are subject to. The elevation of heteronomous values for art, literature and morals is, at best, fairly arbitrary. If one believes that the goal of art is the production of 'beauty', one can certainly discern progress in some of the changes of style – except that one will end up by realising that 'beauty' itself is a value which is subject to paradigm shifts. If beauty will not do, one could try, for art, 'accuracy of depiction' and then assess progress in terms of an approach to accuracy of depiction. However, 'accuracy of depiction' is itself a heteronomous standard for art because it is not essentially part of the artistic enterprise, but only one of its many possible goals. By this heteronomous standard, Andy Warhol's *Coca Cola* would be a progress over Picasso or Jackson Pollock. On a more sophisticated level, Suzan Gablik[21] has argued that one can see the history of Western art as a series of cognitive revolutions, the last of which is the modern period in which the artist has at long last learnt to reason purely in terms of verbal propositions without recourse to images or other concrete materials. Titian and Rembrandt may have aesthetic merit and be praiseworthy, but are on a lower level of development than Don Judd or Sol LeWitt. Modern art, in this analysis, is at long last on the level of thought exhibited by adults.

This approach really depends on the establishment of art as a cognitive enterprise and on the consequent elimination from art of aesthetic criteria. If one abides by aesthetic criteria, one cannot see the changes of style of which the history of art consists as progress; this must lead to the acceptance, in the history of art, of relativism. If one is afraid of relativism, one will be driven to attempts to assimilate art to cognition. The intellectual progress of E.H. Gombrich is a telling example of what happens when fear of relativism intrudes into the history of art. In his early book *Art and Illusion*,[22] Gombrich argued that no artist has an 'innocent eye'. An artist, he claimed, can never start with the observation or imitation of nature; all art, therefore, must remain conceptual. The manifestations of visual expression, on this view, are conventions. If there is a shift of conventions – a paradigm shift – it cannot be counted as progress and cannot be explained in rational terms as a 'better' solution to a problem or as a solution of a larger number of problems. In this view, Gombrich committed himself to a view of the history of art in which differences of style are utterly relative and beyond rational criticism. In a more recent collection of essays, *The Image and the Eye*,[23] Gombrich, wary of relativism, prefers to assimilate art to cognition and is moving in the direction of treating artistic expression as a form of knowledge. According to a relative view of art, the depiction of the moon as a square is as good as a depiction of the moon as a circle. If aesthetic considerations prevail, there is no reason why these two depictions should not be equally good, provided they satisfy certain aesthetic considerations. But if one treats artistic expression as a form of knowledge, then the moon as a square is not as accurate as the moon as a circle. In this last volume, Gombrich is trying to look upon the history of art as a non-relativistic enterprise which aims at conformity to visual perception. Gombrich now starts with the visual image, considers it to be inherently truthful because of the evolutionary pressures which would have eliminated men had their visual perceptions been consistently inaccurate or misleading, and then proceeds to judge artistic production in terms of visual perception. In this way, he goes diametrically against the argument in his *Art and Illusion*, but manages to establish that there is progress in art and succeeds in eliminating relativism from the succession of styles.

The question at the heart of this matter is whether one can reasonably consider art as a form of cognition or not. If one does, then Gombrich's assimilation of art to knowledge and the consequent detection of progress in art is valid. However, if one considers art to be guided by aesthetic considerations, this assimilation to knowledge is unacceptable and one is left with the conclusion that there is no progress in art. In such a case, Gombrich's attempt to set up visual perception as a criterion for art must remain an attempt to set up a heteronomous goal.[24]

The denial of progress in art does not necessarily mean that changes in style are entirely random and incapable of rational explanation. There are styles of art which create real problems. Impressionism, in solving the problems posed by romantic realists or naturalists, eventually created a new problem. Realists such as Delacroix or Ingres had managed to paint people and objects that looked like 'real' people. But in so doing they had done violence to the mechanisms of visual perception. We do not see outlines of landscapes, the impressionists argued, but bits and pieces of colour in different shapes; if we do manage to spot a human being or a landscape, it is only by summing up the total impression created by the bits and pieces. Thus, they concentrated on the spots of colour. This, in turn, created a new problem because when we have lots of bits of colour, the canvas to be filled by them has to be organised in its own terms and cannot be considered a medium to be used. Cézanne accordingly concentrated on the patterns of colour which covered the canvas and, in so doing, opened the way for cubism. The cubists, in turn, explored the shape of the bits of colour and organised them in formal patterns, even though often enough they ceased to be clearly recognisable people or landscapes. And from here there was only one little step to the utter formalisation of art and to abstract art. Here, we have a development of styles of painting which is the result of problem solutions. However, one cannot really detect progress. For there is no reason why we should consider Kandinsky or Picasso a progress over Ingres and Delacroix. There certainly has been no net gain by Picasso, even though we can see that he 'solved' problems posed by the alleged naturalism of Delacroix.

Or consider the law of progress in art discovered by Wölfflin.[25] According to this law, art develops from a geometric or linear style to a convoluted or 'painterly' style. Wölfflin had no difficulty in showing that in Europe the art of the Renaissance had changed from the linear style of, say, Fra Angelico to the painterly style of Rembrandt. Had he looked for examples outside Europe he would have found confirmations. The changes in style in Moghul tombs in India can be explained very well by Wölfflin's law. The earlier Humayun tombs are linear. From there we get the more convoluted composition of the Taj Mahal and, finally, the utterly 'painterly' appearance of the tomb of Aurangzeb's wife in Aurangabad. This development can always be explained as the result of exploration. First, one draws in lines and outlines; then one experiments with the colours inside the outlines; eventually, one leaves out the outlines and produces forms and shapes by an organisation of the colours alone. However, there is again no progress in these changes. The changes are the result of experiments suggested by the techniques of drawing and of using colour and of the chemistry and viscosity of the materials one uses for making colours. One's preferences for linear art or for painterly art will be governed by heteronomous standards which in themselves have nothing to do with art as such and are not an essential part of art. The difference between art and knowledge is obvious. In knowledge, we are aiming at universality right from the start. An increase of universality is an essential part of improved knowledge and the progress which is produced by such an increase is not a progress in accordance with a heteronomous standard, but a progress in the autonomous standard of knowledge itself.

Without the inbuilt notion of universality, changes in knowledge and the entire historicity of knowledge could never be seen as growth and progress. There are in fact many philosophies of science – and I am not thinking only of the extreme case of Positivism and its view of all changes in knowledge merely as discarding errors – which do not consider the inbuilt notion of universality and which see, therefore, no progress in knowledge at all. Without the inbuilt notion of universality one is very readily left with the laconic view that knowledge is not different from art and literature. Positivism had its simple idea of progress. It believed that progress resulted from the elimination of error, and that errors kept being eliminated because careful observation of nature and of people would constrain one to eliminate error. Progress would thus be obtained by the minute reproduction and duplication of everything one picked up by observation. Knowledge was seen as a second world, a mirror-image of the world or a reflection of the world in the mirror of the mind. Once one lets go of this simplistic Positivism in which knowledge is a duplication of what is 'out there', one is left without an appreciation of progress – unless one understands the role of universality. When that role is not understood, one is left with a variety of choices each of which eliminates the possibility of progress in knowledge. Among the alternatives to a Positivistic determination of knowledge by observation, we can take our pick: according to some, knowledge consists in unfalsified guesses; according to others, knowledge is what happens to be advantageous to the ruling class; and others, again, think that knowledge is determined by the social relations or the social structure to which the people who hold it are subject. None of these views considers the universality factor and all are therefore left to see no progress in the growth of knowledge or the changes to which knowledge is subject. We discover here a stance which is diametrically opposed to that of Gombrich. Where Gombrich wanted to combat relativism by assimilating art to knowledge, we find here a number of thinkers who want to establish relativism by assimilating knowledge to art and by wiping out the reality of the distinction.

Some centuries ago, the belief in alchemy and witchcraft was fashionable. In some places in the modern world, it is the custom to believe in voodoo. Some millennia ago, people had confidence in sympathetic magic. In the modern world, where Western culture dominates, some people believe in Quantum Mechanics and General Relativity. Not so very long ago, the ancestors of these same people used to believe that Newtonian Mechanics was true. There is no accounting for tastes and all these fashions are much of a muchness. Who knows, we might find black magic or hermetic cosmology attractive before long. The attentive reader may think that I am here parodying Paul Feyerabend. In fact, I am merely reporting the theories of so respectable and staid a professional anthropologist as Mary Douglas. Little has changed in a thousand years, she writes.[26] We still talk of pollution and danger. A thousand years ago, we were afraid of witches. Today, we are afraid of industrial and nuclear pollution. Some may imagine that we have ceased to fear witches because we have found out that witchcraft is imaginary and cannot be practised. But, according to Mary Douglas, the truth is that we have stopped persecuting witches (persecution was a form of social control) because we have found alternative methods of social control. There has been no growth in knowledge, merely a shift of the *locus* of authority from the centre to the borders, so that we now fear pollution from industry where before we feared pollution from witches. With this kind of argument, the pursuit of knowledge is completely relativised and shows no more progress than the pursuit of art or literature or the changing pattern of social control on which all the other pursuits depend.

Once the distinction between the pursuit of knowledge and all other human activities has become blurred, it becomes also increasingly difficult to distinguish between different kinds of knowledge such as black magic and Quantum Mechanics. And, finally, it appears as a puzzle that Newtonian Mechanics should have been replaced by General Relativity or, for that matter, why Aristotle's theory of motion should have given way to Galileo's theory. 'Viewed *sub specie aeternitas* scientists (even physical scientists) are a fickle lot. The history of science is a tale of multifarious shifts of allegiance from theory to theory.'[27] The problem appears precisely when one is looking at science *sub specie aeternitas* instead of looking at it as a historical phenomenon. The difficulty is compounded if one assimilates the pursuit of knowledge to all other human pursuits, for then one can see nothing but changes and the change from Newton to Einstein must appear mysterious. Only when one sees the pursuit of knowledge as a special phenomenon and understands that it is a pursuit which shows progress rather than mere change.[28] can one grasp how misplaced the expression 'fickle' is in this context.

So far, knowledge has been characterised by two features: alternative pieces of knowledge (rather than error and truth or strictly incompatible alternatives), and universality. The presence of alternatives has led us to the essential historicity of knowledge and the presence of universality in all knowledge has shown that the notion of progress is inherent in the conception of knowledge, and that the historicity which depends on the presence of alternatives is unilinear in the direction of increasing universality.

The terms 'science' and 'knowledge' have been used interchangeably, as if they were synonyms. This usage was intentional. In common usage, 'knowledge' is a wider concept than 'science'. However, it seems to me that nothing but confusion can arise when one is seeking to maintain a rigid distinction between the two terms. If one maintains a distinction, one will be tempted to include in knowledge false knowledge (hermetic cosmology or witchcraft, for instance) and tempted to imagine that science is that part of knowledge which is absolutely true knowledge, knowledge of which one can be certain. Such temptations ought to be resisted and one of the surest ways of resisting them is by treating 'knowledge' and 'science' as synonymous.

Any decision between competing pieces of knowledge should be taken to be a question of preference, not a matter of either/or. One's preference is determined by comparing the degrees of universality of the knowledge in question and consistent preference of the more universal produces progress. Such progress is rational because it results from the unrelenting criticism[29] of the less universal and the consistent preference of the more universal.

Knowledge is also characterised by other qualities. First, there is a common-sense preference for quantifiable and precise knowledge. But quantification and precision are only valuable because they make criticism easier. They have no intrinsic value. Second, one tends to prefer knowledge which leads to predictions, and by that standard much of Freudian psychoanalytical knowledge is ruled out. Nevertheless, it can often enlighten and enrich[30] and no knowledge should be ruled out simply because it does not lead to predictions. Third, one tends to prefer knowledge which has been 'accepted' to theories which are held by people in solitude. But if one prefers knowledge which has been 'accepted', one allows that the people who have accepted it have removed it from criticism by their 'acceptance'. This is not to say that knowledge which has withstood criticism should not be 'accepted'. It is merely to say that 'acceptance' as such cannot be a characteristic of knowledge.

Fourth, one tends to regard certainty as an essential quality of knowledge. But since knowledge is knowledge of universal regularities, no such knowledge can be in any sense certain. Fifth, to many people knowledge is cumulative. But since progress of knowledge consists in our ability to explain more and more of the known particular facts by fewer and fewer general laws, knowledge cannot be said to have grown by accumulation of information about particular events. The above list of properties of knowledge is a list of accidental properties which are valuable if and only if they make criticism easier or more convenient. In no instance ought one to criticise any knowledge because it fails to live up to any preconceived and dogmatic standards of quantification or certainty; or because it does not yield predictions or does not add new particular pieces of information to the store we already have.

The Mechanics provided by Criticism

We are thus left, in addition to the notion of alternatives and universality, with the notion that knowledge can count as knowledge only when it is criticised. The best definition of knowledge, therefore (leaving aside alternatives and universality), is that we count as knowledge every theory which is left standing when all conceivable criticism has been temporarily exhausted.

If criticism is to play such a crucial role in the characterisation of knowledge, and if it is to join the presence of alternatives and the inbuilt notion of universality as senior partner, so to speak, one will have to make sure one understands what one means by it and whether it is the same as 'rationality'.

On principle, in making criticism the crucial quality of knowledge, one is saying that in knowledge all statements are open to criticism. This initial move invites an immediate rejoinder: the statement that all statements are open to criticism is open to criticism. If it is not, the counter-move continues, it ceases to be part of our knowledge and, what is more, it ceases to be part of our knowledge of knowledge.[31]

I do not consider this counter-move to be significant. The counter-move may well be legitimate and, indeed, should be legitimate. But it does not follow from such legitimacy that it will lead to *valid* criticism of the statement that all statements are open to criticism. All it says is that the statement that all statements are open to criticism *could* be criticised. This amounts to saying that the statement that all statements can be criticised is not a dogma or an article of faith and that it does not enjoy any privileged status. If and when it has been criticised validly, we will have to think again. This I take to be the meaning of W.W. Bartley's Panrationalism. As he himself says, Panrationalism is more a matter of attitude than of logic.[32] This Panrationalism also draws our attention to the intimate connection between criticism and rationalism. We say, if we are Panrationalists, that it is rational to criticise everything and to hold on to only those statements which have so far withstood criticism. In this view, 'reason' does not denote a substantive faculty or a correct method of arriving at statements which are true; but a negative quality. When one is rational, one is open to criticism and an absolutely limitless invitation to criticism is the essence of rationality. Any view held in defiance of criticism, for whatever reason at all, is an irrational view. If rationality is not a substantive faculty like 'the dictate of right reason' or 'obedience to observation', but merely total criticism with no holds barred, it is perfectly conceivable that two people who make opposite conjectures and hold incompatible views are *both* rational as long as they will encourage and tolerate and digest criticism of their views.

In Panrationalism, nothing is exempt from criticism and *all* criticism is legitimate. It is just as legitimate to criticise by saying, 'I have a gut feeling that . . .' as by saying, 'It is self-evident that . . .' as by saying, 'Observation shows that . . .' There is no criticism that is privileged or more 'rational' than any other. Somebody may criticise by appealing to authority; somebody else, by appealing to tradition or to consensus. It is then open to the opponent to rebut and an appeal to, say, authority is only reprehensible if it implies a denial of Panrationalism – that is, if it implies an invitation that the authority appealed to must not be criticised. No criticism can be ruled out in advance. One has to allow any criticism and see what happens. One cannot lay down guidelines that the criticism that position A is contrary to observation is a 'better' criticism than the criticism that position A is contrary to gut feeling.

Mostly when invitations for criticism are issued, it is implied that criticism must follow certain 'rules'. For example, one may start by pointing out certain inconsistencies in the views of one's opponent. Then one may demand to know what observations entitle him to hold his views, and so forth. In short, one behaves as if there were guidelines for criticism and as if criticism meant simply a standard scrutiny of one's opponent. If all standards are met, it is assumed, criticism must stop. But all guidelines (does the view satisfy experience? is it consistent? is it formulated correctly in the linguistic sense?) are nothing but disguised attempts to define correct knowledge in advance. If there were such guidelines, one would have to know what kind of knowledge one is seeking; one would have to know, in other words, what one seeks to know. Such guidelines are then nothing but standard checks to see whether any proposed knowledge actually conforms to one's definition of knowledge.

The crux of the matter is that one cannot, in advance of having knowledge, say what knowledge is and then determine the royal road for getting there. In order to find knowledge we must proceed 'rationally'. But we do not mean by proceeding 'rationally' that we know beforehand what we want to find and that in employing the correct method (say, observation) we will be sure to get there. On the contrary, 'rationality' is just a word to describe the correct way of finding out what is going on by using unlimited criticism. Let us go briefly through all possible meanings of 'rational' to see what we will be left with when all trivial or false uses have been eliminated.

To be rational is to make valid inferences. In this sense, the word 'rational' has a substantive meaning, but the procedure is trivial.

We also say that we are 'rational' when we are behaving intelligently. Intelligence, however, is not a rational faculty at all. It is a state of mind where we are aware of the fact that we have a choice between at least two possible courses of action or thought and we choose the 'right' one. If we are guided by experience and if we can make a proper judgment by drawing on our evaluation of the consequences, we are acting intelligently. Such choice cannot, however, be described as a rational choice.

One could, however, define arbitrarily what would be the 'right' choice. There are two possible ways of defining 'right' in this context. We could define 'right' as what is compatible with sense observation (leaving the question of whether there ought to be falsification by observation, verification by observation, corroboration by observation, etc., aside). Or we could say that to make the 'right' choice is to obtain the consensus of a speech community, of the participants in a language game, of professional colleagues, etc.

If we decide on the first definition of 'right', we are pretending to know what the world is really like. We assume we have an ontology and that the world is the sort of entity which can best be fathomed by observation. This way of defining 'right' must be dismissed because it forces us to pretend that we really know what we are setting out to find. The inadvisability of such a procedure becomes very clear when we try, for argument's sake, a different ontology. Suppose somebody says that the world was created by God. It would, in this case, be 'rational' and 'right' to abide by the authoritative verdict of a person who claims that God had revealed Himself to him. In this case, tradition and an authoritative interpretation of that tradition would appear more 'rational' than observation.

If we decide on the second definition, we next have to decide the question as to *who* is a rightful member of the community whose consensus we will go by and *why* a majority decision of such a community should be accorded privileged status. Following Wittgenstein, there have been many philosophers who have advocated that we must abide by the rulings of such a community. Pragmatically, this is quite commendable. But one must resist the temptation (which Wittgenstein and his many diverse followers have not been able to resist) to mistake that kind of consensus for the truth about the world. Nevertheless, if one sets up the rules obtaining in community as the ultimate criterion and prefers that criterion to an ontology, one will be forced to conclude that 'rational' behaviour in thought and action is 'obedience to the rules'.

It takes very little reflection to see that in the two cases examined – deference to observation and deference to rules – one is using the word 'rational' to describe the means to reach an end and not to describe the 'correct method'; at least, it describes 'correct method' only in so far as the end to be attained is independently known. 'Rationality', in both cases, is not a procedure to find the truth, but a method for getting to a goal which, in turn, is set up independently and not subject to rational scrutiny. Though this kind of rationality is a substantive procedure, it is a procedure which will not go far towards the acquisition of knowledge.

It is also possible to turn this whole matter around. One can say that one abides by observation as something rational *because* the rules of the community one is a member of decree that the word 'observation' be used in a certain way. Here, we find that 'observation' is a function of being a member of a community and gets its credentials from the rules obtaining in that community.

Conversely, one can say that the people who abide by observation as something rational form a community, and that the membership of that community is defined by 'willingness to abide by observation'. People who are so willing are people who believe, irrationally, in a certain ontology, i.e. in the ontology which makes observation the most likely method to make true statements about the world.

No matter which way one turns this matter around, one is always left with the same conclusion: rationality is a means to an end. The end is either an ontology, belief in which defines membership of a community; or membership of a community, which membership decrees that the word 'observation' be used in the way the community decrees. Either the ontology in question is the non-rational and unquestioned goal or the membership of a community is the non-rational, unquestioned, ultimate, brute fact. Either way, the exercise of 'rationality' is a means to an end which is itself not capable of rational examination.

Thus, we conclude that if we make the first definition of 'right', we are in reality using the word 'right' to describe a means to an end: that is, a means for discovering the true qualities of the world which we seem to know before we even start our journey of exploration. If, on the other hand, we are making the second definition and define 'right' as obedience to the consensus or rules of a community, we are also using 'rational' and 'right' as a means to an end, i.e. the end of determining by whose decision we will abide. In either case, the value or validity of the end itself is extra-rational.

Thus, we come to the last and only reasonable meaning of 'rational'. It means free, total, uninhibited and unlimited criticism. The only rule for rational behaviour is that no criticism can be ruled out.[33] In this sense, 'rationality' is not a substantive faculty which, if used, yields the desired truths. It is a purely negative exercise, something performed on and against positions and statements. We say a person is rational when he is prepared to offer his non-rational thoughts or behaviour to criticism. Rationality, then, has nothing to do with discovering thoughts or assuming stances, but with the criticism of these thoughts and stances.

It may seem as if there were a *prima facie* similarity between scepticism and rationalism. Scepticism and rationality have, in fact, something in common. They both agree that we must reject the view that knowledge is true if we have a compelling or good reason for it or if we have arrived at it by the correct road. But then comes the difference. Rationality leaves knowledge standing if there is no good reason for rejecting it. Scepticism, on the other hand, is dogmatic. It doubts or rejects even when there is no good reason for rejection. Scepticism, in other words, is merely the dogmatic opposite of dogmatism.

Panrationalism is an extension or extrapolation from biological evolution. In evolution, proposals are made and the decision as to which organism will be selected is left to the consequences of the proposal. There is no initial plan and no correct way in which mutations will have to occur, not even a preliminary sizing-up as to which mutations (i.e. proposals) are likely to have a better chance. Any philosophy of science which leaves the ultimate decision entirely to criticism and forgoes preliminary knowledge as to what one wants to know, how one ought to go about it and what procedure is most certain to lead to the right goal, is constructed on the model of biology. By contrast, any philosophy of science which sees the acquisition of knowledge as the result of 'right' procedure and which validates knowledge by reference to, and in terms of, the procedure employed in finding it, is constructed on the model of physics, where causation is energy transfer.[34] In such a philosophy of science, correct knowledge is the result of an acknowledgment of a stimulus. Provided the stimulus is allowed to transfer its energy without hindrance or distortion, the resulting knowledge must be correct knowledge of the object in which the stimulus originated. The philosophy of science extrapolated from biological evolution operates without causal connections between knower and known. It assumes that there are proposals and that these proposals are relentlessly criticised.

In following the example of evolution, we can also get a clearer appreciation of what we mean by rationality. Rationality, we argued, is not a substantive faculty which allows us to follow a procedure which would be 'right' and which would lead to the desired results. It is a negative faculty of relentless criticism. However, in taking biology and evolution as our guide, we can also see that criticism which appeals to observation and uses observations to falsify pieces of knowledge (regardless as to whether they are general theories or particular statements) is preferable to any other kind of criticism. If one were to allege such a view in cold blood – that is, without biology and *in vacuo*, so to speak – as if it were absolutely true, one would stand on very shaky ground. Why, a critic might legitimately ask, is a referral to observation and falsification preferable to an appeal to authority or to a referral to tradition or intuition? *In vacuo* one cannot have an answer to such a question; and this is the reason why all old philosophies, from Bacon to Locke right down to the Vienna Circle, must break down. They imagine, without any good reason, that sense experience or observation is somehow privileged. However, when one is speaking in a biological context and understands knowledge as a relationship between an organism which has evolved in a certain environment and that environment, one can see that *observation* does indeed occupy a privileged position. Moreover, it occupies this privileged position when it is used to falsify, for falsification is a procedure in harmony with the general process of evolution. The proposals which are made in the form of theories are not induced from, or induced by, observations; nor are they incorporated, as Lamarck would have us believe,[35] through observation (or learned adaptation), into either organism or theory. The proposals are thrown up spontaneously and, having been thrown up, are checked, tested and possibly falsified by the environment. For this reason, the use of observation for falsification is biologically justified. We thus get a double presumption. First, there is a preference for observation as against other sources of knowledge; and second, there is a mandatory preference for using observation to falsify rather than to verify or induce because, like organisms, nervous systems propose knowledge to the environment but do not build it up piecemeal by making random observations.

However, we must end this discussion of rationality with a word of caution. In evolution, the consequences of non-fitting proposals are relentless and merciless. As soon as *Homo sapiens* arrives on the scene, there is a fundamental change which has important consequences for the philosophy of knowledge one derives by extrapolation from biological evolution. Man is capable of creating societies which differ from species in that they are artificially circumscribed by culture. Any culture interferes with the process of critical selection of theories because it consists, in an important sense, of the nurture of a body of knowledge which enables people to gauge in advance what they set out to discover. Proposals in the form of theories are therefore not exposed to radical and relentless criticism but are shielded by the prevailing knowledge embodied in the culture. Unlike organisms, theories are protected artificially from the consequences of falsity. For this reason, it has been possible for false theories to flourish for millennia without falling victim to rational criticism. In a culture, rational criticism cannot be permitted lest the knowledge which forms part of the social bond be endangered. The only rational thinking which is permitted is of the means–end type. The end is set by the prevailing culture and can therefore not be falsified by further criticism. This phenomenon has been well observed and described by the many sociologists of knowledge who have been able to show how, in any one culture, the knowledge considered valid is a fairly rational outcome of the intelligent means available in that particular culture.

Culture shields us also in a different sense from the consequences of false theories. Every culture creates a mutual-aid system which makes it impossible for people to suffer directly the consequences of their folly and of their cognitive failures. It organises co-operation between its members and this co-operation enables societies to flourish in spite of their maintenance of false knowledge. We will return to this topic in chapter 7.

Reason, then, is the negative activity of criticism – and, moreover, the negative force of total criticism. If one exempts any proposition from criticism, one is not rational. Truth is what is left standing when all criticisms are exhausted for the time being. In that sense, reason and truth are interdependent. There can be no such thing as an irrational truth. Truths are *found* by methods other than rational procedures. They become rational truths if and in so far as they withstand criticism. Thus, when we speak of the rationality of science, we do not mean that science is the sum total of all the propositions we have been led to by following the dictates of reason; rather, we mean that we believe those propositions to be true which have not fallen a victim to criticism.

If reason is not a substantive force but merely an attitude (i.e. we should speak of having a rational attitude to knowledge) rather than an ability to find knowledge, it is ultimately linked with the notion of radical criticism. Criticism can demolish knowledge, but never assure us that what is left is known with certainty; for what is left can always be criticised the following day. A rational attitude to knowledge is an attitude one has *after* the knowledge has been invented; not a device for inventing it.

By the same token, genuine knowledge can never be *certain* knowledge. It is common usage to equate science with certainty. If we follow the correct method, it is alleged, the findings will be securely established and we will have *certain* knowledge as opposed to superstition, guesswork, hearsay, revelation or subjective musings – all of which are the results of seemingly incorrect ways of finding knowledge. The real reason why they lead to incorrect knowledge is that they are often exempt from criticism or that they are insufficiently criticised; not that they have been discovered by following an 'incorrect' method. These and similar methods are not suspect in themselves, but are made suspect by the fact that they are either linked to the avoidance of criticism or are considered proof against criticism *because* they are alleged to yield true knowledge.

It makes no sense to use the word 'scientific' as an adjective. One should never deny scientific status to any piece of knowledge as distinct from any criticism one can make of its contents. Followers of Marx defend the 'scientific' status of Marxist knowledge; opponents of Marx reject the claim that Marxism has 'scientific' status. In this debate, the discussion centres upon the question whether the truths of Marxism have been arrived at by the 'correct' method. If so, Marxism has 'scientific' status and one need not examine whether its theories are true. Such a debate is senseless. It is based on the idea that there is a 'correct' method and that one can distinguish in advance between scientific knowledge and non-scientific knowledge. If one does, one implies that there is a special kind of knowledge which has been reached by the 'correct' method. What one is really saying is that since it is 'scientific' because it has been reached by the 'correct' method, it is not open to criticism. If one wants to use the word 'scientific' as an adjective, one can use it to describe only that knowledge which has been left standing when all criticism has been exhausted. Since such exhaustion can be only temporary, there is really no point in using the adjective at all.

The consequences of the conclusion that there can be no certain knowledge must also be applied to our knowledge of knowledge. There are not only limits to our knowledge of the world and of ourselves, but also limits to our knowledge of knowledge. If our knowledge of the world remains open-ended, so does our knowledge of that knowledge.

There is a certain presumption that our cognitive apparatus, being an adaptive response to the world, does not get its messages and responses totally wrong. If it did, we would not be here. Organisms who make habitual mistakes are not here to wonder about it. A monkey who keeps misjudging the distance from one branch to the next branch would soon be a dead monkey and have very few offspring to perpetuate that kind of error about the environment. However, *Homo sapiens* is not just a monkey. He conceptualises his 'knowledge' and, in conceptualising, can easily make mistakes. Unlike the monkey, the concepts, regardless of whether they are right or wrong or misleading, can be used to construct cultures. They can, for example, be used as social bonds. All men who subscribe to certain concepts are constituting a certain culturally defined society. People in such a society will practise co-operation and mutual aid and thus effectively protect themselves from the disastrous consequences of the mistaken concepts they are using as social bonds rather than as instruments for orienting themselves in the world.

In view of this process by which *Homo sapiens* has been able to exempt himself from the relentless natural selection to which all other organisms are subject, it is frequently suggested that *Homo sapiens* has only one way open to him. Since he cannot rely on natural selection to weed out his conceptual mistakes, he has to give his allegiance to whatever concepts happen to be going in the culture of which he is a part and to the protection of which he owes his survival in the face of his mistakes. This suggestion is the main burden of Richard Rorty's *Philosophy and the Mirror of Nature*.[36] Having lost (though Rorty does not spell this out but takes it for granted) the stern corrective selectivity of nature, man can avoid mistakes only by voluntary submission to the epistemic authority of his culture. Above all, he must submit by depriving philosophers of their arrogant habit of criticising cultures.

Without being able to contradict the argument that man has indeed lost the natural correctivity of nature by his ability to use concepts for the construction of cultures, and mindful of the fact that even our knowledge of knowledge is uncertain, I would nevertheless argue for a different strategy. Rather than recommending submission to the authority of our culture, I would plead that we see to it that our cultures are reorganised in such a way as to remove artificial protective barriers – such as dogmatic adherence to certain kinds of knowledge or dogmatic rules governing the use of words – and create instead as open a situation as possible in which there is competition between alternative theories, between alternative usages of words and concepts. Hence, the mistakes made in the formation of concepts can be criticised and corrected.

To be sure, not even the availability of alternatives is the same as suffering the direct consequences of mistakes in the animal world. The consideration of alternatives and the selection of the least criticised one is quite different from natural selection. Nature kills the organism which is not adapted. The most we can do is to kill the theory we can criticise. If we don't, we will still survive. Thus, the consequences of mistakes are never really dire – unless we imagine ourselves in a totally unreal situation in which we have no families and no friends and no social support at all. No matter how open a culture, the minimum support which would protect us against mistaken selection of concepts would always be there. Inside a culture, no matter how open the culture, when one has chosen critically one of the available alternatives, one would still be protected from the immediate consequences in case one has chosen the wrong one. One would at least be protected from the immediate consequences. Seeing that we cannot achieve certainty, and least of all certainty about knowledge, we must leave the matter here and merely confess that, in leaving it, we are more honest than those followers of Rorty who are prepared to seek refuge behind the epistemic authorities of their culture, thus using a stratagem to create the semblance of certain truthfulness.

Descriptive Epistemology

The connection between knowledge and its history is intimate. Even the most daring scientist and researcher must watch other researchers and it is only from the history of science that he can learn what constitutes an experiment; how far he may go in inventing *ad hoc* hypotheses in order to salvage a theory contradicted by observations; under what circumstances he may dismiss an observation as an accident; and what the implications of incompatibility are. One could give hundreds of examples. But these brief indications suffice to show that, in an important sense, the scientist learns his craft from history, i.e. from the examples of others. This does not mean that scientists do not learn from their contemporaries as well. It merely means that scientists have to learn their craft and that since much of their craft was practised in the past, they learn from history as well as from their fellow-scientists. Even learning from an older teacher is like learning from history.

History is a sort of schooling. At the same time, it is also more than schooling. The philosophy of science is no longer 'abstemiously restricted to a logical analysis of the status of scientific truth,' D.T. Campbell writes. 'While there is a strong interest in explicating the normative decision rules science should use in deciding between theories, this gets mixed up with arguments about which decision rules science *has* used, implicitly or explicitly, in presumably valid decisions in the past, and thus can be seen as a hypothetical, contingent search for normative rules . . . For such theory of science, the history of science is fundamentally relevant.'[37] For this reason, some of the finest books on science are cast in a historical mould: L.N. Cooper's *Introduction to the Structure and Meaning of Physics*,[38] R. Gregory's *Mind in Science*,[39] François Jacob's *The Logic of Life*,[40] as well as Jonathan Miller's more popular *The Body in Question*.[41] It is true that there are still a few philosophers of science who persist with a purely formal approach to the philosophy of science. This approach has been christened the 'Received View' and is presented as an introduction in Frederick Suppe's *The Structure of Scientific Theories*.[42] But when one looks at Suppe's alternatives to the Received View, one finds Toulmin, Kuhn, Hanson, Popper and Feyerabend. These philosophers of science have nothing in common except the fact that their alternatives are all history-oriented. Each one of them has a philosophy of science which deals with, and accounts for, the historical dimension of science. It would seem that in the philosophy of science we are faced by an impending paradigm shift away from Suppe's 'Received View'. We cannot tell yet quite in what direction the paradigm is going to shift. The present book is meant to determine this direction. But whatever the ultimate direction, it seems bound to move towards an acceptance of the historicity of science and away from the static Received View which has enabled philosophers of science to treat science in a purely formal and systematic way, as if it had no history or as if its history were an accidental by-product and of no relevance to science itself.

If the history of science is basically a sort of descriptive epistemology because it is concerned with how people have acquired knowledge, it can, by itself, be no guarantee that the knowledge so acquired is true. For this reason, philosophers of science, and especially scientists themselves, have often shown no interest in the history of science. But this is only one side to the question. The other side consists in the fact that we *have* acquired knowledge and in learning *how* we have succeeded in doing so, we can learn something about the constitution of the world which has made it possible for us to do so. To quote D.T. Campbell again: 'I also want descriptive epistemology to include the theory of how these processes could produce truth or useful approximations to it: in what possible worlds, in what hypothetical ontologies, would which knowledge-seeking processes work?'[43]

Look at the emergence of the molecular theory of gases. At first, it seems, it was an ingenious metaphor, culled from French sociology.[44] This 'how' was no indication of truth. But tests enabled the metaphor to be declared literally true. It became a dead metaphor[45] and now these molecules can even be observed by means of electron microscopy. The study of this particular history of science involved description as well as normative considerations; the normative precepts derived from it tell us something about the constitution of the world in which one can arrive at some truth by starting with metaphors. 'The rationality of science,' S. Toulmin says, 'cannot depend solely on the formal validity of the inferences drawn within the scientific theories of any given time . . . We can recognise the source of science's explanatory power only if we come to understand also what is involved in the processes of conceptual change: in particular, how the character of these processes can give authority to new concepts, new theories, even new methods of thought, inquiry and argument.'[46] The concept of field, for example, 'was introduced by Faraday to aid him in visualising the effects of charges on other charges,' writes L.N. Cooper.[47] 'Maxwell attempted to visualise the electric field as a mechanical stress in the medium of space, the ether. Since that time, the electric field has acquired a significance deeper than any such mechanical interpretation and, like some other concepts, such as momentum or energy, finally becomes more important than the specific theories out of which it came.'

There is a peculiar irony here. For a Positivist, the nature of the material itself decides all questions of truth, experiment and *ad hoc* hypotheses. It is only to the non-Positivist that these questions are not themselves part of the subject-matter of science. For this reason, however, the non-Positivist becomes the very man who has to find out what actually happened in the history of science (i.e. he is the man who has to ask a question which bears a notoriously Positivist stamp). To the Positivist, on the other hand, this notoriously Positivist-sounding question is a matter of peripheral and negligible curiosity.

If this kind of connection between knowledge and history is

intimate, there is another kind of link which is constitutive of the very conception of knowledge. The human nervous system – and I will take it for granted that we mean by knowledge a certain relationship between that nervous system and the environment – has evolved on a large planet moving with a comparatively low velocity. This means that for all practical purposes and certainly so far as the mere survival of that nervous system is concerned, the nervous system is adapted to large masses and low velocities. Its powers of perception as well as its faculties of concept-formation are therefore primarily formed in attempts, by trial and error, to adapt to this kind of environment in which bodies move and in which their position in space and time is always known.[48] When sophisticated apparatus and sophisticated interpretations of the observations made with sophisticated apparatus became known, it turned out that human beings have considerable difficulty in adjusting their powers of perception and intuition to the idea that there are sub-atomic particles moving with velocities approaching the speed of light and whose position in time or space cannot be known with certainty or, if we know their position in space, we cannot also, at the same time, know their position in time and vice versa.

In inviting the reader to imagine what it might be like to live on an atom, I am inviting him to imagine what it might be like to have *evolved* on an atom or electron and to be adapted to it. This is quite different from inviting somebody to imagine that he is an atom or that he is the size of an atom or electron so that he can witness what happens when electrons jump from one orbit to another. The second invitation has been proposed as a thought experiment to help with the ontological problems created by Quantum Mechanics.[49] I am not here concerned with a thought experiment, but with the important fact that there is an essential link between the fact that we are here on earth and not on an electron and the faculties at our disposal for understanding that we are here.

Our nervous system has evolved as a successful adaptation to a space which contains bodies and which is something absolute, not something which results from the relations between bodies. When asked to consider that space is a 'property' of bodies, our mind boggles and an intuitive grasp of such a consideration becomes well-nigh impossible. This indicates that there is a sort of historical significance in the fact that Euclidean geometry and absolute space were discovered before we began to use Riemannian space and the

Uncertainty Principle. It is indeed inconceivable that it could have been the other way round. By contrast, we could try an experiment of thought. What would the history of science have been like for creatures existing on sub-atomic particles moving with the speed of light? One could argue convincingly that, for such creatures, the discovery of Riemannian space and of the Uncertainty Principle would have been easy and natural; probably as natural or no more difficult than the discovery of Euclidean space and the principles of causality presupposed by the laws of gravity in absolute, Newtonian space was for human beings living on a comparatively large planet moving slowly round the sun. However this may be, it would seem that there is a real and significant link between the growth of knowledge and the progression from Euclid to Newton, and from Newton to Quantum Mechanics. It is no accident, given the evolutionary pressures our nervous system is subject to, that the progression of knowledge was not the other way round. We could, in other words, not conceivably have started with Quantum Mechanics.

Physicists frequently state that the description of their theories in 'plain language will be a criterion of the degree of understanding that has been reached.'[50] Professional scientists may not take such statements too literally; but they enshrine an important truth about the historicity of the whole scientific enterprise. First, there comes common-sense understanding; later, sophisticated mathematical formulation. However, since our senses and the nervous systems which control them are adaptations to the common-sense environment, the eventual reduction of complicated concepts to common-sense language is by no means just a matter of scientific popularisation and of attempts at science for the layman. It is, on the contrary, an essential part of the whole scientific enterprise. Vision has become specially adaptive, and more adaptive than smell, to bipedal creatures. On top of vision we get the adaptiveness of consciousness and of the words that are linked to consciousness. This trio – eyes, consciousness and words – determines nine-tenths of our perception of the world. Thus, we are creatures to whom the presence of a limited object such as a chair or a table is the referent of a word and an entity which is located at a given time in a certain space. When we see the same entity somewhere else, we must conclude that it has moved and that time must have elapsed. In this way, our evolutionary conditioning militates all along against an intuitive grasp of Quantum Mechanics.

Frege believed that true knowledge must be based on changeless, ahistorical properties and relations. This view is untenable. First, our neurophysiology is the product of natural selection by an earth environment. This means that, at best, its mental imagery is compatible with macro-events. It cannot grasp or formulate concepts which are an exact fit to macro-events, let alone to micro-events. Hence, it can never be a precise mirror of nature; only a lamp which partially illuminates nature. Next, knowledge is always growing knowledge. Like species themselves, any bit of knowledge is unstable and can be eliminated. Hence, there cannot be unchanging and ahistorical properties of knowledge. To say that there are, is like saying that no matter what the species, light sensitivity is always the same and always interpreted by its owner in the same way. In the growth of knowledge, we always operate with such loose concepts as 'force' or 'energy'. At one point, Newton succeeded in giving a precise mathematical definition to 'force at a distance'. It turned out 200 years later that while the concept had been defined with the utmost precision, there was nothing it referred to because Newton's gravity (i.e. 'force at a distance') was instantaneous and there can be nothing faster than light. The concept of 'maximum velocity' was loose, too. Then it came to be defined precisely; and now some scientists are beginning to wonder whether light *does* move with the maximum velocity possible.

All efforts to establish that our knowledge is based on unchanging and precise concepts and their relations to propositions, etc., are efforts to establish rules, in advance, for right knowledge and wrong knowledge. Both Frege and his opponents – Kripke, for instance – are, ultimately, inductivists. They believe they can arrive at truth not by error elimination, but by following the correct procedures for formulating propositions. Some of their propositions, they grant, may turn out to be empirically false. But they think that half the battle is won if the words have the precise referent. Knowledge being what it is, nothing is won – even if the words had the precise referent.

We are quite used to speaking of 'curved space' when light is bent as it passes near the sun. Such an expression must be a metaphor to bring the complicated calculation involved in General Relativity within the layman's reach. But the apparatus used for the measuring of the effect of the bending is not a metaphor. Not only does it exist on earth and can be handled, but the correctness and accuracy of the observations involved depend on what the human eye can see with the help of that apparatus. In the end, even in physics and chemistry, data have to be analysed with the help of the eye. True, we have electronic microscopes and sophisticated scanning devices. But, in the end, the pointer readings have to be made by the human eye. In physiology and biochemistry, many experiments are designed to elucidate 'invisible' spatial structures. But the ultimate goal of these experiments is to produce three-dimensional pictures or a series of pictures of atoms in space. 'Visual perception,' John Ziman writes, 'plays a vital part in the most aristocratic branch of experimental science – the physics of elementary particles.'[51] In the bubble chamber, high-energy-charged particles make visible tracks which can be photographed in order to be examined by the human eye and inspected for unusual 'events'. These and many other considerations show that the historical connection between common-sense reasoning and sophisticated mathematical formulation of theories has always to be kept alive and that the unilinear development of scientific theories from ordinary observation and learning to abstract theories is an essential and inevitable ingredient in scientific knowledge. The connection is indeed historical in essence and in its nature. It is not just a 'historical' accident in the sense that we might be able to conceive that the physics of elementary particles could have been generated in some other way. The connection has evolved and could continue to evolve. It is not static. All efforts to give a permanently valid description of the connection between formal languages and natural languages is therefore misguided; and so is the Frege enterprise and everything which goes with it to determine the eternally valid links between language and reality, reference and referent.

The historicity of knowledge is further underlined by the development of modern physics. For a long time now, we have looked to physicists for information about what the world is really like. In an important sense, the trust that physicists would find out was linked to some form of materialism. If the world is made of matter, then it was reasonable to expect that people who study the behaviour of matter would be able to tell us what the world is like. Physics was at first phenomenally successful in the quest for the real world. Whenever there were discrepancies between intuitive observation and the findings of physicists, one explained them in terms of the differences between appearance and reality. The world, we used to say, appears one way and *is* another. It may *be* as in Plato's *Timaeus,* but *appears* as in Aristotle's *De Anima.*[52] Motion may appear to be the result of a push, as Aristotle observed; but is in reality a permanent condition unless stopped, as Galileo reasoned.

Eventually, however, the belief that one was tracking down matter disintegrated. Matter turned out not to be a stuff, but particles; and atomic particles revealed themselves more and more sub-divisible until finally the sub-atomic particles turned out to behave as if there were no local causes, no absolute locations, and as if communications between them were instantaneous and faster than light. If this were not enough, even the old gap between matter and life and between matter and mind seemed capable of being bridged – not because life and mind turned out to be material events, but because matter turned out to be less and less like solid stuff: even when fairly solid, matter emerged as capable of negentropy and self-organisation and thus similar to the activity performed by what we thought were purposeful minds. If we stick with the distinction between appearance and reality, we are now faced with such a huge discrepancy between the world as it appears – the world with local causes and determined movement of particles which have velocity and at any moment in time a determined location – and the world as it is alleged to be in reality according to Quantum Mechanics and the Principle of Indeterminacy. These two worlds are so much at variance that the old explanation that the one is the world of appearance and the other the world of reality, will not sound plausible. On one hand, we have Quantum Mechanics and, on the other, a macroscopic world in which we are living, in which everything has a cause, in which one can locate particles, and in which we are rationally entitled to insist that events are either like bullets or like undulations but that they cannot be, under any circumstances, both at the same time. There have been many attempts to bridge the gap. We have been given theories about hidden variables and infinite worlds to resolve the paradoxes of Schrödinger's cat and Wigner's friend, paradoxes which arise when one is looking with eyes formed and evolved in one world at the events taking place in the other world.

It will be helpful if one applies historical reasoning to this problem. Our cognitive apparatus has evolved in a macroscopic world and we are living in a mesocosm[53] and are adapted to it. The stuff which has evolved is made of the stuff to which we are adapted.

This historical process is quite intelligible and has led us to perceptions in which local causes are paramount and ultimate. Knowledge of this ultimateness and paramountcy is a historical product of the interaction of molecules with each other, from the primeval soup in which life originated to the evolution of the nervous system of *Homo sapiens*. This historical process is not an illusion or an appearance of an underlying, different reality. It is simply what has happened when molecules behaved in a certain way. The knowledge which we derive from the historical end product is a sort of self-reference of molecules. Molecules, organised in a certain manner, will react to other molecules in an adaptive manner, i.e. tell us about local causes and the relationship between velocity and location in time and space.

However, these same molecules can also stand in a different relationship to each other. When, instead of letting them evolve as living systems *vis-à-vis* non-living molecules and *vis-à-vis* other living systems, we start bombarding them with sub-atomic particles and split them up into the sub-atomic particles they consist of, we simply get a totally different kind of relationship between electrons and protons and muons, etc. The difference in these relationships is not due to the fact that one is an error or that one is an appearance of an underlying reality; neither is it that one is governed by hidden variables and the other is not. The difference results from two lines of evolution. In one line, we get living systems in relation to their environment; and in the other, sub-atomic particles in relation to each other. Though both sets of relationships are made up of the same 'stuff', they reveal themselves in different ways. If one bombards sub-atomic particles with sub-atomic particles, one will get one set of relations between them. If one allows atoms to form molecules and then lets molecules self-select each other to produce living matter, one will find that the relationship between such molecules is different from the relationship which emerges when sub-atomic particles are related to sub-atomic particles. Looking at the problem in this historical way, the variance the mesocosm we are conscious in and the microcosm we are only conscious of is not only not surprising, but is precisely what one would expect. At bottom, there is only one world. But depending whether the knowledge we have of it is one kind of self-reference or a different kind of self-reference, this one world refers to itself in at least two different ways. In one way, the self-reference is molecules as living organisms to each other and to non-living molecules; and in the other way, the self-reference is sub-atomic particles to sub-atomic particles. In one self-reference, there are local causes and in the other, there are not.[54] One arrives at this view of the problem by realising that our knowledge of local causes is neither a chimera nor an error, and that the absence of local causes is not a fault in our understanding of Quantum Mechanics[55] but that the knowledge of local causes is the result of a very specific historical process to which molecules have subjected themselves. If one studies the sub-atomic components of these molecules by bombarding them with other sub-atomic components, there are no local causes.

The relationship between scientific knowledge and its history is made even more complex by the fact that the growth itself is no validation of the knowledge acquired, not even of knowledge tentatively and temporarily held. Both in individual life-spans and in mankind as a whole, knowledge is acquired, discovered and learnt. All this takes time and is slow. Allowing for the fact that some of the preconditions for all these acquisitions are to a certain extent genetically programmed, we are merely shifting the problem of the historicity of science further back. For the genetic programming in, say, a human being, is itself the result of millennia of evolution by natural selection which is at bottom a process of knowledge-acquisition. At any rate, taking the genetic preconditions into account, there still remains the fact that the process of subsequent learning and acquisition cannot be automatically a validation of the knowledge acquired. Biological organisms which make too many mistakes in this acquisition get eliminated by natural selection. But theories learnt and formulated by conscious human beings have to be scrutinised artificially. The mere acquisition and survival, in this particular case, cannot be a guarantee of validity. Hence, the need for a philosophy of science and, more specifically, for a philosophy of science which takes cognisance of the fact of the historicity of science.

The Sociology of Knowledge

Finally, we come to an almost accidental link between knowledge and history. Ever since it was discovered that cognition is not completely constrained by nature and that there is a gap between what we know and what our observations might oblige us to know, philosophers have realised that the way the gap is to be filled might be determined by sociological factors and, further, if filled by sociological factors, they must vary with the passage of time so that what we know changes with the passage of time. Thus was born the sociology of knowledge.

The sociology of knowledge consists of a formal part and a substantive part. The formal part seeks to derive our ability to abstract and to form expectations about the regularities in the environment from man's social experience. Examples of this derivation have been discussed above, in the section entitled 'The Faculty of Abstraction'.

The substantive part of the sociology of knowledge deals with the actual content of knowledge and seeks to explain it as a function of social experience or social self-interest. Since thought is not rationally determined, the sociology of knowledge says, it must have a social or existential basis.[56] There is ample room for speculation and exploration here. Some sociologists have tried their hand at explaining the rise of Protestantism as the result of the penetration of sixteenth-century regimes by vested interests. This penetration weakened the regimes and made the Catholic belief in the immanence of God implausible.[57] Other sociologists have attempted to explain the support of scientific research at the expense of magic, astrology and alchemy in the seventeenth century as the result of the Puritan spirit of prudential calculation.[58] There is a famous book which relates the rise of Newton's Mechanics entirely to the growth of the bourgeoisie in early-eighteenth-century Britain,[59] and another in which the coming of Quantum Mechanics is explained in terms of the social turbulence of the German Weimar Republic. The Uncertainty Principle, we are told, sounded plausible and quite certain in a society in which all traditions and values had become uncertain.[60] Similarly, we have often been told that the reception of the theory of natural selection in the nineteenth century owed a lot to the aspirations of the liberal bourgeoisie because the theory appeared to countenance capitalistic competitiveness. Cartesian mechanism, to look at another example, with its emphasis on single elements and the clock-like relations between them, mirrored a society of alienated individuals and the division of labour governed by iron laws of economic self-interest. And again, the Central Dogma of molecular biology (DNA instructs proteins and proteins carry out these instructions) appeals to people who are used to a society in which intellectual labour dominates mere production and designs, execution. It is the science, the argument goes, of the white-collar elitist. In yet another example, we are told that seventeenth-century mechanical philosophers insisted on the passivity of matter and the view that particles do not move or do not stop by themselves and on a divine ordering of natural law because these views seemed plausible in the light of their latitudinarian social and religious convictions.[61]

In a famous pronouncement, Marx generalised this explanation of knowledge by saying that the ruling ideas in each epoch are the ideas of the ruling class. The German socialist philosopher Ernst Bloch maintained that formal logic is a bourgeois invention to validate the status quo. Formal logic, he says, never yields new truths. By logic, one can make explicit only what was implicit in the premisses. Hence, formal logic is the paradigm of conservatism and ought to be rejected by revolutionaries who are trying to change society.[62]

On a more systematic basis, Mary Douglas has endeavoured to explain cosmological theories in terms of the social structures of the societies in which they are prevalent. Societies with a strong centre of authority have one kind of theory; societies with a weak centre, another.[63] Even more systematically, Berger and Luckmann have produced a famous book in which they seek to show that our entire knowledge of reality is a function of our social experience and varies with our social experience.[64] In all these pursuits there is a very strong realisation of the links between history and knowledge; for as social structures change with history, so does the knowledge which appears plausible to people experiencing the structure or is inspired by the structure.

The rise of the sociology of knowledge is intimately linked to the decline of Positivism. As long as people thought that knowledge is what observation obliges us to believe, there was no need to seek an explanation for why certain people hold certain pieces of knowledge outside observation. At most, one went to the psychology of perception and the mechanisms of speech acts to explain delusions of perception and errors of expression. The great founders of the sociology of knowledge, from Marx on, have all been Positivists of sorts and have therefore argued that our knowledge of nature, being based on observation, is exempt from sociological explanation because it can be explained satisfactorily in observational terms.

Even Durkheim argued that there was no need to doubt the objectivity of scientific knowledge of nature just because we know that our ideas of time, space and cause, and our ability to classify, are constructed out of *social* elements.[65] Mannheim, too, considered knowledge of nature exempt and capable of standing on its own feet. While other knowledge varies and fluctuates, knowledge of the immutable laws of nature grows by simple accumulation which represents the growth of knowledge. As far as our knowledge of nature was concerned, there was no need to run to sociology to explain its presence and its growth.[66] Even the younger generation of sociologists of knowledge openly confess to some kind of Positivism. David Bloor, for example, argues that we can distinguish between perception and thinking in our knowledge. In so far as knowledge is grounded on perception, there is no call for a sociology of perception. It is only when we are faced by the 'thinking' part, i.e. by the theoretical component, that a sociological explanation is required. The theoretical is the social; the observational is governed by nature.[67]

There is, then, a long tradition in the sociology of knowledge in which knowledge of nature is identified with Positivism and observation; on this view, only non-observational knowledge as it displays itself in religion, art, literature, morals and politics is in need of a sociological explanation. At first glance, one might therefore think that our entire rejection of Positivism as an explanation for the acquisition and growth of knowledge of nature would drive us all the more firmly into the arms of the sociology of knowledge. If not even knowledge of nature itself (contrary to the ideas of Durkheim and Mannheim) cannot be exhaustively justified in terms of observation or reduced to protocol sentences, it must be explained as the function of something other than experience of nature. The recourse to the sociology of knowledge, it would seem, becomes all the more urgent, the firmer one is in one's rejection of Positivism.

There is, however, a third way out. If we all reject Positivism nowadays, we still have a choice between a sociological explanation of knowledge and a biological explanation of knowledge. The correct rejoinder to the sociologists who would welcome us into their parlour now that we have given up Positivism is that the non-experiential and *a priori* parts of knowledge can be explained biologically and that the recourse to a sociological explanation is unnecessary. It is perfectly true that one cannot justify any theory exhaustively and conclusively in observational terms. But it does not help and seems unfruitful to argue that therefore the theory in question must be explained as the dictate of class interest or a reflection of a social structure in which the people holding it are living. If one chose this recourse to sociology, one would soon deprive knowledge of its relational character and reduce it, as indeed the sociology of knowledge does, to some kind of narcissistic reflection of the known in the mirror of one's own social existence. If biology does not work and if the biological derivation of the non-experiential component in all knowledge had to be given up, we might indeed be left with nothing better than a recourse to sociology. But until such time as the biological explanations are refuted, we should not wilfully and voluntarily embrace a sociology of knowledge which impoverishes our knowledge of knowledge. As long as we have biology up our sleeve, it does so needlessly.

If the main link between knowledge and the recourse to a sociological explanation merely results from a disregard of biology, there is also a more sinister link. On the old view of knowledge, knowledge was the result of correct observation and correct reasoning. Provided one did not make mistakes and provided one did not allow oneself to be side-tracked by neurotic obsessions and phobias, one would be entitled to expect that correct reasoning and correct observation would lead to correct knowledge. However, for some time now we have recognised that there can be no such 'correct' reasoning and no such 'correct' observation because in order to distinguish between 'correct' and 'incorrect' observation and reasoning, one would have to have an ontology – i.e. one would have to know in advance what the world one wants to know is like. Since one cannot have such an ontology without knowledge, the derivation of the 'correct' method of acquiring knowledge from prior knowledge of an ontology has proved futile. The reasonable move, once this is recognised, is to admit that knowledge is not acquired by the pursuit of a 'correct' method; rather, it is what is left standing when criticism has been exhausted. We have seen in the above section on 'The Mechanics provided by Criticism' that this move is the sensible answer to the demise of Positivism.

The sociologists of knowledge, however, have refused to accept this answer. Instead, they have continued to think that if there is knowledge, it must be the result of a 'correct' method of getting it.

Seeing that there can be no 'correct' method, they have jumped to the conclusion that the reason why it is not correct and why it does not yield universally true knowledge is that it is the dictate of class hatred or of a prevailing mode of production, or reflects a social structure. In other words, the contribution of the sociology of knowledge to this whole debate has consisted in an attempt to unmask and expose the real reason why people have pursued a certain method to acquire knowledge. Instead of giving up the notion that if one has knowledge there must be a correct way of getting it, the sociologists of knowledge have engaged in what appears as an enlightening manoeuvre: if one exposes the real reason behind scientific method, one will know more than one did before the real reason was exposed. In this sense, the sociology of knowledge has been able to parade as a form of enlightenment because it has purported to reveal what is *behind* the so-called 'correct' method. In the present argument one must, however, conclude that the pursuit of such a strategy is not enlightening but a form of deception. Genuine enlightenment would consist in the recognition that there is no correct method; not in the revelation that there is an ulterior purpose in the pursuit of the correct method.

Suppose, however, that the pursuit of knowledge is not a rational pursuit and not the result of following the dictates of substantive reason. Suppose, instead, that we pursue knowledge by allowing proposals and hypotheses to be put forward and then expose them to criticism. In such a situation, we consider those beliefs to be knowledge which has withstood criticism. Truth is what is left over, after criticisms have been exhausted. On such a view of the growth of knowledge, there is no denying the gap. But there is no need for a systematic investigation as to how the gap was filled and what factors had to be invoked to follow the path of reason from observation and experience to perfect knowledge. On the view that the growth of knowledge is the result of criticism rather than the result of obedience to the dictates of substantive reason, and on the view that rationalism is the pursuit of criticism rather than an enslavement to the rules of 'reason' – the sociology of knowledge becomes superfluous.

Nevertheless, sociology has a very important contribution to make to our knowledge of the growth of knowledge. Its contribution does not consist in the substantive explanation of how the content of knowledge is determined sociologically, but in a negative explanation of why knowledge is rare and intermittent and why it needs very special social conditions in which it can grow. It is common knowledge that the growth of knowledge is very intermittent and discontinuous, and that it happens only in very few places. Most of it occurred during the last three centuries, though there was a certain amount in ancient Greece. It is therefore not far fetched if one seeks an explanation for this curious phenomenon in history or, more specifically, in the history of social structures.

While certain basic knowledge about the weather, the growth of seeds, the nurture of animals, and similar matters, is subject to the selective pressures of the environment – people who believe that animals reproduce non-sexually cannot survive if they are dependent on meat and other animal products – there are many pieces of knowledge held consciously which have very little direct bearing on physical survival. They can be held or discarded regardless of the environment in which the people who hold them are living. Nevertheless, they are frequently used for a very useful function. They are used as a social bond so that societies can be formed with defined members and these societies can survive because defined membership makes co-operation and division of labour possible. Membership, we might say, is defined by subscription to certain beliefs about God, nature, the universe, man and his destiny, and so forth. One might describe this kind of social bonding as catechismic, for membership of such a society depends on being able to give the 'correct' answers to a catechism. Clearly, in such a society the contents of the beliefs used as a catechism are not available for criticism and therefore cannot be examined. They are held dogmatically. Such dogmatism should, however, not blind us to the fact that it performs a very useful and essential function in keeping the society together. One might say that knowledge, in such cases, is being used for non-cognitive purposes. One could compare such non-cognitive purposes with the non-monetary purposes for which money is frequently used. Money is intended as a means of exchange. But given modern opportunities for communication, it has turned out that it can also be used as a commodity and that its value, in such cases, is not determined by the availability of the goods and services it represents, but by the supply and demand for money itself. There is no denying that the non-monetary use of money serves a useful purpose, just as the non-cognitive use of knowledge can serve a useful purpose. In such catechismic societies, one has to protect knowledge artificially from criticism. Knowledge has to be elevated to the rank of dogma. The easiest way of doing this is by stopping communication with outside societies in which other knowledge is used, possibly also catechismically. If communication has to occur, one has to take other steps for protecting one's own knowledge, lest it be criticised and, at least in part, abandoned. If it were to be abandoned, the bonds of society would become loosened. If knowledge were submitted to trial and error, this would be tantamount to dissolving the social system. In catechismic societies, people have to adopt a mercantilistic attitude to knowledge. In catechismic societies, people practise cognitive mercantilism and thus exempt knowledge from the pressures of a free market.

Though there are many societies which are quite literally catechismic because they require a confession of faith or a subscription to a set of beliefs as a qualification for membership, there are many other societies which are only metaphorically so. In these societies, there is a catechism but no formal declaration is required for membership. On the contrary, members are born into the society and in being born into it they become automatically committed through nurture and possibly even through heredity to certain axioms, values, sentiments and beliefs which remain impervious to experience and indifferent to contradiction. They are present in the society before the individual is born and will continue after his death. In this sense, they are not psychological features but social constraints. To an outsider, it will appear as if every baby, at birth, is baptised to a certain catechism; but in reality, the catechism involved is merely a hypostatisation. In reality, it is part of the social constraint which shapes every individual's life and does not permit questioning because of the character of the social order concerned.[68] It follows, therefore, that only in societies where the social order is non-catechismic (i.e. cognitively neutral) can beliefs and theories be examined critically. For trial-and-error testing one needs the presence of alternative theories. When a social system consists of a given set of theories about the world, it is impossible for alternatives to be entertained. But when a social system is open or neutral, then the presence and entertainment of alternative theories will make no difference to the social system. In this way, the progression of scientific knowledge is accidentally related to social systems. This is not to say, as so many people have alleged, that one can take one look at the structure of a social system and determine from that structure what kind of theories the people in that social system will believe to be true. On the contrary, the truth of any theory is quite unaffected by the social structure of the society in which it is held to be true. But it does mean that since knowledge depends on the possibility of trial and error and that since trial and error depends on the presence of alternative theories which, if the old ones do not pass the trial, can be substituted and, in turn, subjected to further trial and error, there are certain kinds of society in which genuine knowledge cannot grow. If one recognises this, one will still not be able to determine what special kind of knowledge can grow in societies in which knowledge can grow; but one will be able to detect the kinds of societies in which beliefs must be held dogmatically because they are part of the very social structure itself, the kinds of societies in which genuine knowledge cannot progress. By the same token, we can determine the optimum social conditions for the growth of knowledge, although none of these conditions in itself will enable us to say what kind of knowledge will grow or, after it has grown, why this particular kind of knowledge grew under these particular conditions. This connection between social conditions and the opportunities for the growth of knowledge constitutes a sort of negative sociology of knowledge.

This negative sociology provides two explanations. First, it explains the optimum conditions for the growth of knowledge. These conditions are at their best when cognitively and intellectually there is something resembling perfect competition. This means that there are no exigencies of social bonding which would exempt any piece of knowledge or belief from radical criticism. This, in turn, would mean that there is absolutely no belief or knowledge which is required to fulfil an extraneous social or psychological function, such as encouraging co-operation or providing emotional comfort. This, in turn, would require a situation in which co-operation is derived from and based upon a different mechanism (i.e. different from the community-forming power of shared beliefs and shared rituals). It would also require a situation in which people are either not in need of emotional comfort from certain beliefs – that is, they are so integrated emotionally and so regenerate that comfort is unnecessary – or that comfort is provided by some force other than solacing beliefs. However this may be, one can clearly see that it is just as difficult to obtain a social field in which there is perfect intellectual competition as it is to construct a field in which there is perfect economic competition.

Second, negative sociology explains why the growth of knowledge has been so rare and so intermittent in human history. In most of the situations we find in history, the degree of perfect competition has been so low that knowledge was not able to grow. The presence of perfect competition – even of competition approximating perfection – is very rare. In this way, negative sociology can explain the absence of the growth of knowledge and explain why in a few societies, at certain times, there has been a growth of knowledge. Unlike the conventional, positive sociology of knowledge, the negative sociology of knowledge does not claim to be able to explain the content of knowledge or the reasons why knowledge with content A is, in certain societies, preferred to knowledge with content B.

The negative sociology of knowledge provides an explanation for the growth of knowledge which is in marked contrast to the explanation given, for example, by Joseph Needham.[69] According to Needham, archaic, practical knowledge can be transformed into experimental and growing knowledge provided a number of specific institutional changes are made in society. There has to be a removal of those class barriers which separate artisans from theoreticians; the development of a special attitude of curiosity about nature and society; and, finally, the growth of a specific ideology in which quality is reduced to quantity and a mathematical reality affirmed to be behind all phenomena and a proclamation of a space and time uniform throughout the universe. One can see that if such changes were to occur, a certain kind of knowledge would be likely to emerge. But in specifying the kind of knowledge likely to emerge (doctrines about uniformity of space and time, proposals to reduce quality to quantity), one is claiming to know in advance what the world is like and what kind of knowledge will be most likely to do justice to it. Such a claim, as we pointed out above, is not legitimate because it prejudges the issue by laying down guidelines for a successful inquiry. The negative sociology suggests, instead, that knowledge is most likely to grow when the social order is maintained in a non-catechismic way – that is, when it is sustained by bonds which are not made up of bits and pieces of knowledge. In such an order, knowledge can be set free and exposed to unrelenting criticism. This unrelenting criticism is, however, a luxury which most societies, depending on pieces of knowledge for their social bonding, cannot afford to enjoy. Negative sociology of knowledge also suggests that societies in disorder – for example, Renaissance Florence[70] or the

German Weimar Republic – are likely to be as favourable to the growth of knowledge as societies in which social bonds are cognitively fairly neutral. Periods of disorder and social disequilibrium have a destructiveness of their own. But they may countenance a great growth of knowledge. Take Leonardo da Vinci as an example. We may suppose that when he noticed that the Archbishop of Pisa had conspired to have the Medici brothers Lorenzo and Giuliano murdered during Mass in front of the high altar of the Cathedral of Florence, he concluded that he was living in a social disorder in which people were obviously taking liberties. Hence, he decided that it was in order for him to take liberties, too, break a taboo and study anatomy by dissecting corpses.

It is frequently argued that the discontinuity in the growth of knowledge and the stubborn survival of false but dogmatically adhered to pieces of knowledge, is due to the slow evolution of the human mind and its cognitive apparatus. The minds of mankind, it is alleged, have developed slowly. At first, their powers of perception, of reasoning and of logic were like those of young children. Piaget has documented the slow development of these faculties in children and shown how these powers improve and reach full maturity only after puberty. But long before Piaget, as long ago as the seventeenth century, philosophers like Francis Bacon, in the Preface to his *De Sapientia*, maintained that the earliest men were capable of only pre-logical and confused thinking, that they were unable to tell the difference between a metaphor and a literal description. The only thing Piaget has contributed to this line of argument is the evidence which seems to indicate that the mental growth of every child recapitulates during the first dozen years the mental development of mankind. We will leave aside the question of whether Piaget's researches were initially guided by the thought that children must be like primitive men or whether he researched and found independently that the mental and cognitive faculties of children were similar to those of primitive human beings.

The view that primitive men cannot think logically and failed to categorise their perceptions correctly has had, ever since Bacon, a large number of supporters. In the eighteenth century, it played a crucial part in the thought of Vico, Herder and Rousseau.[71] In the nineteenth century, it became the starting-point for the systematic history of human thought in Hegel, and was used in a slightly different way by the great nineteenth-century evolutionists, Comte,

Tylor and Frazer. They held that mankind had been prey to magic and religion before ascending to the liberating power of science because it simply takes time for human beings to grow up. In the twentieth century, the theory that primitive humans are incapable of rational thought and that their cognitive faculties are therefore stunted, has been revived by Lévy-Bruhl and Bruno Cassirer. The latest and most carefully documented study to this effect, by C.R. Hallpike,[72] appeared as recently as 1979. His is an important book which covers the whole ground more systematically than any of its predecessors and provides a great deal of ethnological evidence to support the claim that the mental and cognitive faculties of primitive men are not sufficiently developed to allow for the growth of knowledge, let alone for the development of science, with its abstractions, generalisations and its deductive reasoning.

Needless to say, the evaluation of all these findings is greatly influenced by the personal values of the observers. To rationalists like Comte and Frazer, this primitive mentality was contemptible. They rejoiced in the fact that we had left it behind. Romantics like Wordsworth and Herder welcomed it and developed nostalgia for it. They deplored the fact that we had left it behind and regretted that children, in growing older, abandon their straight intuitive powers. In between, there are the values of Lévy-Bruhl and Cassirer, who both took a more balanced view of the development. They appreciated the advantages of pre-logical thinking for community life and for being in tune with nature itself. They also appreciated the development of cognitive and logical faculties in modern man without regarding this development as a fall from grace, as the romantics had done.

In the twentieth century, on the other hand, many scholars, conscious of the 'racist' implications of the view that primitive men think pre-logically and modern men do not, often prefer to stress the continuity of mental faculties – either by saying that both primitive men and modern men are capable of logical thought, or by saying that both primitive men and modern men are swayed by non-logical thinking. While one must appreciate the ethical considerations which prompt such a refusal to spot a difference in logical power between primitive men and modern men, such a view does not exactly help to explain why knowledge took so long to grow. Nothing was done to resolve this debate when Quine showed[73] that the supposed cornerstones of modern rational knowledge – the dogma that there is an absolute distinction between analytic and synthetic truth, and the dogma that all meaningful statements can be reduced to terms which refer to immediate experience – have very shaky foundations. In abandoning these two dogmas, Quine writes, the supposed boundary between speculative metaphysics and natural science must become blurred and bring about a shift towards mere pragmatism. Thus, 'primitive' and 'modern' cease to be the antithetical terms which might have explained the difference between primitive man's persistent harbouring of false knowledge and the modern growth of knowledge. If Quine is right, not even modern men can take an ability for rational knowledge for granted and such differences in knowledge as there undoubtedly are, must be explained pragmatically. A pragmatic view may have much to commend itself. In taking it, however, one must face the fact that the next question is likely to be a political one. If the prevalence of superstition is a matter of cultural accident and if the growth of critical knowledge is also a cultural accident, one recognises the justice of Foucault's remark that questions of knowledge turn out to be questions of power: Who issues the decrees? Who controls funds? Who wields influence? Surprising though it may sound, people who start with Quine may end with Foucault.[74]

Lévi-Strauss, on the other hand, approaches the question in a different way, combining a strict egalitarian rationalism with some of the pragmatic considerations suggested to be necessary by Quine. There are, he admits, cognitive differences between children and adults as well as between primitive men and modern men. But *all* human beings, he says, are capable of counting and of making binary distinctions: totemic animals are not for eating but for counting. The fact that primitive men use totemic animals for counting and for making binary distinctions rather than abstract numbers and digital computers, is to be explained by the peculiarities of their cultures. Unlike Quine, Lévi-Strauss is confident that the logical potential in man is universal and *can* be taken for granted. If it displays itself in different and seemingly incompatible ways in different cultures, the differences can be explained by the accidental contents of the cultures – not by an appeal to a pre-logical mental faculty as the romantics from Bacon to Lévy-Bruhl and Cassirer would have it. Such evolution as there has been, concerns only the content of cultures, not human nature. Take away the totem from a primitive man and replace it by an abacus or a digital computer, he is saying, and you will soon see that men are all alike in their rational faculties.

The arguments on all sides are transparently shot through with evaluations of childhood and nostalgia or with contempt for childhood and primitive life – though it has to be admitted that Quine's argument claims to be logical and is certainly not based on ethnographic data. There also has to be considered the purely psychological evidence often advanced by Evans-Pritchard. When all things are said and done, we find that there are innumerable people in the modern world, fully grown up and living in industrialised societies, who are as superstitious and as incapable of logical inference as any Zande or Nuer. Evans-Pritchard and other British social anthropologists have very successfully explained how the seemingly strangest beliefs of primitive people are part and parcel of their social system and, therefore, as long as one is standing inside that social system, not in the least 'irrational'. Given certain social institutions of accountability, for example, some witchcraft beliefs seem almost inevitable and certainly quite plausible. This method of explaining what are to us untenable beliefs, however successful for the insider and for the practising field anthropologist who makes himself an insider, begs the question. Our question is not whether under certain special circumstances a belief in witchcraft is not as strange and improbable as it might appear to us. Our question is why and when certain people ceased to hold strange and improbable beliefs. The method of looking at every belief from inside the society in which it is held, and from the inside only, is unable to answer this question.

The negative sociology of knowledge suggests that the mind of primitive man is primitive because it lives perpetually under shelter. Primitive minds are not exposed to competing claims and to competing concepts. They do not have to evaluate and compare even when they are free to exercise choices. Without competition there is no criticism and no critical selection. As a result, no concepts and no beliefs are abandoned for better or more suitable ones. This protectionism rather than a special structure of the mind of early man, makes for the primitive nature of his thought.

Whether one is prepared to follow Quine or Evans-Pritchard, Lévy-Bruhl or Lévi-Strauss, one must make sure to ask the right question. The right question is whether all human beings have an ultimate rational baseline or not. If they do, the absence of logic and science in so many societies must be explained by our negative sociology. Negative sociology explains their absence by the fact that in primitive societies logical reasoning and abstract concept-formation are inhibited because counting and binary distinctions are inhibited. The inhibition is due to the fact that these faculties are artificially protected because they are used catechismically for non-cognitive purposes as social bonds. If they do not have such a baseline, the absence of logic and abstract, consistent concepts, and the prevalence of intuition and metaphor (i.e. of what strikes us, modern observers, as metaphor) must still be explained by a negative sociology. If primitive men were *naturally* pre-logical in their thinking, negative sociology of knowledge provides an explanation for the persistence of such pre-logical cognitive habits. In using these habits as social bonds, primitive men were not exposing themselves to criticism and thus found in their social order an artificial protection of those habits which under open competition would soon have been weeded out. In both cases, the lack of development of logic or the continued presence of metaphorical intuitions must be explained by lack of competition and critical selection. This lack is due to the fact that metaphors or logic – whichever – are artificially protected by the exclusion of alternatives. They are used to define the boundaries of societies and not treated as instruments of cognition. The factor which has changed with time as we approach Western modernity, whichever way one is looking at it, is not human nature but the nature of the social constraints under which it is operating.

The best available explanation for the discontinuity of the growth of knowledge and for the variety of its occurrence must, therefore, be sought in changes in social structure and can best be explained by a negative sociology of knowledge. In early and primitive societies, people could not afford to allow such knowledge as they had about the weather, the growth of plants, sickness and the seasons, etc., to be exposed to criticism. They had to use it to define their societies and social boundaries and this use was more important for human survival than veracity. People who subscribed to that knowledge, whatever it was, were insiders; and people who did not were outsiders. Knowledge and subscription to knowledge is a more flexible form of bonding than the kind of bonding provided by blood relationships or by such physical characteristics as race and skin-colour. The bonds circumscribed by blood relationships are far too narrow and would oblige one to keep on marrying and choosing wives and husbands from far too narrow a circle. The bonds circumscribed by raçe or colour are far too wide and would include, in any geographical area, far too many people and include them indiscriminately. To make co-operation, mutual help and division of labour effective, the society has to be large; but not too large. Knowledge and the ritualistic practices which follow from it are the best available form for this kind of bonding and hence there grew up the universally practised principle *extra ecclesiam nulla salus*. The prostitution of knowledge for this purpose is bad; but its adaptive value in the history of mankind has been enormous. Clearly, knowledge so protected could not be subject to criticism and therefore had to remain at a very low level of adequacy and truthfulness. The prevalence of what we describe as primitive thought or pre-logical thinking is therefore a secondary phenomenon. It is the result of social protectionism. The requirements of some social structures inhibit the growth of knowledge in two ways. First, they protect false beliefs because adherence to those beliefs constitutes a social bond; and second, they prevent, in doing so, a critical appraisal of the differences between metaphor and less metaphorical expressions. The first inhibition concerns content; the second, the cognitive apparatus itself.

While there is obviously considerable doubt as to whether man's rational potential is universal or not or whether it has evolved gradually and if it has evolved, what the most suitable conditions for such an evolution might have been, a negative sociology of knowledge manages to by-pass this entire debate. According to the negative sociology of knowledge, whichever side one is on, one is always left with the same conclusion. According to the negative sociology of knowledge, there is no need to make up one's mind on this question or to take sides. The negative sociology accepts the findings of scholars like Hallpike: primitive men are pre-logical. However, there is no need to decide whether they are naturally so (as Bacon and Lévy-Bruhl claim) or whether they are so because of the accident of their local culture (as Lévi-Strauss claims). They are either inhibited from displaying their natural, logical potential because they have to use the beliefs they have as social bonds. Thus, they cannot expose them to competition and criticism and remain caught with whatever happens to be going. They are stuck with totemism not because they are pre-logical, but because they cannot afford to look at alternatives lest their social bonding break down. Or, they are prevented from developing forward towards logical reasoning because the kind of social order they are living in makes trial and error impossible. If the first alternative applies, they are logical but cannot avail themselves of their logicality because they cannot change the content of their culture according to the dictates of their logic. If the second alternative applies, they are pre-logical and cannot move forward towards logic because their social order inhibits the sort of discussion which alone can promote the growth of logic. Either way, there is no growth of knowledge – regardless as to whether pre-logical behaviour is natural or a cultural accident. All one should add is that the primitive mentality which is inimical to the growth of knowledge is not confined to people who are technically known as 'primitive'.

When, for a number of reasons, societies developed which were not entirely dependent on subscription to a given system of knowledge for the definition of their bonds, it became possible to criticise knowledge and release it from the bondage in which it had been kept. Thus, we find that wherever more neutral forms of bonding have developed, knowledge began to grow. Most of traditional knowledge gave way to criticism, new knowledge was invented only to give way to further criticism, and so forth. This cannot, of course, be taken literally. There is no society – not even the most modern, post-industrial, urban mass society of atomised individuals – in which the bonds are completely neutral. For that matter, even if it were, radical criticism would not be practised by everybody all the time. Even in such societies, radical criticism is really practised only by 'scientists', that is, by some people. Negative sociology merely states that the societies of such radical criticism practitioners find it impossible to exist when most of the knowledge which is available or held is pressed into the service of social bonding. When it is not, societies of criticism practitioners are tolerated. These societies – or, better, sub-societies – are held together by shared practice of criticism, not by a particular belief; not even by the belief that one ought to practise criticism. The practice of radical criticism is not based on the belief that radical criticism is 'right'. If it were, one would call such practice a commitment to a belief which, in turn, cannot be criticised. There is, however, no such commitment. Radical criticism is the simple operation of reason. While reason is not a substantive force which can tell us what is the right thing to do, it is self-sustaining or self-supporting; for it would simply be against reason to accept any knowledge without criticising it.

Finally, one should not underrate the positive contribution made by the dogmatic preservation of knowledge and by its artificial protection and the comparative stunting of the cognitive apparatus that goes with it. During the millennia of such protection, people developed the art of writing and the whole conceptual apparatus which accompanied it. In this way, even the dogmatic protection of knowledge helped to prepare the ground for the cognitive apparatus on which the eventual growth of knowledge came to depend.

The negative sociology of knowledge indicates that both Milton and Mill were wrong. Milton, in one of his most purple passages, pleaded for freedom of thought because, he argued, the truth will eventually survive and triumph over everything else. Mill concurred, though he struck a more cautious note. To silence discussion, he said, is a presumption of infallibility. The negative sociology of knowledge makes a different case. Milton was wrong because truth is not something which is there, held by some lucky people so that, when there is freedom, untruths will disappear and truth will be left standing. The negative sociology of knowledge says nobody knows what the truth is – not even what it might be. But if there is completely free discussion, some opinions or theories will emerge temporarily because people cannot think of cogent criticisms, for the time being. Mill was equally wrong. When discussion had to be silenced, people did not silence it because they thought themselves infallible, but because the knowledge they protected artificially from discussion and criticism was too precious: it was being used not as knowledge but as a social bond. The question of infallibility did not come up. Claims to explicit infallibility can only come up, and then presumptuously, when there is free intellectual competition; and, in such a situation, they cannot stand up to criticism and will be laughed out of court.

Chapter 2

The Conditions of Historical Knowledge

The Difficulty with Events

Having established that there is, in several different though not unconnected senses, an intimate link between knowledge and the growth of knowledge and having argued that this link is more intimate and more necessary than the link between the art, literature or society and the histories of these pursuits or institutions, we are now left to face an unenviable problem. The history of science is as uncertain and as relative a piece of knowledge as the history of any other pursuit or institution. It would be a comforting world if we could say that there is a history of science which we can look at and study in the way in which we can look at a beetle or a glacier.

The pursuit of science consists of events. There is Galileo observing the moons of Jupiter, Newton working out the infinitesimal calculus, a modern physicist watching a cloud chamber, Einstein pondering the meaning of simultaneity. Nobody would deny that these events must have their place in the history of science. But nobody can say with certainty what place any of these events actually has and how one event led to the next.

The history of science here is in no way different from the history of any pursuit or institution and if we have argued above that the pursuit of science and the philosophy of science depend intimately on the history of science, we are now left with the recognition that science and the philosophy of science are intimately dependent on something which we do not really know at all.

The difficulty in the history of science, as in the history of anything else, derives entirely from the concept 'event'. There are small and large events. It is left entirely to the observer how large any event is believed to be. We can call the Second World War an event. We can also call the several battles and negotiations which made up the war, events. We can further call the movements of the separate soldiers in every battle 'events', and so forth. If one now asks which event led to which event and how events hung together, one is left with a bewildering array of choices. The same is true, *mutatis mutandis,* for the history of science.

Moreover, any event one looks at is infinitely sub-divisible. Every battle consists of little battles and every little battle of the movements of soldiers and the movements of the caterpillars of their tanks which, in turn, contain events concerning fuel, military orders, plans, decisions at headquarters, and so forth. In short, the study of events, no matter how meticulously carried out and no matter how objectively reported and listed and classified, will never yield a comprehensible historical series. As if this were not enough, there is a quite different problem for the historian. Slippery soil can retard the caterpillars of tanks and cause the loss of the battle. But slippery soil as such is not obviously part of military history unless one is able to establish the quite complicated mechanism involved in making the caterpillars slip. People who do not understand that mechanism or who believe the caterpillars to have been so well built as to be immune from slippery soil, will not link the condition of the soil to the outcome of the battle.

The Difficulty with 'Succession in Time'

Or consider a different angle of this problem. Those who hope to find the relevant link between events in the way events succeed one another in time, must be disappointed. If mere temporal succession of events – leaving aside the thorny problem as to what size event one is thinking of – were a guide, it would follow that the establishment of Dominion Status in New Zealand was 'caused' by the arrival of the ship carrying the instructions issued at Whitehall rather than by a decision made in London months earlier and 12,000 miles away.

There is an old belief that, provided one rules out subjectivity and bias, one will at least be left with some real raw material, the reality of which cannot be in question. But given the above considerations, bias and prejudice are our least worries. Given sufficient care, they can certainly be eliminated – only to leave the poor observer with an unmanageable and sizeable hotch-potch of ill-assorted events of varying sizes the relevance of which to one another is unintelligible.

There is another old belief that if only one can stick to the succession of events in time, one cannot go wrong. If one follows the thread of time, the advice says, one must come up with the correct knowledge of how one event led to the next. But the above considerations show that this solacing method, too, is not available. Clearly, in a series of events presented in such a way that one event leads to the next event, one is not only presupposing a decision as to the sizes of events one is dealing with, but also jumping completely clear of the thread in which events are alleged to hang together in their succession in time. Not only would such a series exclude the statement that the occurrence of the Second World War 'led' to the marks of the pencil on a voting paper which was part of the ballot in the election which toppled Churchill from power in Britain in 1945. The advice would also make it impossible to decide, having stated that event A took place, whether it was followed by B or C because the gap of time between A, B and C can conceivably and quite readily be filled by hundreds of other events.

General Laws

In spite of these difficulties, we have historical knowledge. In spite of these problems, we know that there are historical sequences and that some events led to other events. How do we have such knowledge?

We have such knowledge because, as historians, we not only deal with events but we also have at our beck and call a large number of general laws which we believe to be true and which will tell us in advance which events hang together and which events do not hang together. We know, for example, that a bullet fired into a man's heart will kill that man or, at least, immobilise him. We know that low incomes in an age of high prices will make it difficult for some people to procure food. We know that in certain societies, orders issued by certain people will be obeyed; and that in other situations, orders issued by certain people will cause resentment rather than obedience, and so forth. Many of these general laws are culled from economics or psychology; some are daring and interesting, others are trivial. None is absolute or universal. Most of them, or a large number of them, are very limited in their operation to certain places and certain times. All of them may be errors of judgment and not really true. None of them should be taken to have 'determined' the particular events which they appear to connect as cause and effect. These general laws are used in order to enable us to look back, to understand what led to what. Even the people involved in the events concerned have to understand these events. They, too, can do so only by looking back – that is, by employing general laws to link one event to another. Whichever way we look at them, we can see that it can only be with the assistance of such general laws that we can sort out which events hang together and which events do not hang together. In principle, the establishment of any historical sequence consists in finding an initial condition and a prognosis.

I am using these terms in the sense in which they are used in Popper's *Logic of Scientific Discovery*. The connection between an initial condition and a prognosis depends on the employment of a general law. One general law will point to one prognosis; another general law, given the same initial condition, will point to another prognosis. The determination of which two events are linked does not, therefore, depend on the initial condition and the prognosis as such, but on the choice of the general law. The use of this terminology in history may, at first sight, seem idiosyncratic, for one cannot know what the prognosis will be until one has stated both the initial condition and the general law. In historical knowledge the situation is, however, different. All events to be linked are events which have happened in the past. The event we designate in history as a prognosis is not really a 'prediction' as the word would suggest, but merely an event known to have happened after the initial condition. In historical knowledge, the occurrence of the so-called prognosis is not in doubt. The only matter which is in doubt is which general law can link an initial condition to a prognosis; or, for that matter, which general law can link any given 'prognosis' to an initial condition; or, given a prognosis *and* a general law, where we can find the initial condition. Popper's terminology was designed for those sciences in which one makes predictions. Historical knowledge makes no predictions about events which have not yet been observed. It is, therefore, completely backward-looking. This difference in the temporal location of the single events dealt with should, however, not be allowed to obscure the all-important fact that two events can be linked only with the help of a general law, regardless of whether one of these events is in the past and the other in the future, or whether both events are in the past.

The expression 'general law' need not and should not be taken too literally. The laws do not have to be absolutely general. Obviously, at different places and different times, people will use different generalisations. The laws must be somehow universal, but this universality can be a limited universality. Thus, it is a general law that when people shake hands they mean to be friendly. But in other places, the shaking of hands may not be a sign of friendliness and in some places friendliness can be established by different means. The crucial point is that we need, in order to connect one single event with another single event, a statement about a regularity of occurrence. This statement can best be described as a general law with or without unlimited universality. All that is required is that it should be a statement of a regularity of *some* universality.

An initial condition together with a general law and a prognosis can be summed up as one event. Such an event can then, in turn, be the initial condition or prognosis of another series, provided we can find a suitable general law. This new triad can, in turn, become the initial condition or prognosis for a third series, and so forth. If we look at any event in this fashion, we can see that it is made up of sub-events and the sub-events of further sub-events, and so on. The size of any event we use as an initial condition or as a prognosis is quite arbitrary, at least in the sense that the historian can decide, by his choice of general laws, what size he wants to settle for.

To make a long story short, we can say that we can establish a historical series of how event A led to B and then to C, if we have at the back of our mind a general law which tells us that they do so hang together. This leads us then to the conclusion that the historical knowledge we can have is dependent on the general laws we know of, and that any series we can construct is relative to the general law used to construct it. This does not mean that all historical knowledge is absolutely relative; but it does mean that all historical knowledge is relative to the general law we employ in constructing it. The general laws help us to decide on the size of the events we select and they help us to decide which events to select. But there follows one important conclusion. There are as many historical series of events as there are laws employed in constructing them. *Quot leges, tot historiae.* If, for argument's sake, we consider a series of events 1, 2, 3, 4, 5, 6, 7, then we will find that a general law A to the effect 'if 1, then 3,' will link 1 and 3, whereas a general law B to the effect 'if 3, then 6,' will link 3 and 6. The laws in question do not have to be absolutely universal. In many cases, mere generalisations will do; and in some cases, a general law valid only for a certain time in a certain place will do.

This conclusion should be no comfort to relativists. It says no more than that our historical knowledge is relative to something. It does not say that all historical knowledge is absolutely and irretrievably relative and that any story is as good as any other story. We cannot decide the truth of any story by just looking at the events which have been selected. But we most certainly can decide the truth of any story by looking at the general laws which have been used to select the events.

Res Gestae and *Historiae Rerum Gestarum*

Moreover, the conclusion is by no means new. Good historians have for centuries distinguished between the totality of everything that has ever happened – in short, the past – and the stories that are told about the past. They have called the former *res gestae*; and the latter, *historiae rerum gestarum*. Good historians have always known that the truth of any *historia rerum gestarum* cannot be established by a simple look at *res gestae* because the *res gestae*, the past as a totality, is not the sort of thing one can simply look at. One can only look at it selectively and at isolated strands of connected events. The ability to watch *res gestae* in this selective fashion depends on the presence, in the historian's mind, of general laws, generalisations or concrete universals.[1]

When we are looking at *res gestae* with the intention of producing a *historia rerum gestarum scientificarum* – that is, a history of science – the general laws we will mostly employ will have to be general laws or generalisations about scientific behaviour and the emergence and evaluation of scientific ideas and the nature of scientific discussion. In short, we will use sets of general laws which constitute a philosophy of science. If we use different philosophies of science, we will get different series of events and each series (i.e. each history of science) will be relative to the philosophy of science used.

Hutton and Lyell

We can find support for this theory about the construction of historical series from the method of study employed by the most successful historians of the earth and of biological species. Between them, Hutton, Lyell and Darwin adhered to, and practised, a way of establishing the series of events which led to the present condition of the earth and of biological species. Their method is best described by James Hutton in his *Theory of the Earth*. 'We must read,' Hutton wrote, 'the transactions of time past, in the present state of natural bodies; and, for the reading of this character, we have nothing but the laws of nature.'[2] He simply meant that we must assume that the laws of nature, as they affect earth and rocks, water and climate, laws about gravity, viscosity, erosion, density, and so forth, have been operative in the past and thus reconstruct the events which from the earliest state of the earth we know have led, one after another, to the present state of the earth. Both Lyell and Darwin appropriated this basic methodological rule. The history of the earth and the history of species is therefore relative to the general laws employed by the historians writing that history. But nobody would wish to infer from this that our knowledge of the history of the earth and of species is therefore 'relative', and that one story about the earth and about species is as good as any other.[3]

Geologists and biologists have, of course, a slightly easier task than other historians. In an important sense, the particular objects they have to put together to make a story – events relating to rocks and water, events relating to genes and living cells – are all events about circumscribed and definable objects. The number of laws they can employ to build a historical series is therefore limited. Even so, change the laws and one gets a very different story. The most dramatic changes have thus taken place in the history of the story of living organisms. Darwin knew nothing of laws relating to genetics and Mendel knew nothing of molecular biology and its laws. But within the spheres of living cells, given the important changes of general laws used, we can quite clearly see how the stories which have been told about the evolution of species are always relative to the general laws which have been used.

Historians of science, of art, of society and human institutions are not so lucky. The objects they are dealing with are not neatly circumscribed, and therefore the choice of general laws at their disposal at any time is infinitely larger than the choices open to geologists and biologists. But in principle, the problem which confronts the historians of science, of art, of societies and institutions is not different from the problem which confronts the historian of living cells and of the earth. In all cases, the stories they come up with are always relative to the general laws they employ.

Qualified Uniformitarianism

If the scope of available choices creates difficulties, there are two further, more fundamental differences between the method used for the history of biology and geology, on one side, and the methods used for the history of science, art, literature and institutions, on the other. The first difficulty which the historians of the earth and of life do not encounter consists in the fact that people, unlike stones and organic cells, are capable of thinking and therefore have general laws of their own; as a result, they will have views of their own as to how separate events hang together. For the historian of subjects who can think, these general laws and the resulting links between events are themselves part of the subject-matter. This presents no special difficulty in those cases in which the historian has confidence that these general laws are valid ones. But it does create special difficulties in those countless cases in which the historian has no such confidence. Ought he then disregard them? Ought he to reinterpret them? There are many possible strategies for dealing with this problem.[4] Whichever is chosen, we have here a set of problems about which historians of the earth and of pre-conscious life need not worry. As far as the earth is concerned, the distinction between the general laws inherent in the subject-matter and the general laws known to the historian (i.e. the geologist) is neat and absolute. Where life is concerned, the distinction may not be equally neat. When the historian is dealing with conscious life, he clearly has to face the fact that there are general laws used by his subjects. When life is totally unconscious, he can disregard the possibility that such general laws are part of the subject-matter. But then we do not really know where consciousness exactly starts in the evolutionary scale. Moreover, the ability to spot some regularities in the environment is an essential part of living cells. All living cells, therefore, behave as if they 'knew' of some general laws. Since they are unable to put them forward as objective knowledge and can merely display them in their behaviour, we tend – probably justifiably so – to regard those general laws as identical with the sorts of general laws which we would formulate if we were living cells and nothing else. In this case, the living cell and all organisms below the level of articulate consciousness do not represent a problem different from the problem presented to the historian of non-living matter (i.e. atoms, molecules, rocks, and steam). Perhaps we should regard the ability to make mistakes and to survive them, either as a society or as individuals, as the criterion of distinction between subjects which have general laws of their own which the historian has to take into account as part of the subject-matter, and subjects which have no articulate general laws of their own. To be sure, all organisms can make mistakes. But none of them survives them for long. It takes a human being, with his highly developed nervous system, his active imagination and his ability to socialise, to compensate for mistakes sufficiently well to be able to survive them. Indeed, human beings, alone among all animals, have even developed the ability to make mistakes systematically and to use these mistakes as the basis for social bonds, bonds which, in turn, will assist the members of such societies to evade the consequences of these mistakes. At any rate, there is no need here to pursue this matter. Suffice it to say that there is a distinctive difference between the problems encountered by the historian of science and the historian of the earth. The latter does not have to worry about general laws other than the ones he believes to be true.

The second fundamental difference between the historian of the earth and the historian of science consists in the fact that where human beings are concerned, the sets of general laws held to be valid change. This is not the case where the earth is concerned. Since rocks and water do not put forward laws of their own, the historian of rocks and water only deals with the laws he takes to be valid. To be sure, *these* laws do change. A historian unacquainted with laws about viscosity and laws governing gas pressures and magnetism, will write a very different kind of geology from the historian acquainted with those laws. The history of the earth, therefore, has a history.[5] But when the historian is concerned with human beings, he is also concerned with the laws they have used in the past. For this reason, there exists not only a history of science and a history of the history of science, but also the irreducible and ineluctable fact that one cannot be sure which of the histories of science is better. When one can be certain, for all practical purposes, that the laws governing the behaviour of water and rocks have never changed, one can be equally certain that the latest and most up-to-date history of the earth is the best history. But where human beings are concerned, we know perfectly well that the laws they believe to govern the behaviour of scientists have changed, and there is no obvious way in which we can tell whether they have changed for the better or for worse. For this reason, the history of the history of science does not simply allow us to regard the latest and most up-to-date history as the best. Indeed, in this case, it is very difficult to say what would constitute 'up-to-dateness'.

Given these two fundamental differences between the method of the historian of inarticulate subjects and the historian of articulate subjects, historians have usually tended to give preference to the story they meet in the sources from which they derive their basic information. Allowing for the fact that the compilers of the sources can have been biased or may have written propaganda, it is always a safe working principle for the historian to allow himself to be guided by the general laws inherent in the sources and thus take the way in which single events have been made to hang together in the sources as a *prima facie* sequence of events.

The Faraday Effect

However, in this area the historian of science faces a difficulty almost unknown to the historian of art, literature and institutions. For the sources in the history of science show a bias which is wholly honest and ineradicable – unlike the bias often met in the sources relating to art, literature and institutions. We may call this honest bias the 'Faraday Effect' for nobody has formulated for us the nature of that honest bias more clearly than Faraday. In Paragraph 45 of his *Experimental Researches in Electricity*, Faraday writes: 'These results I purpose to describing not as they were obtained, but in such a manner as to give the most concise view of the whole.' Though I have never found an equally explicit confession of historical distortion undertaken for wholly honest purposes, it is clear that similar thoughts have guided the writings of almost all scientists. The historian of science, therefore, cannot apply his usual rules to the treatment of the scientific source material. The usual rules are, first, 'back to the sources' and, second, to interpret the sources by subtracting obvious or latent personal and ideological bias. In the history of science, however, the Faraday Effect makes it difficult for the historian to allow himself to be guided by these rules. For the problem as to what to select and how to select is made specially difficult when the scientists who provide a large proportion of the sources, present their researches logically rather than historically. In the history of science, therefore, a reliance on the sources, presented as they are logically rather than historically, is fundamentally misleading and likely to disguise rather than to disclose what actually happened. For in the history of science, the sources enshrine an *honest* bias and therefore tend to create a mist which does not pertain to the sources in other fields.

The syndromes created by the Faraday Effect have often been noticed. The discovery and its proofs are presented in order to convince rather than to show how they were come by. Such presentation is itself, as it well might be, unhistorical. It pre-selects the historian's source material in a way very different from the way in which such source material is pre-selected in other fields. A compiler of source material for a political party or for the history of the church pre-selects, too. But he pre-selects to give his own version of how things came into being. He pre-selects to present his own version of how things came to pass. He may be mendacious, biased, propagandist, deluded or anything you like. But in all cases he is *not* unhistorical. Not so the compiler of the source material in the sciences. He is honestly disinterested in the historical process and pre-selects his material to present unhistorical evidence. This kind of pre-selection predisposes the historian to evaluate past science relative to the *present* state of scientific knowledge rather than relative to contemporary alternatives.[6]

This matter has often been remarked upon by historians of science and there would be no need to enlarge on it here were it not for the fact that the above-mentioned differences between the historian of the earth and the historian of science (or art, literature and institutions) left us with the conclusion that the general reliance on the sources, at least in the first instance, is both inevitable and sound. Now, however, we see that for the historian of science such reliance is fraught with quite special pitfalls because of the peculiar nature of much of the source material relating to the history of science. There are, of course, some scientists who are fond of writing their memoirs or of talking to journalists like Judson and Nigel Calder about them. But there are also many scientists – Einstein, for example – who are extremely reluctant to do so and such reluctance leaves the historian of science with a kind of source material which is, from a historical point of view, honestly biased and genuinely misleading.

The Faraday Effect distorts the source material so that it cannot be used as it stands to tell a story of what actually happened. This distortion is not accidental but is inherent in the nature of the scientific enterprise. For the historian of science, the strategy of allowing oneself to be taken in hand by the sources is rarely available and hardly commendable. When Fustel de Coulanges, in an impassioned moment, lent forward during a lecture and reminded his audience that it was not he who was speaking but the sources (i.e. history itself), he may have been guilty of exaggeration. But the historian of science, given the inbuilt bias of most of his sources, is rarely in a position to commit similar exaggerations.

All in all, the sum total of general laws available to the historian of science for his reconstruction of what actually happened is his estimate of the human nature of scientists as it performs under certain cultural and economic constraints, plus the philosophy of science he holds to be correct; it cannot be the sources by themselves. His task is even less enviable than the task of the historian of all other human enterprises. The historian of science cannot even use his sources as a starting-point for determining what scientists have done and how they have gone about their tasks. He must have a view of his own which he cannot really derive from the sources themselves as ordinary historians are wont to do. This view must cover such matters as what scientists will do, how they will investigate, what puzzles them, how they regard their peers, whom they will take to be their peers, whose authority they will respect, how they will evaluate their inspirations, how they will treat their psychological hang-ups, what is likely to lead to an inspiration, and suchlike.

The historian of science can therefore rely less on his source material than the ordinary historian. The history of science cannot, therefore, be used as a *basis* for the philosophy of science, which is the discipline whose aim is to provide the answers to the above questions.[7]

The impasse cannot be avoided by a simple definition of what constitutes a scientist and then by watching what that sort of man has done. There is no way in which we can establish in advance what would be a 'scientist.' The impossibility of such a definition is neatly and charmingly illustrated by the first meeting between Planck's assistant, Max von Laue, and Einstein, in the summer of 1906. Laue journeyed to Bern to meet Einstein. He assumed automatically that a man of Einstein's stature would be teaching at the university in Bern. He did not find him there. 'Certainly Laue was surprised to discover that the man who had conceived the ideas of time and space that had so impressed Planck was the unimposing, shirt-sleeved employee whom Laue at first gave scarcely a glance when he sought out Einstein at the Patent Office.'[8] Had Laue stuck to his preconceived idea of where 'scientists' worked, he might never have found Einstein.

The philosophy of science, even more than the philosophy of literature or sociology, determines what history of science the historian of science will find. The tenuous relationship between the sources and the story of art, literature, society, politics and economics upon which historians of these subjects can rely – at least to start with – is infinitely more tenuous when one is dealing with the source material of the history of science. It is so tenuous as to be practically non-existent. From all this there results a certain anarchy in the history of all these pursuits. But in our understanding of art, literature and society, such anarchy and uncertainty does not really matter because our knowledge of these pursuits and institutions is not intimately tied up with our knowledge of their growth. It is helpful to have knowledge of how one art-form developed out of another and how one society with certain problems transformed itself into a different kind of society. But since there is no progress in any of these pursuits and institutions, we can understand them perfectly well without looking at their histories. In science, by contrast, growth is an essential part of the pursuit and the uncertainty of our knowledge of that growth affects our knowledge of the pursuit.

Science versus History?

There is a widely held view that science and history do not mix. This view is very pervasive and is based, though it comes in many different forms, upon the belief that history deals with matters that are temporal and evolving and changing, while science is atemporal. It leads to the conclusion that historical evolution and scientific understanding are totally different things and separated by a wide and unbridgeable gap. The gap, however, is imaginary. We have scientific understanding of evolution, including the evolution and growth of science itself. Indeed, it is this scientific understanding of evolution which leads us to the understanding that science is evolutionary. The preceding argument has shown that the alleged incompatibility is illusory. One cannot construct a historical sequence without the help of general laws. The laws themselves may be, in some cases, abstract and atemporal; but the particular conditions which they bring into a temporal and historical relationship to one another, represent evolution (i.e. historical sequences).

Many people understand science to be a pursuit which has no history. To be sure, they admit that people in the past have pursued science. But the past, so the argument goes, has no bearing on the present. The past, in science, is simply the sum total of theories which have been discarded. All a scientist needs to know is the theories which are now true. This rejection of the historical dimension of science cannot stand up to scrutiny. It assumes that the knowledge held to be true today is held to be true because of compelling empirical evidence. It is held to be true because it corresponds to nature or to our observation of nature. This is the line taken by all Positivists who, taking this line, can then disregard the past. Such Positivists consider the study of the history of science to be a peculiarly irrelevant, though charming and edifying, occupation. Like the whole of Positivism, this Positivistic disregard of the historical dimension of knowledge is based on the erroneous assumption that one can tell a true theory from a false theory by showing that the true theory has the support of observations and the false theory does not have such support. As soon as one realises that in knowledge theories are preferred not because observations compel one to prefer them but because they represent progress over older theories, one has to pay attention to the historical dimension. For one can decide which theory is a progress and which theory is not, only by looking at the theories of the past. In this sense, the historical study of the growth of knowledge is an integral part of one's appreciation of knowledge.

Positivism, however, dies hard. When philosophers of science had to admit that this simple disregard of the history of science was untenable, they fell back upon a different line of reasoning. If we have to study history, they seemed to be saying, we are really only studying how scientists came to hold the theories they are holding. It is hard to think of anything which would be a good reason for suggesting a theory but not a good reason for accepting that theory.[9] For this reason, when we are investigating the history of science, we are really only investigating the reasons scientists have had for putting forward certain theories. If these theories now turn out to be false because we have observations to this effect, all we can conclude is that the earlier scientists were wrong in suggesting their theories. They ought not to have suggested them in the first place. With this view, the earlier Positivism seeks now to fortify itself by a sort of history-oriented Positivism.

Cohen and the Raw Material

If one examines a book on the history of science, one will readily see that this approach reveals an inherent ambiguity. In his *The Newtonian Revolution*,[10] I. Bernard Cohen is writing as a self-confessed historian. 'The historian's task may legitimately be restricted to determining what features of Newton's science seemed so extraordinary in the age of Newton as to earn the designation of revolution.'[11] In thus legitimately restricting his task to what can be expected of a historian, Cohen avows that he wants to eschew any philosophical discussion and simply report what happened. Cohen manages to show that the Newtonian revolution was a turning-point in the history of the exact sciences,[12] and in doing so is still believing that he is doing no more than one can expect from a historian. But he also says – and this is where the rub lies – that Newton did not really know that he was doing anything revolutionary in his use of the Newtonian 'style'.[13] Now this 'style' is very carefully analysed by

Cohen.[14] This analysis and detection of Newton's 'style' shows us what Newton did as distinct from what he thought he was doing. Again, one might concede that even here Cohen is not transgressing the limits he set himself as a historian. But then it turns out that Newton was not himself aware of this 'style' and that the 'style' is Cohen's distillation of a philosophy of science which Newton practised but apparently did not know that he was practising. At this point, Cohen is definitely going beyond the limits he has imposed on himself as a historian. He has every reason for doing so. Had Newton confined himself to his own 'scenario', he would never have achieved his success. If Cohen wants to account for that success, he has to satisfy himself that such accounting is done in the *correct* terms – that is, can be explained as a function of a correct philosophy of science. Could it not be so accounted, it would not count as success. In other words, when Cohen is writing as a historian to find out what happened, he cannot confine himself to what Newton thought happened, but has to add what Cohen's philosophy of science obliges Cohen to believe to have happened.

There is indeed a great difference between Newton's style, as determined by Cohen the philosopher of science, and Newton's practice, as determined by Cohen the Positivistic historian trying to find out what really happened. The link between the philosophy of science Cohen says was behind the success and the guidelines which Cohen says Newton thought he had followed is, however, not accidental. One cannot say that in one capacity Cohen is finding out what happened (the scenario) as a historian, and that in a quite different capacity Cohen is determining how one can justify Newton's astonishing success by outlining his style. On the contrary, Cohen must convince himself that though Newton did not say so, he was actually practising his style and disregarding his scenario and, what is more, he must convince himself as a historian. Could he not convince himself so, he could not explain why Newton was so eminently successful; for success could not be accounted for by the faulty philosophy of science manifest in Newton's scenario. In short, Cohen is always writing as a historian trying to find out what happened; but in being a historian he cannot eschew the task of a philosopher of science and has, therefore, to distinguish between a good philosophy of science and a bad one.

The historian Cohen is intimately dependent on Cohen the philosopher of science. Newton believed that he not merely supposed his conclusions, but had derived them from experiments.[15] Newton, Cohen says,[16] would have us believe that he followed this 'scenario': first, to reveal by 'analysis' some simple results that were generalised by induction, thus proceeding from effects to causes; then, on the basis of these causes considered as principles, to explain by 'synthesis' the phenomena of observation and experiment that may be derived or deduced from them. But eventually Cohen finds that Newton did not follow this scenario at all, but practised his 'style'.[17]

And now let us look at the 'style', something altogether different from the 'scenario'. Every reader will spot at once that Cohen the historian has here tracked down the heart of Newton's genius. The style consists of two phases. In the first, the consequences of an imaginative mathematical construct are determined by the application of mathematical techniques to initial conditions concerning mathematical entities in a mathematical domain. In the second phase, the physical counterparts of the initial conditions are compared or contrasted with observations of nature. This suggests some alterations to the initial construct and thus produces a new first phase, followed by a new second phase, and so forth. 'Such a mathematical construct is founded on a simplified and idealised natural system of which it is the mathematicisation and the analogue.' Observation enters only obliquely as a corrective and not, as Newton said, as the starting-point from which conclusions are derived. Hence, the revolution which it is the historian's task to discover is thus discovered historically with the help of a philosophy of science which differs markedly from what Cohen finds explicitly stated in the sources. But the historical discovery of a successful revolution could not have been made had Cohen interpreted his role as a historian too strictly and not allowed philosophy-of-science considerations to come in.

One might think, taking a first glance, that Cohen is really reporting, as a historian, what happened. He has found out that Newton did not practise what he preached and that the revolution he brought about was due to this failure. Alternatively, one might think that Cohen has shown that Newton did not bring about a revolution and that it only seems to us in retrospect that he did. However, there is contemporary testimony to contradict both alternatives. John Locke in *An Essay Concerning Human Understanding* says towards the end of chapter 7 that Newton brought about a revolution, though he says no more than that he brought it about by not making proper use of the 'general maxims' discussed in an earlier part of that chapter, this would clearly eliminate the second alternative. The first alternative is eliminated by the testimony of David Hume, who wrote in his *History of England* (chapter 61) that Newton admitted no principles 'but such as were founded on experiment' and was 'resolute to adopt every such principle'. Hume, in other words, abides with Newton's scenario and appears unaware of the 'style' Cohen has discovered to have been practised by the scientist.

Holton and the Raw Material

Even more convinced of the possibility to get to the heart of the matter by accurate historical investigation than Cohen, G. Holton writes that 'it is through the dispassionate examination of historically valid cases that we can best become aware of the preconceptions which underlie all philosophical study' of, for example, Einstein's view of the Lorentz transformations.[18] Such dispassionate study would ultimately revolve around how Einstein interpreted the Lorentz theory and, initially, one would expect that there would be no better source than Einstein himself. The historian, in other words, by finding out what Einstein thought, can solve the question as to what happened when Einstein proposed his Special Theory of Relativity and this discovery will, finally, be relevant to the philosophy of science by showing whether Einstein solved a real problem and whether his solution was comparable to the Lorentz theory, and so forth. Such historical investigation is believed, with Einstein's own testimony, to strike rock-bottom brute fact, raw material (i.e. historically primary sources). After all, he must have known what he was doing. But here we find that, first of all, he said one thing in 1905 and the opposite in 1915.[19] It is a well-known and often quoted story that when Heisenberg pleaded with Einstein to accept the Copenhagen interpretation of Quantum Mechanics by reminding the latter that it was based on exactly the same identification of reality with the methods one uses to observe reality as had been employed by Einstein in the Special Theory of Relativity, Einstein replied: 'Yes, I know that; but it was nonsense all the same'. We realise then that the ultimate evidence is not what Einstein thought, but what he thought he thought, and that Einstein can be as wrong about his own motives as any outside observer. Hence, historical investigation will get us nowhere when we are concerned with the evaluation of rival theories, though it may shed some light on the psychological states of the protagonists – states which are, it is generally agreed, irrelevant to the one question of interest to the philosophy of science.

The 'Actual' and the 'Real'

In writing history, the choice of general laws must be determined by a fundamental consideration. If one wants to be *objective* and exclude as much as possible one's own knowledge and interests, one must choose only those laws which were known or could have been known (there is a slight ambiguity here) by the people one is writing about. In this way, one will be able to see events as those people saw them or might have seen them, and one gets to know what *actually* happened.

If, on the other hand, one wants to find out what *really* happened, one has to use for preference (that is, in cases where there is a conflict) those laws one believes to be true today. In this way, one finds out how events really hang together, as opposed to how the people involved in them thought they hung together. However, this gain in real knowledge is made at the expense of objectivity. For in this method, we are obtruding our own knowledge and understanding and are brushing aside the knowledge of the people we are writing about. Thus we get the seeming paradox that *real* knowledge is more subjective and less objective than knowledge of what *actually* happened.

Consider Erikson's book on Luther as an example.[20] Erikson notes that in late adolescence Luther entered a monastery. He explains Luther's decision in terms of modern psychology. Adolescents need a moratorium from parental pressure and Luther must have entered the monastery in order to get away from his parents. Explained in this way, with the help of psychological laws we know to be true, Luther's entry into a monastery makes sense to us. We have *real* knowledge, even though such knowledge is subjective and does not tell us what Luther himself thought.

Luther himself, so the sources reveal, thought that he entered the monastery in order to step up the discipline he was pursuing in order to achieve not only salvation, but assurance of salvation. He did not think he was running away from his parents; he thought that he wanted to increase the discipline he had been subjected to. Once we understand this, we understand what *actually* happened. We gain an objective understanding of Luther – even though, given our modern psychological knowledge, the story seems to us very fishy.

For the working historian, the reasons for the choice are determined by what he wants to find out. He is free to change one set of laws for another according to whether he is interested in actuality or in reality. Whatever he is interested in, either method explains change. Since change is all the historian of most pursuits and institutions is interested in, there is no great problem here.

For the historian of science, however, there is a very real problem. For he has to account for *progress* and growth; not just for *change*.

If the historian of science seeks actuality, he will tell the story of relativity as Einstein saw it, or at least as Einstein saw it in 1905 – that is, without reference to the Michelson–Morley experiment. If, however, he wants to find out what really happened he must tell it as his philosophy of science obliges him to see it. Suppose he is a falsificationist in the philosophy of science. He will then tell how the Michelson–Morley experiment 'falsified' the ether theory; and that Einstein, knowing that the old theory had been falsified, proposed a new theory in which the velocity of light was constant.

However, if he is looking for actuality and wants to know what actually happened, he must follow Einstein's philosophy of science, in so far as it is ascertainable, and use Einstein's own testimony about his (Einstein's) method of discovery. Using this kind of evidence, the Michelson–Morley experiment will not appear in the story.

So far, the historian of science finds himself in exactly the same position as any other historian. He has to decide what he is looking for. But since he is a historian of the growth of knowledge, he has to account not just for change, but for change which made for progress and growth. Knowledge would not be knowledge had it grown according to a path other than to the path in which knowledge grows. Thus, if we want to find out what *really* happened – that is, if we want to find out how we have come to have knowledge – the story we tell must be the story of radical criticism and of trial and error. This story may be very different from what actually happened – that is, from what scientists, let alone others, thought happened. Our knowledge of art and politics and our knowledge of how art and politics have changed, must of necessity change with those changes, and the historian of art and politics must, therefore, keep an eye on both reality and actuality and must be aware that even his presumption of what *really* happened can change. But knowledge about the growth of knowledge refers to itself. Our knowledge of art and politics is subject to constant changes as knowledge evolves. But our knowledge of knowledge is self-constituting, for knowledge of the growth of knowledge cannot have other criteria than the criteria of knowledge itself. Knowledge of knowledge would not be knowledge if it developed or were assumed to have developed according to criteria other than those valid for knowledge. One form of art follows another form of art, whether we know it or whether we ignore it and regardless of our understanding of why it did so. Hence, it is immaterial for the history of art whether we reconstruct it by looking for what really happened or by looking for what actually happened. In art, it does not matter whether we have 'wrong' knowledge of the reasons for the changes in art. Since art is not a form of knowledge, there is no reason why our knowledge of changes in art should tell us how *we* think they occurred or tell us how, say, Vasari thought they occurred. But the same does not apply to our knowledge of the growth of knowledge. No matter how people in the past thought their knowledge had grown, we can have correct knowledge of that growth only if we can show that it has grown in the way that we consider to be necessary for the growth of knowledge (i.e. by trial and error). For if it has grown by any other method, we would not regard it as knowledge. Knowledge, in short, would not be 'knowledge' if it developed according to false criteria.

It follows, therefore, that in our knowledge of knowledge we not only have a situation in which we cannot derive the knowledge we need from the history of knowledge, but also one in which there is the problem that we have to make doubly sure that we have the correct philosophy of knowledge so that we can understand the essentially historical dimension of knowledge.

In the history of science, the philosophy of science plays the role of meta-history. One can arrange the meta-histories used in the reconstruction of historical sequences in a hierarchy, depending on the potential for conflict between actuality and reality – that is, on the degree of difference between the employment of laws known to the subject-matter and the laws known to the historian.

At the lowest level, there are the histories of the earth and of living matter. The series begins with short-term natural events, the history of the earth and of living organisms. In these fields, meta-history consists of the laws of physics and chemistry. There is no conflict between what actually happened and what really happened. Neither rocks nor water nor living organisms have thoughts about their own history and it would make no sense to demand that the history of the earth be written by taking into account not only what really happened (i.e. what the laws of physics and chemistry oblige us to think), but also what actually happened (i.e. what the earth, the water, the rocks and living organisms *thought* happened). The general laws to be employed change only when we think they are false, i.e. when our knowledge grows. Today, we are certain that a history of the earth without the law of inertia and without laws governing viscosity, would be a false history. A history of living organisms without bio-chemistry would not only be false, but probably even impossible to write.

At the next level, we come to the history of long-term natural events, the history of the cosmos. In cosmogony we use the laws of physics and chemistry as meta-history and here, too, there can be no conflict between actuality and reality because electrons and atoms do not think for themselves and have no views about their own history. But there are changes in the physical and chemical laws. For example, there is good reason for believing that gravity diminishes as time passes and that the force of gravity today is less strong than it was at the beginning of the universe. In writing cosmogony, one ought to take account of this change in the general laws one employs and realise that one cannot just use one and the same meta-history throughout.

At the next level, we come to the history of human beings and their cultures. Here, meta-history will consist largely of laws about sociology, psychology and economics. In this region, there must always be manifest conflict between the laws we today believe to be true and the laws which the people we are investigating believed to be true. There is conflict between the actual and the real histories one can obtain. Moreover, what we consider to be really true about psychology, sociology and economics is itself subject to change.

Finally, we come to the history of knowledge itself. Here, too, there is conflict between what people who knew in the past believed about the method of the acquisition of their knowledge and what we today believe about the method of acquisition of knowledge. But in this case, the only meta-history we are entitled to employ is the *correct* philosophy of science. The 'actual' certainly took place. In many places, people believed that such knowledge as they had was revealed by the gods or by a shaman. In others, it was held to have been handed down by tradition. Some people believed that their knowledge is the result of induction, and others, again, have thought that it is obtained by following the dictates of right reason. But in this case, where the knowledge of the growth of knowledge is concerned, the actual knowledge people have had at different times in different places has to be discounted, for knowledge could not have grown by false paths. Or, paradoxically, if it had, we would not count it as knowledge. Less paradoxically and more seriously, such knowledge as is demonstratively due to divine revelation or positive observation and nothing else, and is maintained by the artful exclusion of trial and error and criticism, is not to be considered 'knowledge'. Its history, whatever else it may be, is not the history of knowledge and our knowledge of it is not knowledge of the growth of knowledge.

In this way, moving from absence of conflict to conflict and then to absence of conflict again, we can see that the conflicts are determined by the nature of the subject-matter. In some cases, there is no conflict because the laws do not change and the subject-matter has no thoughts of its own. Then we come to the subject-matter where there are still no thoughts by the subject-matter, but where there are changes of laws. Then we come to the region in which there are both changes of laws and of the thoughts of the subject-matter about itself. And finally, we come to the knowledge of knowledge, where we know that the subject-matter has had thoughts about itself but where these thoughts have to be discarded if they differ from our own knowledge of knowledge.

Tot Historiae quot Leges

Although there have been innumerable and incompatible histories of science, both small scale and large scale, the significance and the consequences of this phenomenon were first clearly confronted in full and amply documented by Joseph Agassi in his *Towards an Historiography of Science,* published in 1963.[21] Agassi shows in this book exactly what a proper understanding of the difficulties of historical method, as outlined in the previous section, would lead one to expect. Since the facts of the history of science are not placed before us for inspection in the sense in which we might be able to look at a horse in a paddock to decide whether it has four legs or five and test whether the quality of the grass has affected its muscle-tone, we must make use of general laws. In this particular case, the general laws are philosophies of science. These general laws and these laws alone can help historians of science to assemble the separate events, to decide at which size and level to focus on them, and how the one led to the next.

Agassi's analysis proves that my contention in this chapter is correct — i.e. *tot historiae quot leges*. The theoretical part of his account is in more general terms than my account and he does not base his contention on a close analysis of the nature of historical knowledge as such. The ultimate demonstration that there are as many histories of science as there are philosophies of science follows from the argument that any historical sequence is distinct from all temporal sequences and that, in the absence of purely chronological links, events in any historical sequence can be linked only with the help of general laws.

Agassi distinguished six different philosophies of science, each of which yields a different story of how science developed and grew and increased our knowledge: (1) inductivism; (2) conventionalism; (3) the philosophy of scientific continuity (Duhem); (4) reductionism (Marx); (5) Hegelian dialectics; (6) the philosophy of continuing comparison (Agassi). Agassi provides many examples for each type of history and explains in detail how each story is indebted to one particular philosophy of science. Popper's falsificationism is conspicuous by its absence. Nobody has tried to write a history of science with the help of a purely falsificationist philosophy of science. This is most probably due to the fact that falsificationism by itself – that is, without the biological dimension it received eventually in Popper's thought – whatever its philosophical merits, is not a fruitful perspective for a history of science.[22] Obviously, however, Agassi's list is not exhaustive and one could envisage alternative classifications as proposed, for example, by Imre Lakatos in his *History of Science and its Rational Reconstructions*,[23] in which he, too, argued that the history of science one gets depends on the philosophy of science one employs. Unlike Agassi, Lakatos included Popper's philosophy of falsification in his list: (1) inductivism; (2)

conventionalism; (3) falsificationism (Popper); (4) the philosophy of research programmes (Lakatos).

Whatever the merits of these lists,[24] they both suffer from the defect that their authors accord a privileged status to their own philosophies of science – Agassi to his number 6, and Lakatos to his number 4 – thus suggesting that there is, after all, an unqualified preference for that history of science which is written with the help of one particular, privileged, philosophy of science.

Chapter 3

Historical Circularity

Kuhn's Circularity

About the same time as when Agassi's book was published, there appeared Thomas S. Kuhn's *The Structure of Scientific Revolutions*.[1] Kuhn addressed himself very much to the same problem as Agassi. Unlike Agassi's book, Kuhn's book has become something of a classic. Kuhn's success is truly astonishing, for he paid no attention at all to the essential circularity involved in the problem and blithely went ahead to propose a philosophy of science, whose validity he justified by an appeal to the history of science. To all intents and purposes, Kuhn is completely unaware of the circularity of his method. He seems to suppose that the history of science is something ready-made, available for inspection; that if we only look at it carefully enough, we will discover the true philosophy of science. Unlike Agassi, who squarely confronted all the problems raised in chapter 2, Kuhn simply evaded all these problems.

Kuhn's argument is too well known to require more than a summary description. Kuhn maintains that one must distinguish between fundamental scientific theories, which he calls 'paradigms', and normal scientific theories. Paradigms come and go. According to Kuhn, they are set up for no compelling scientific reason other than an accumulation of doubts and vague dissatisfactions with an earlier paradigm. The paradigms gain both ground and adherents simply because an older generation of scientists wedded to their defence, dies out. Eventually, the new paradigm is established in the scientific community. Once established, the new paradigm leads to the pursuit of normal science. That is, to the solution of scientific puzzles on the assumption that the paradigm itself is beyond question and beyond criticism. One paradigm, Kuhn argues, is as good as any other and is incommensurable with any other paradigm. As one would expect, Kuhn has no difficulty in buttressing this philosophy of science with historical examples. Once he has got his philosophy of science, he can use it as a set of general laws which will serve to select the relevant events, establish their size and their relevance to each other. Given the analysis of historical knowledge put forward in chapter 2, it can be no surprise that Kuhn's philosophy of science should yield a history of science. If Agassi were to publish a revised edition of his book, he could well add Kuhn's philosophy of science to his list and treat it as the seventh philosophy. What is astonishing is that Kuhn himself has not noticed this circularity. Perhaps it is not incumbent on a philosopher to criticise his own work. But it is somewhat astonishing that his many admirers, who are legion, have not been worried by this circularity. It is even more astonishing that not even his many critics have been able to spot the one fundamental and fatal flaw in his reasoning.[2]

As we have seen, it is possible to base a history of science on a philosophy of science; but it is not possible to do it the other way round. The advantages and disadvantages of Kuhn's philosophy of science will be discussed in the next chapter. Here, we must investigate his reasons for his philosophy of science and examine them as he produces them. Kuhn bases his philosophy of science exclusively on the history of science and argues that our observation of the history of science teaches us this particular philosophy of science. Contrary to the arguments advanced in chapters 1 and 2, Kuhn assumes that history is something that is given. His derivation of the philosophy of science from the history of science is to be taken quite literally. Joseph D. Snell writes:

> I regard . . . Kuhn's thesis as substantive, historical claims about how theories of mathematical physics (or scientific theories in general) come into being, or how people come to have them. People could, conceivably, come to have theories in quite a different way. That they do not, is a claim to be argued for by looking at the historical record.[3]

There have been many critics of Kuhn – although not nearly as many as he deserves and not nearly as many as there are disciples and supporters. It is especially relevant, as I will show in the following section, that a large proportion of his supporters and disciples are social scientists and philosophers at large, rather than philosophers of science, scientists and historians of science. Such critics as he has had, have all concentrated on minor issues. Thus, it has been pointed out that he uses the word 'paradigm' in at least twenty-one different senses, some of which are actually incompatible with each other. Other critics, more to the point, have rejected his theory that paradigms are incommensurable with each other and have argued that if Kuhn were right, he would make nonsense of the whole scientific enterprise and reduce the growth of knowledge to something like the history of art or literature. This criticism is valid as far as it goes. But *if* Kuhn is right, we may have to resign ourselves to the conclusion that the pursuit of science and knowledge is not different from the pursuit of art and literature. This kind of criticism, therefore, can be said to beg the question.

Kuhn's History of Copernicus

In order to show that Kuhn is wrong and that one cannot consider his philosophy of science to be the correct philosophy of science, one simply has to demonstrate that his argument is circular. First, Kuhn writes his own history of science. He did so some six years before he published his influential book, in a volume entitled *The Copernican Revolution* (first edition 1957). In this book, Kuhn presented the history of the Copernican revolution and its aftermath of normal science in the wake of the new paradigm. He then turned round and derived his philosophy of science from that history and, finally, offered the history of science he had written as proof that his philosophy of science was correct. In his *The Structure of Scientific Revolutions* (1963) there are lots of different, assorted historical examples. But it is much more fruitful to assess the circularity in terms of Kuhn's own coherent example as presented in *The Copernican Revolution.*[4] Kuhn himself says we should not, for he is *either* historian *or* philosopher, but never both at the same time. But since he bases his philosophy on historical evidence, there can be no reason why we should accept his protestation of intellectual schizophrenia at its face-value.

Kuhn's story goes as follows. Copernicus, by placing the sun at the centre, created a new paradigm. The reasons for the choice of the new paradigm were largely irrational. Copernicus was really concerned with mathematics[5] and was aware that heliocentricity had been put forward earlier. His main interest was technical mathematics. Copernicus's narrow technicalities delayed the recognition of his theory and slowed down the reception of his book. But eventually the old conceptual schemes faded away, even though Copernicus's readers could not grasp the mathematical reasoning on which the new paradigm was based. In Kuhn's story, there are no compelling reasons for this fading away.[6] By the time Kepler came along, the new paradigm was firmly established and Kepler was able to do normal science in finding the correct laws which govern the orbit of the planets around the sun. Kepler himself was very critical of Copernicus's mathematics, but accepted the new paradigm nevertheless so that he could do normal science. There appears, therefore, a certain irrationality in Kepler's approach when he criticised Copernicus's mathematics but believed nevertheless in the heliocentricity upon which these mathematics were based.[7] In Kuhn's story, it is made quite clear that Kepler's enterprise was governed by an irrational acceptance of heliocentricity and that heliocentricity was also the most irrational of Copernicus's convictions.

In Kuhn's story, the paradigm change is as irrational as any event can be. There had been earlier heliocentric theories and Copernicus's own mathematics were very clumsy, he says. In so far as Kepler's correct mathematics helped to buttress the paradigm, his (Kepler's) adherence to the new paradigm was again based on the irrational faith that the sun ought to be in the centre[8] because Kepler was a Neoplatonist.

Other Histories of Copernicus

Kuhn's story makes perfect sense as it stands. If, however, one consults other historians of the same epoch in the history of science, one will find different versions. In his *The Sleepwalkers,* Koestler[9] distinguishes at least two paradigm changes. After the acceptance of Copernicus's heliocentric paradigm, Kepler introduced an entirely new direction of thought by injecting 'physical causality into the formal geometry' of the skies.[10] Had it not been for this additional paradigm, Kepler would have found it impossible to ignore the famous crucial eight-minute arc. According to Koestler, Copernicus was mortally and neurotically afraid to have his views published. Other historians think that Copernicus's reluctance to rush into print was not due to a neurosis but to fear of the new medium, the printing press. He seemed to have had no hesitation about communicating his ideas in writing (personal communication from Paul Levinson). According to Kuhn, Copernicus was always and widely read;[11] and if there was delay in acceptance, it was due to Copernicus's preoccupation with narrow mathematical complexities. According to most other writers, Copernicus did not become widely known and there can, therefore, be no reason for thinking that the old heliocentric paradigm simply 'faded away'. Toulmin, in *The Fabric of the Heavens*,[12] argues that Copernicus's heliocentricity came simply 'at the right time'. Toulmin tells nothing of an irrational decision in favour of it, nothing of the fading away of the old paradigm and nothing of Kepler's 'normal science' after the paradigm was well accepted. In Toulmin, Copernicus is credited with a sort of prescience of what rational thought really required. This is more like an appeal or a resort to some kind of Providence. Certainly, no paradigm shift for irrational reasons, let alone a rational falsification of earlier theories. If we consult E.A. Burtt's famous *The Metaphysical Foundations of Modern Science*,[13] we are told on page 39 that Copernicus's interest in mathematics was far from narrow and technical. Unlike Kuhn, Burtt connects Copernicus's famous sentence 'mathematics is for mathematicians' with Copernicus's metaphysically inspired wish to produce a simple and harmonious theory. This version and this interpretation of the famous remark on mathematicians is also to be found in Charles C. Gillispie's *The Edge of Objectivity*.[14] This version is incompatible with the interpretation of this sentence by Kuhn[15] and by Toulmin.[16]

These examples are quite random and there is no merit in multiplying them. I have simply used them in order to show that Kuhn's story of the paradigm change and of Kepler's relation to it is only one of many possible stories, and that other historians, using different philosophies of science, have produced very different stories of the theory of the planets in the sixteenth and seventeenth centuries. All this is no fundamental criticism of Kuhn as a historian. But it fatally flaws his argument that his own history provides the evidence of his philosophy of science as it appears in his book of 1963. It certainly refutes his own argument that the historian has the 'facts'[17] and shows that, when it comes to history, Kuhn is not a Kuhnian. Had he read his *Structure of Scientific Revolutions* and applied its theory to history, one might argue ironically, he would not have invoked historical evidence and 'facts' to prove his philosophy of science.

Historical Tests of Kuhn

As one might expect, attempts have been made to settle the question of whether Kuhn's view of the role of paradigms is correct or not by historical investigations. It was natural for scholars to assume that if Kuhn is not worried by the circularity involved in such appeals to history, there is no reason why other scholars should be worried. However, if the preceding analysis of the relationship between paradigm (or philosophies of history or philosophies of science) and the composition of historical narratives is correct, such investigations, far from settling the question, will turn out to be completely inconclusive. Again, I will take a random example, from a book edited by Gary Gutting.[18]

The example concerns the paradigm shift alleged to have occurred in biology and geology in the nineteenth century. In a paper entitled 'Kuhnian Paradigm and Darwinian Revolution', John C. Grene investigates the history of biology and geology in the nineteenth century and finds that at no time were there any 'anomalies' in the practice of normal science and that, therefore, if Kuhn is right, there ought not to have been a paradigm shift. However, as everybody knows, there *was* a paradigm shift. Grene's story looks perfectly convincing until one decides to put the same or contiguous historical facts together with the help of a paradigm other than the one used by Grene. On page 312 Grene says, for example, that there

> is little evidence . . . that Lyell's great book was a response to a state of crisis in geological science. Instead it seems to have been conceived as a reaffirmation of uniformitarian principles, and, what was crucial for the development of evolutionary ideas, an extension of them to the organic world, at least in regard to the extinction of species.

But on the following page Grene himself refers to a 'hard fact' which, when seen in a light different from the light in which Grene sees it, would show that there was a real anomaly and crisis. Supposing one approaches the period in question with the idea that Kuhn is right and that the paradigm shift in favour of uniformitarianism was due to a 'crisis'. One will then look for signs of crisis and find them ready to hand in Lyell himself. Thus, Grene himself says that

> the elements of a non-Lamarckian theory of evolution, stressing the struggle for existence and the survival of the fittest, were present in his [Lyell's] work cheek by jowl with his systematic exposition and discussion of the Lamarckian alternative to his own steady-state concept of earth history.

Every reader of Lyell will know that Grene's description of the situation is correct. The question, however, is whether one should consider this 'cheek by jowl' situation as evidence of 'crisis' or whether one should not. My argument is that the answer to this question must depend entirely on the paradigm one uses. If one is a Kuhnian, one will use this situation as evidence of crisis and consider the paradigm shift 'explained'. If one is not, one will take it simply to be an expression of a certain uncertainty which, moreover, lasted well into Darwin's own thinking – and force oneself to seek an explanation for the paradigm shift elsewhere. Grene considers that a shift took place, but that the revolution came 'from outside, not from within'. Thus, Grene's story seems to prove Kuhn wrong. But this proof cannot settle the matter for, as we have seen, one could compose a different story with more or less the same facts and then find that Kuhn is right.

Kuhn's Exemption of History

Looking again at the famous *The Structure of Scientific Revolutions*, one will find only one single theoretical argument to the effect that Kuhn's philosophy of science is a correct philosophy. In the opening paragraph of chapter 8, he reminds his readers of a fundamental difficulty. He states that at no time can any theory be falsified by direct comparison with nature. Although Kuhn does not say so, this is an obvious tilt at Popper's theory of falsification and its difficulties. I will return to this matter in chapter 6, where I will try to argue that these difficulties can be and have been removed by Popper's evolutionism. For the moment, it is important to see that Kuhn has a valid theoretical argument (i.e. one not derived from the history of science) against all those philosophies of science which seek to explain paradigm change in terms of rational rejection of false paradigms, and also against all philosophies of science, derived from Positivism, which hold that valid knowledge – whether in the shape of particular statements, general theories or paradigms – is valid because and only when it is constrained by observation. But it does not follow from this single theoretical argument produced by Kuhn that his own explanations of why and how paradigms are changed are correct. The correctness of his own arguments as to how these changes take place, why and under what circumstances, depends entirely and exclusively upon his analysis of the history of science; for this reason, his one piece of theory, whatever it does, does not help to commend or support his philosophy of science. So convinced is Kuhn that the 'hard facts' of history simply prove him correct that he explicitly rejects the possibility that the historian of science might benefit from a philosophy of science. He denies that C.G. Hempel's theory of historical explanation (which is identical with the Popperian theory put forward in chapter 2) is of any use to the historian of science, and adds that philosophers of science would gain many advantages if they bothered to take a closer look at the 'hard facts' of history.[19] He simply assumes that historical knowledge is exceptional and that whereas all 'facts' are paradigm-dependent, historical 'facts' are not. This exceptionality is specially stressed[20] and justified cavalierly by an argument about the role of general laws in historical knowledge which one can only describe as a travesty or caricature of the genuine argument. Kuhn, it appears, is under the impression that general laws can play no part in historical knowledge because the ones which frequently do are either trivial or not quantifiable or not completely universal.

The circularity of Kuhn's reasoning is particularly damaging to his case if one considers for a moment that historical knowledge itself is part of scientific knowledge – at least, part of our scientific knowledge of the past. After all, there is no reason why scientific knowledge should be exclusively about gases and atoms, light rays and gravity. Here, we can reduce Kuhn to absurdity. Let us suppose that his philosophy of science is correct and that paradigms are changed for irrational reasons because no single observation of anything has ever enough bite to explain or recommend a rational change of paradigm. In this case, if no observation has enough bite to establish any theory rationally, none of his historical examples have enough bite to establish any theory rationally. The most he can do is to invite his readers to abandon all earlier philosophies of history and hope they will fade away. But Kuhn does not do this. He allows historical examples in the history of science the absolute bite which he denies to all other facts of nature so called. History, so it seems, is for Kuhn the one exception. Here, for once in the whole and entire realm of human knowledge, we have a set of hard and brute facts which invite, indeed compel, us rationally to give up old paradigms for the philosophy of science advocated by Kuhn. There is no need for further comment. One can simply sum up the absurdity and irrationality of this argument by saying that Kuhn's philosophy of science must be wrong if his argument that, since no theory can ever be falsified by confrontation with nature or history, is right. In short, if Kuhn is right in saying that paradigms are changed and accepted for irrational reasons, he must be wrong in saying so. For he offers us what he considers to be rational reasons for leaving behind all other philosophies of science – the very thing he maintains cannot be done.

Kuhn's 'Colligation'

Kuhn's understanding of historical understanding is completely naive. He argues[21] that historical understanding is derived from the grasp of 'structures' which exhibit a 'meaning' which unrelated, single events do not possess. Nobody would wish to deny this. But every perceptive reader would carry this analysis a little further.

Kuhn takes the 'structure' as final and ultimate and declares that its meaning is not derived from the fact that the constituent elements of this structure are covered by a general law. If they are not covered by a general law, the constituent elements would not congeal into a structure! Where does Kuhn imagine the 'structure' which exhibits 'meaning' comes from?[22]

In fairness to Kuhn, one has to admit that there are several reputable philosophers of history who maintain that there is an inherent connection between single events and that there is no need for a recourse to a general law or a covering law. They maintain that single events are simply 'colligated' to one another and that the historian finds these colligations ready-made.[23] Michael Oakeshott, for example, manages even to dispense with the notion of colligation. He states that there is a continuity of contingent events and that in tracing how one leads to the other, the historian has 'abated the mystery'.[24] Though the single events are contingent to one another, the last one in the series ceases to be mysterious and seems explained when it appears as the last one. One can then see, Oakeshott says, how all the contingent events lead up to this last one.

The notion of colligation introduces a confusion. Single events cannot be colligated to one another unless somebody has done the colligating. Now it is perfectly conceivable that the historian does find single events colligated to each other. There is then no reason why he need or ought to break up such colligation and recolligate to his own satisfaction. He can do so; but he need not. If he does, he is, following the argument of chapter 2, subjective; if he does not, he is objective. If he preserves the original colligation he finds, he is however relying on the fact that the original colligation was made by somebody else. It is simply logically inconceivable that single events should be permanently and necessarily colligated to each other so that each set of colligations presents a fixed and immutable pattern of meaning which the historian can simply pick up and portray.

The Oakeshott part of the argument is not confusing, but quite simply false. Since events *are* contingent to each other and just because they are not *necessarily* connected with one another, it is impossible to trace a single line of single events leading up to a last event in such a series. If it *could* be done, the mystery of the last event would indeed be not only abated, but disappear. It would cease to be mysterious. Moreover, though Oakeshott would not like this consequence at all, the whole series would appear as a pattern, configuration or structure which would exhibit meaning in exactly the way required by Kuhn's procedure. But there is no need for Oakeshott or Oakeshottians to feel worried lest there might emerge more meaning than they would allow or care for. The path recommended by Oakeshott does not exist. It is not open to a historian or anyone else to trace a progression from one single event to another. All single events – no matter what their size on the time-scale, i.e. no matter whether they are the Second World War or Chamberlain's announcement of the state of being at war – consist of smaller events which are separated from each other by a time-gap. In all cases, there are many possibilities as to how this gap could be filled so that when one produces the next event *without* bridging the gap by a covering law, that next event will appear to be *so* contingent that it explains nothing at all.

Burke or Tocqueville on Revolutions

Every experienced historian, be it a historian of science, of society, of art, of law or of politics, must immediately see how untenable Kuhn's procedure is. Let us look at one crucial example taken from the beginning of chapter 11 of *The Structure of Scientific Revolutions*. He says there that those events in the history of science which he has described as revolutions (i.e. paradigm changes) have been treated by most other historians of science as 'additions to scientific knowledge'. Kuhn is here inviting us to believe that one can establish by historical detection and investigation whether an event is a 'revolution' or an 'addition'. Anybody even superficially acquainted with the study of the French Revolution and the vast literature on the subject will immediately recognise the weakness of Kuhn's contention. As the examples of Tocqueville's narrative of the events of 1789 and Burke's book on the same subject show, it is perfectly possible to tell the story of the French Revolution either as an addition to the *ancien régime* or as the story of the violent and revolutionary overthrow of the *ancien régime*. It depends entirely on the series of events the authors have selected. Tocqueville tells us that during the century and a half preceding the so-called revolution, the monarchy itself prepared a number of changes which almost completely eroded the *ancien régime* so that the so-called revolution was merely the last straw in its removal. In reality, he writes, the revolution was an addition to the many events which had gradually brought about a complete transformation of French society. Burke, selecting very different events and fixing his sights upon events of a different size, tells a very different story. He argues that the *ancien régime* was a well-functioning, prosperous and orderly institution and that it was violently overthrown as the result of a political conspiracy in 1789. This overthrow was brought about for no good purpose, as a sort of irrational expression of dissatisfaction by a few people.

Agassi would have no difficulty in coping with these two different histories of the same period. He would point out that Tocqueville used one philosophy of history and that Burke used a different sort of philosophy of history. In Agassi's terms, neither Burke nor Tocqueville were inductivists, for neither held that the *ancien régime* had been rationally and persuasively criticised by a very large number of people who had then come to the conclusion that the sheer accumulation of critical evidence compelled rational people to abandon the institution. Following Agassi, one would class Tocqueville as a follower of Duhem and consider him an 'accumulationist'; one would class Burke as a 'comparative conventionalist' who held that one system can be replaced by another, but that the two systems ought to be weighed and compared with each other. Kuhn, on the other hand, by his own philosophy of science and his own philosophy of history, is completely helpless in the face of evidence presented by the books of Burke and Tocqueville. All he might offer is the argument that revolutions are real, that if they appear as 'additions' people are being misled by textbooks and that therefore Burke must be right and Tocqueville, wrong.

If the question were put to historians in Kuhnian terms, they would not hesitate with an answer. The verdict would go entirely against Kuhn and in favour of 'addition'. Tocqueville and his view that the events usually described as the French Revolution are really an 'addition' has an infinitely higher credit-rating than Burke's thesis; even though Burke, too, has his defenders and admirers, no sound historian would be prepared to admit that Tocqueville was the victim of deception or self-deception. Unfortunately, the question is never put in this fashion. There are innumerable historians who are only too ready to pay lip-service to Kuhn's philosophy of science, to apply it to fields other than science and to repeat what he says about paradigm changes, the incommensurability of paradigms, and the irrationality which governs paradigm changes.[25] The only explanation I can offer for this surprising state of affairs is that most historians, no matter how erudite and sophisticated they are in their own fields, are usually quite ignorant of the history of science. Somehow, it seems, they feel that Kuhn, a historian of science, *must* know what he is talking about. His conclusions must, therefore, be accepted by historians who feel out of their depth when it comes to the history of science. And, so they seem to reason, if it is true for the history of science, it must be true for all history. Indeed, many historians believe that Kuhn has merely historicised science and by introducing a historical dimension into science, happens to have discovered that the emergence and disappearance of paradigms are irrational events. The truth is that Kuhn was not the first to historicise science and that nobody is quarrelling with the historicisation of science. On the contrary, the importance of the relationship between the history of science and the philosophy of science is due precisely to the realisation that the scientific enterprise is a historical phenomenon and to our understanding of the historicity of science. Kuhn's special contribution is that though science has a history, there is no particular importance to be attached to that history. As time passes, he argues, paradigms change. The distinction between earlier and later is of no significance and the connection between the passage of time and changes of paradigm, though real, is completely random. Progress, he writes on page 170, is nothing but a move away from a primitive condition. At any rate, Kuhn's particular conception that the historicity of science consists in irrational paradigm changes is incapable of being supported by the historical evidence because the history of science follows upon the philosophy of science, and not the other way round.

One has to bear in mind that the idea of progress has three very distinct meanings. First, it means that if one speaks of progress, one is speaking of a movement away from an initial or primitive condition. In this sense of progress, Kuhn is firmly on the side of progress. Second, it means that if one thinks of progress, one is thinking of a gradual fulfilment of a divine plan, of teleology or some other kind of pre-ordained Providence. Kuhn is not thinking of this kind of progress and everybody would agree with him. Third, it means that if one is supporting the idea that there is progress, one is supporting the notion that it is self-generating and self-planned. Design, in this sense, results automatically from the so-called *invisible* hand – or, in Darwinian terms, design produces itself without plan by natural selection. According to Popper, as we shall argue in chapter 6, this kind of progress applies also to the growth of knowledge. According to Kuhn, the growth of knowledge does not exhibit this kind of progress. It is a major flaw in Kuhn that he fails to distinguish these three different meanings of progress and thinks that, having correctly dismissed the second possibility, he must be left with nothing but the first possibility. In reality, the third possibility ought, at least, to be considered. One can see, however, why Kuhn is not in a position to consider the third possibility. Having argued that all paradigms are incommensurable and that one will do for some problems or observations and another for others, he is really saying that from the eyes of God, as it were, they are equidistant. Such equidistance precludes the possibility of any kind of progress other than progress in the first sense, where it means nothing more than that all paradigms are different from an initial pre-paradigmatic state. We will return to the concept of equidistance in chapter 4.

In order to criticise Kuhn, one has to consider the above example of the French Revolution and show ordinary historians and social scientists the sort of difficulties they find themselves committed to in regard to Burke and Tocqueville if they keep on believing in the truth of what Kuhn is saying. They may have difficulty in detecting the flaws in Kuhn's arguments about the history of science, but they should have no difficulty in detecting the flaws when confronted with the consequences which Kuhn's reasoning has for our knowledge of the French Revolution.

The Two Postulates

The circularity in Kuhn's argumentation is a very formidable problem. But Kuhn is not alone: there are many people who might wish to throw the towel in. In chapter 2 I explained that history is something which has to be composed with the help of general laws, the sum total of which one might describe as a philosophy of history. If all historical knowledge is relative to a philosophy of history, one might conclude, then Kuhn's philosophy of science is relative to his history of science, and his history of science is relative to his philosophy of science. He is no worse than any other historian. Like all other historians, he cannot break out of this vicious circle. If there is nothing much to recommend him, people might say, there is also very little to condemn him. Circularity is simply a fact of historical knowledge. Moreover, there was nothing in chapter 2 to dispel such a defeatist attitude.

Nevertheless, such a defeatist conclusion is not warranted. The relativity of a history to a set of general laws is undeniable. But one can set up at least two postulates which will attenuate such circularity. If Kuhn had been more cautious and had paid some attention to such postulates, he might have been able to avoid complete circularity. He would then, in all probability, not have been able to come up with the striking conclusion that history shows that paradigm switches are always revolutionary and that such revolutions make for progress only in the negative sense that one is getting away from the original.

The two postulates concern the problem of circularity in historical composition. First, there is the 'Postulate of Sufficient Variety'. It demands that there ought to be a high level of difference between any criterion of selection and the general laws derived from or tested by the history composed with the help of any criterion. Kuhn totally fails to satisfy this postulate. He first writes his own history of science about Copernicus and Kepler, selecting and interpreting the events in terms of his idea that paradigm changes are revolutionary, fundamental and irrational; that old paradigms fade away; and that after the acceptance of a new paradigm people start to do normal science, and so forth. Next, he turns round and invites us to believe that this particular history 'proves' that his philosophy of science about paradigm changes is correct. There is no difference between the input and the output and, therefore, there is total circularity. Given the nature of historical knowledge, the failure to observe this postulate has proved fatal. Had Kuhn taken Burtt's history of the same period and used it as evidence and then come up with the finding that, on Burtt's story's evidence, paradigms are changed irrationally and normal science follows upon revolutionary paradigm changes, the postulate would have been observed in full. Burtt's story was obviously not composed by using Kuhn's philosophy of science as a criterion of selection. If Kuhn had been able to discover evidence for his philosophy of science in Burtt's story, this would have been an important and telling discovery.

The second postulate is the 'Postulate of Sufficient Specification'. It states that any philosophy of history or any philosophy of science used as a criterion of selection must have sufficient specification of time and place. For if one uses as a criterion of selection a philosophy of science without stating the time and place to which it applies and then considers the whole world and all ages as fair hunting-ground for events likely to support that philosophy of science, one cannot achieve much and cannot hope to command much credibility. The world is a large place and there have been many centuries to search in. But if one specifically states that science was practised in accordance with a certain philosophy of science in Britain in the eighteenth century and then manages to produce, using that philosophy of science as a criterion of selection, a large number of events to support the original contention, obviously the credibility of the arguments must increase. In this second postulate, Kuhn fails completely in his *The Structure of Scientific Revolutions*. His examples are chosen from all places and all ages and it is hardly surprising that he has come up with a formidable array of examples to make a convincing case. Using all centuries and the whole world as a hunting-ground, one could find examples for almost anything. But by the same token, his earlier book, *The Copernican Revolution*, scores fairly well by this postulate. He has, here, specified that this particular philosophy of science applies to the sixteenth century in Central Europe, and the mere fact that in this specified, limited area of time and place he has been able to find a coherent set of examples to bear out his contention, is impressive. The fact that he has done so does not 'prove' anything, as the counter-examples from Toulmin, Koestler and Burtt and Gillispie have shown. But at least it does not rule his argument, in this particular area, out of court. The circularity here, has been attenuated.

Lakatos's Predicament

In the opening sentence of *History of Science and its Rational Reconstruction*,[26] Imre Lakatos stated that the philosophy of science without history is empty and that the history of science without philosophy of science is blind. Although the present argument has sought to show that the history of science is more dependent on the philosophy of science than the other way round, and that the relationship between history and philosophy is therefore not completely symmetrical, this statement is sufficiently compatible with my argument to make it imperative to subject Lakatos's argument to a close scrutiny. Unfortunately, it turns out that in

History of Science and its Rational Reconstruction Lakatos did not deliver the goods promised by his proclamation of symmetry between the philosophy and the history of science. On the contrary, in spite of certain important differences, Lakatos appears to believe, like Kuhn, that we can know the history of science, that it provides us with real hard information as to what happened in the past, and that that knowledge of what actually happened can be appraised in the light of a *rational* reconstruction of what happened.

Kuhn, as we have seen, simply allows history the final say as to which philosophy of science is correct. Lakatos is more circumspect. He will allow such a final say only to a very special kind of history – that is, to the 'internal' history of science. By 'internal' is meant the history which is a *rational* reconstruction of the history of science. It differs from 'external' history of science, which includes all the irrational and accidental circumstances which surround the discovery of problems and the discovery of solutions of problems. His insistence that only internal history should be allowed to provide the decision as to which philosophy of science is correct, is marginally better than Kuhn's simple reliance on the history of science as such. But in the last analysis, Lakatos, too, makes the particular philosophy of science which he believes to be the correct philosophy of science completely dependent on a special version of the history of science.

On the face of it, it seems as if Lakatos sought to avoid the Kuhnian impasse. He says that methodologies (i.e. philosophies of science) can be criticised so that among several competing ones the correct one will emerge, without direct reference to an epistemological or even logical theory.[27] He points out, correctly, that all philosophies of science function as meta-historical theories and that any history of science one can obtain is dependent on a meta-historical philosophy of science. So far, so good. But then he goes on to say that these meta-historical theories can be 'criticised by criticising the rational historical reconstructions to which they lead.'

How does Lakatos envisage a criticism of a rational historical reconstruction? He admits that such a reconstruction is originally dependent on a meta-historical theory. Being so dependent, it is not very likely that an internal history of science, constructed with the help of a meta-historical theory, will be critical of the meta-historical theory which was used to compose it. Lakatos seems aware of the possibility of complete circularity, although he does not say so in so many words. The real question one has to ask is how the internal history of science obtained with the help of a given meta-historical theory can be criticised. One could, of course, criticise the meta-historical theory (i.e. the philosophy of science) which was used. But in order to do so one would have to appeal to epistemological and logical considerations – the very thing Lakatos wants to avoid.

How, then, can the internal history be criticised? In order to criticise it without criticising the meta-historical theory itself, one would have to have *independent* knowledge of what actually happened (i.e. of what that history was *really* like). There is no way in which Lakatos can avoid such a reliance on historical knowledge. If he wants to criticise internal history without criticising the meta-historical theory on which it is based, he must have other, independent historical knowledge up his sleeve. If one supposes that one can have such independent knowledge and that Lakatos does have it, then his argument becomes acceptable. He can then criticise the internal history produced by a meta-historical theory. If the internal history deviates from, or is significantly different from, what actually happened, one must infer that the meta-historical theory on which it was based must be false. Historical knowledge, in this case, can become the arbiter between rival methodologies or rival 'logics of discovery'. In one place he writes as if he were in possession of such independent historical knowledge. He says explicitly that one should resort to external history only where the actual history (*sic*) differs from internal history, thus presuming that the 'actual history' is known or knowable and that there is, in fact, an *actual* history.[28] Nobody, nowadays, would suggest that the truth of Newtonian mechanics can be tested by looking at the *actual* planetary system. Why are there philosophers who believe that history is an exception and that the accuracy of any narrative can be ascertained if one looks at what *actually* happened? If one could know what *actually* happened in the universe, there would be no need for the philosophy of science as distinct from science. And yet, here we have philosophers who suggest that the problems in the philosophy of science – problems created by our inability to know what *actually* happens – can be solved by a recourse to the history of science.

The whole argument of the present book has been designed to show that we cannot have such independent knowledge of the history of science as a whole; not even of the internal history of science. To say that we know what actually happened is like saying that we have knowledge of *res gestae*. In chapter 2 it was shown that such knowledge is impossible. Even an internal history of science which would consist of a rational reconstruction of how argument and test led to argument and test, and so forth, presupposes knowledge of what the scientists in question considered an argument and a test and is thus dependent on a logic of discovery or, more precisely, on the particular logic of discovery which the scientists followed and considered correct.

In the final analysis, therefore, Lakatos's proposal that we can use historical knowledge, even if it is knowledge of the internal history of science, to compare critically rival philosophies of science and decide which is the correct one, is untenable.

Chapter 4

Closed Circles

Cutting the Gordian Knot

Now that we have shown that Kuhn's model of the history of science – that an irrational and largely gratuitous revolutionary change of paradigm is followed by the pursuit of normal science – is not, as he claims, derived from the observation of the history of science, we must inquire as to whence it is derived. I am using the expression 'model of the history of science' in Kuhn's own sense of 'paradigm'. This use seems to be legitimate once it has been established that his version of the structure of scientific revolutions is not just a Positivistic report about what has happened in the history of science. Kuhn claimed to have historical knowledge of *res gestae* as such. Critical scrutiny has revealed, however, that all he had was a particular *historia rerum gestarum*. It is therefore legitimate to refer to his history of science as one of many possible models of the history of science. We must now inquire into the real grounds for advocating this particular model even though such an inquiry might make one feel a bit sheepish, like the psychiatrist who in *Catch 22* is sent to examine the hero suspected of insanity. The psychiatrist offers the hero a cigarette. The hero refuses. The psychiatrist then wants to know why the hero has such an obsessive objection to smoking. The hero answers that, far from being obsessively against smoking, he just put a cigarette out and will not want another one for at least ten minutes. Thereupon, the psychiatrist's eyes light up. 'A very clever answer,' he says, 'but we will soon find out what the *real* reason for your objection is.'

The inquiry into the real genesis of Kuhn's model yields surprising results. Knowledge is a relation between knower and known and we say that it *refers* to what is known. It has been notoriously difficult to account for and define the idea of reference. There is no easy and certainly no obvious way to get between language and its object – that is, to separate the two so that one can check whether and how the one is adequate to the other. No matter how one twists and turns, the concept of reference remains somewhat elusive. How, for example, can a linguistic expression refer to something non-linguistic? Does it have to be a mirror-image before we consider reference established? Is there a special way of coding knowledge? How can language be a mirror-image? And if not a mirror-image, is it necessary for knowledge to be a replica of what is known? And how can we think of language as constructing such replicas or portraits? And if not language, what are the portraits to be made of? Are we to think of them as a genuine duplication? Or may we think of them as imitations or possibly as simulations? 'The only thing incomprehensible about the world,' Einstein used to say, 'is that it is comprehensible.' In desperation, people have come up with the strangest of ideas to account for 'reference'. In so far as knowledge is expressed mathematically and quite a lot of knowledge can be so expressed, it has been seriously maintained that God must have been a mathematician and made the world mathematically so that we can understand it mathematically. I have never come across a similar argument in favour of language in general, though Muslims believe that God spoke Arabic and could therefore be thought to have made the world in conformity with Arabic idiom.

Reference in general is a very untractable phenomenon, even outside the sphere of knowledge. Every society, for example, 'refers' to its own past. The same society in the same place looked different in the past. How can one account for and explain such reference of the past to the present? One can pinpoint certain changes and transformations in some customs or laws or in population density, and so forth. But it is very tricky to establish a referential link between the whole structure and its past. For that matter, it is equally difficult to establish such links between two different, contemporary societies, even though cross-references may be very striking and quite obvious. Historians and sociologists are as uneasy and as bewildered when asked to account for these references as philosophers when asked to explain how knowledge refers to anything it is knowledge of.

In view of these difficulties, it is not surprising to find that time and again people have solved the problem by cutting the Gordian Knot. They have maintained that there is no need to explain 'reference' because 'reference' does not occur. All knowledge, the radical argument goes, is a set of conventions governed by a leading central paradigm. It is derived from and informed by that paradigm and does not refer to anything other than the paradigm it is informed by. The same strategy can be used in regard to the manner in which societies are linked to their past or to each other. They are not linked at all, the argument goes. They are self-contained systems in which all parts are functionally related to each other so that the need to refer any part to a past condition simply disappears. Malinowski's declaration that 'there are no fossils in a society' has its direct counterpart in Wittgenstein's declaration that 'there is no private language'. The first declaration cuts off reference to the past; the second cuts off reference to the outside.

The Closed-circle Model

For Kuhn, science is an activity practised inside a closed circle and the value of the activity is assessed by reference to the paradigm which stands in the centre of the circle. This model is a modern variation on the old theme of cutting the Gordian Knot. There is nothing that is novel about it, except Kuhn's claim that it should be applied to the philosophy of science.[1] As I will try to show, the model has its good and fruitful uses *except* when applied to the history and philosophy of science. Further, once the essential unoriginality of the model is grasped, one can only recommend to all those countless historians and social scientists and philosophers who now use it on Kuhn's authority, that they would be better advised to use it in its traditional and better-tried forms and not to rest their cases on Kuhn's authority.

The Kuhn model, or the philosophy of closed circles, says that the pursuit of science takes place in a system; that each system is a sort of closed whole; that each such closed whole can be replaced by another similar closed whole; that inside each such whole the truth of any statement or theory can be tested by reference to the centre (which is called a paradigm); that each such system is incommensurable with any other system; and that while any theory inside any system can be true inside that system, it will appear false when compared with the centre of any other system.

The philosophy of closed circles has its twin origins in the two main streams of eighteenth-century thought. On one side, it derives from Voltaire's philosophy of history; and, on the other, from the philosophy of the German romantics, especially from Herder. Voltaire believed that the whole of the past history of mankind was a long series of errors, crimes and follies, largely perpetrated by priests and their ignorant victims. However, at the same time, he was also something of a cultural (as distinguished from a geological) 'catastrophist', for he admitted that there had been four periods of enlightened peaks which stood out like islands: Periclean Athens, the Golden Age of imperial Rome, the Florentine Renaissance and the age of Louis XIV. He was at a loss to say how these peaks had managed to emerge in such oceans of ignorance and unlike earlier historians who had seen long paths of decline or ascent, as the case may be, Voltaire saw these islands as sudden, isolated and inexplicable systems of light. Unlike other historians, he therefore had to make a valiant attempt to explain these systems as self-explanatory systems, as systems which cause their own enlightenment and irradiate themselves. Without thinking of the right terminology, he had actually hit, through the sheer accident of his own peculiar and myopic Enlightenment-oriented thinking, upon what we nowadays call 'system theory with feedback'. Unable, because unwilling to explain these four Golden Ages of mankind as the result of, or as related to, epochs which had surrounded or preceded them, he was forced to invent a new kind of historiography in which each of these Golden Ages was a closed whole inside of which each part – politics, art, literature, science, manners, morals, etc. – was explained in terms of every other part.

The other source for this kind of closed-system analysis is to be found in the historical thought of Herder. Herder was much more historical than Voltaire and, unlike Voltaire, only too willing to consider the causal influence of the past on the present. He was dissatisfied with political history and found it insufficient. He therefore considered that behind the ephemeral and transient veils of political events, there lay – sometimes deeply buried – the folk spirit of every single nation. In Herder's day, it really required some power of imagination to see history in this fashion, for, at that time, the 'nations' were hardly visible and could be discerned only dimly behind the dynastic and political configurations which were then the real stuff of political–historical knowledge. But Herder dug deep into the past of languages and poetry and came up with the grand theory that throughout time, the politics, economics, social structures and manners of every nation had been determined by this hidden spring of folk spirit. He, too, like Voltaire, thought in systems. Each system, at the centre of which there was a folk spirit, was a self-contained whole. One could explain everything that had happened to the nation concerned in terms of that folk spirit at its centre. But each folk spirit was different from every other folk spirit. Two folk spirits could not be compared with each other, nor could the separate manners, arts, politics and social structures which had issued from each, be compared with each other. Here again, there were systems and there was incommensurability. In order to understand, one had to grasp or find the centre. The rest could more or less be deduced. Knowledge of the centre enabled one to do 'normal science'. The real difference between Herder's systems and Voltaire's systems was the fact that the former were extended in time, and the latter in space. But the exclusiveness, the separateness, the incommensurability and the feedback were all there. Given the conceptual similarity of the historical methods forged by Herder and Voltaire, it is perhaps a little surprising that the Voltaire systems have become part of enlightened, rational social science and history – leading to Burckhardt and other meritorious people – and that the Herder systems have given birth to the more irrational ways of romanticism, mass movements, demonic folk cults and the worship of irrational nationalism.

It must be stressed that if one thinks in terms of closed circles or systems, one cannot relate either the system itself or any part of it to the passage of time. In this kind of analysis, there is an inbuilt disregard for evolution. It is easy to see how this comes about. If one looks upon any institution or any pursuit as explicable in terms of the other institutions or pursuits with which it is synchronically related and considers the whole as a functioning system of interrelated parts, its position in time is irrelevant. What comes before and what comes after is a matter of accident, and the emergence of any one system is a random event – at least, random in relation to the emergence of other events. In this way, system analysis of the kind described precludes historical explanations and forces one to disregard the possibility that any one system might have evolved and be the precursor of another system.

When one is looking at systems in such a non-evolutionary way, one is obliged to conclude that all systems are of equal value or merit or, as the German historian Leopold von Ranke put it, that they are equidistant from God.[2] With this view of equidistance, evolution is barred. For evolution, whatever its mechanisms, cannot accept that all species or thought-systems or institutions are equidistant from whatever origin or whatever goal. Some are closer and some are more distant not only from the point of departure, but also from one another. In a way, one might say that closed-system analysis is a latter-day version of creationism. It is certainly more compatible with Linnaeus's description of all the different species than with Darwin's view that all species are unstable and that one has evolved from the other. It is true that most supporters of the closed-system method are not creationists and many do not even believe in God. But it is remarkable that one should find this broad similarity and anti-evolutionary bias in all of them. If it is a matter of chance how one system disappears and is replaced by another, one might just as well add that that chance is the result of God's will. The most important change in man's view of himself, of the world and of living nature, came with the idea of evolutionary change. The philosophy of closed circles and of functioning systems would seem a studied attempt to deny this change and to adhere to the overt or hidden opposition to change and to reduce such change as there has been to the result of chance or irrational accidents. By contrast, the most important quality of evolutionary thinking is the ability to see that change is no more random or accidental than that it is decreed arbitrarily by God. Evolutionary thinking maintains, on the contrary, that the relation between change and the passage of time is not random.

In order to avoid misunderstanding, I should add a word about terminology. The closed-circle model which says that every system – whether a system of knowledge or a system of social structures — is closed has often been called historism. To historism, each epoch, each epistemic configuration, each social structure, is totally individual and *sui generis* and can only be explained in its own terms (i.e. as it appears to itself). Conventionally, historism is considered to be an off-shoot of the Romantic Revolution and in this respect the role of Herder in its formation is well appreciated. It is also held to be incompatible with the Enlightenment and conventional histories of historism usually contrast Herder with Gibbon and Voltaire. Enlightenment historians and thinkers are said not to have been historists because they believed that human reason, as well as human nature in general, is the same in all places and at all times. They were therefore not disposed to consider that every society or every age was *sui generis* and a uniquely individual configuration which could not be understood from the outside, as it were. But as soon as one takes a wider perspective and understands the emergence of a historist strategy as a response to the difficulty one encounters when one seeks to explain reference, one can see that the link between romanticism and historism is quite accidental. Voltaire, though anything but a romantic, forged the idea of closed circles through his 'catastrophist' vision of enlightenment and historism has certainly long survived the romantic movement. The role of Voltaire was indeed quite crucial because he not so much formulated the explicit tenets of historism, as provided in his famous book on the age of Louis XIV a practical demonstration as to how a purely historist inquiry has to proceed.

For the most part, the proponents of closed circles or historists, are not much interested in historical development. But sometimes they are. When they are, they will either resort to 'catastrophism' or put forward the idea that closed circles succeed one another according to an iron law of development. This belief in iron laws of development has come to be known as historicism.

Historicism is an unsound idea and comes close to being a contradiction in terms. When one is speaking of laws, one is thinking of regularities. But when one is thinking of a single sequence of closed circles, one cannot be thinking of regularities and to speak of a developmental law therefore cannot make sense. Not even the Second Law of Thermodynamics, which has introduced the idea that there is an arrow of time in the order of nature, can be considered to be a developmental law, for it does not assert that there is a singular succession of unique states of molecules. It says, on the contrary, that molecules behave with certain regularities and that these regularities, as time passes, lead to increasing entropy. Hence, the arrow of time. It is a little difficult to discover why people should have thought of developmental laws at all and why historicism has enjoyed a certain vogue. But when one links it to historism, one can see that it is a sort of desperate attempt to introduce the passage of time into the notion that all societies and all systems of knowledge are closed circles. One could have simply left it at that. But when one wants to look at the succession of closed circles in time and not simply treat them as 'one damned thing after another' (as a famous French film director once put it), one has to resort to historicism and invent the idea that there is a law of development which forces these closed circles to come and go. In sum, all closed-circle thinkers are historists; but not all historists are historicists. But if one is a historist and wishes to account for the passage of time and link closed circles to each other, one has to resort to historicism to do so.

It is not the purpose of this inquiry to trace the precise growth of systemic thinking and of closed circles and historism. From the middle of the nineteenth century onwards, starting with the various fashions of nationalistic historiography, there has not been a single decade in which this kind of systemic thinking in the social sciences has not come forward under a new name and with the claim to have found, at long last, the genuine method of understanding man and his relation to society. This kind of systemic thinking was at the basis of the philosophy of Oswald Spengler.

Spengler distinguished eight or nine such systems in the history of mankind and combined, in each system, the temporal and the spatial extensions of Herder and Voltaire. Each system was a culture, fed by a central core of power – Apollo, in Greece; Faustus, in modern Europe; The Magus, in the case of Middle Eastern culture, and so forth. Each system was self-contained and eventually, for no compelling reason, was bound to wilt. Spengler explained such wilting in purely organic terms and argued that systems wilt the way flowers wilt. There are perfectly good reasons why flowers wilt; but systems are not flowers and Spengler's analogy can therefore not be considered an explanation. Strangely, Kuhn's major explanation why a paradigm and the system that forms around it disappears, is not very different from Spengler's explanation. Kuhn, too, says that paradigms 'fade' because the people who uphold them, of necessity, will eventually die. In Kuhn's case, the organic analogy is more acceptable because he is talking about human beings who are in fact subject to organic decay. Spengler cannot claim such a justification for his analogy because each of his systems spans may generations. But even for Kuhn the use of organic decay as an explanation ought to be questionable. The paradigm in question informs knowledge; and while it is perfectly true that upholders of paradigms die, such death is irrelevant to the validity of the paradigm as knowledge. While each system lasted, Spengler argued, every one of its parts could be explained as a function of its central core of power. Each system was closed and self-contained and could not be compared, let alone understood, in terms of any other system. There was no explanation why one system flowered and faded before another system. One might say that here, in Spengler's thought, there was a historiography to end all historiography. The whole thrust of Spengler's thinking was anti-evolutionary and anti-historical.

While Spengler was working out the details of his grand attack on, and rejection of, historical investigation in Germany, Bronislav Malinowski, a man of completely different stamp, was at work in Britain and Australia. In tracing the history of historism or closed circles, one now discovers peculiar eddies and pathways. Malinowski reacted in the first instance against historicism and more precisely against historicism which had been inspired by historism and closed circles.

During the nineteenth century, Voltaire's 'catastrophism' had gone out of fashion and people had become very much concerned with historical explanations as to why primitive societies had made room for less primitive ones and how less primitive societies had become modern and 'civilised'. The most widely practised method for explaining these changes was historicism – that is, the belief that there was a developmental law which forced all societies sooner or later to 'evolve'. With such a developmental law one could arrange societies on a time-scale. The more primitive a society, the earlier it was. Those societies which were still primitive in the nineteenth century, had not yet evolved. This historicism was greatly inspired by Comte and practised by Tylor, Maine, Morgan, Marx, Frazer and Spencer. These people were and still are considered to have been evolutionists. So they were; but the use of this term is likely to cause misunderstanding. The real theory of evolution as practised by Hutton, Lyell and Darwin was not historicist. Neither the geologists nor Darwin himself appealed to a law of evolution or to any other developmental law. They were not concerned to discover how one state had been succeeded by another state, nor with how the succession of states – be they the forms of the earth or the forms of living organisms – had been brought about by the force of a developmental law. On the contrary, the genuine evolutionists held that one can explain the evolution of the earth and of living organisms by assuming that the causes which are operative today have always been operative in the past. This doctrine, known as uniformitarianism, lies at the heart of all valid evolutionary thinking and is diametrically opposed to the methodology of closed circles or of historism, which precludes genuine evolutionary thinking.

The nineteenth-century historicists differed according to the developmental laws they used. Some were more historicist than others. Thus Comte, for example, considered the succession from magic to religion and from religion to science to have been wholly mysterious. Marx, on the other hand, was less historicist than Comte for he thought that one could account for the transition from feudalism to capitalism by showing up the contradictions which had been inherent in feudalism and which had caused its downfall. No matter what the degree of historicism exactly was, all these historicist accounts of human history assumed that there is a link between the mere passage of time and the eventual approximation of all people to the cultural and social conditions of contemporary Western man. In all these stories, one finds the notion that the connection between the passage of time and the changes which had occurred in history, had come about by some mysterious force so that one could detect how phases of development had succeeded one another. The course went from magic to religion, and from religion to science; or from primitive communism to slavery, from slavery to feudalism and then to capitalism; or from the simple to the complex; or from status to contract. These theories of history were theories of change. But the change which they explained seemed to be predestined or brought about by a developmental law the nature of which nobody really understood – largely because one cannot understand a developmental law. Comte was adamant that magic and religion had made way for science, but he could not say why it had made way. All these theories of change were historicist because they could not go beyond the assertion that change had been of a certain kind – from magic to science, from slavery to feudalism, from simplicity to complexity.

Malinowski reacted against this kind of historicism and against historicism in general and went back to pure, non-historical historism. He advocated the method of closed circles because he was dissatisfied with the evolutionary historicism of Frazer. In so reacting, he was absolved from any lengthy argument to establish or commend the method of closed circles. In pointing out the flaws of historicism, he had done enough and was able to give the idea of closed circles a new and vigorous lease of life. Malinowski taught that every people in any place is a system in which every part is related to every other part. This systemic methodology was christened 'functionalism' because Malinowski was able to show that in every system all parts 'functioned' to support the whole. Religion and economics, art and morals were all functionally integrated to make a complete system. Each system was self-explanatory as an ongoing whole and one need not and ought not compare one system with any other system. Malinowski, unlike Spengler, became an academic orthodoxy in Britain and throughout the British empire.

Meanwhile, in America, obviously fired by Malinowski but avowedly influenced by Spengler, the system idea was taken up and popularised by Ruth Benedict in one of the most influential books on social science ever written: *Patterns of Culture,* first published in England in 1935. It went through innumerable editions and linked the American scene to the rest of the English-speaking world and cut across linguistic boundaries by its explicit ultimate appeal to the authority of Spengler, whom Ruth Benedict managed to deprive of his Teutonic gloom. Although Ruth Benedict never did achieve the status of academic orthodoxy accorded to Malinowski, her book must have helped to broaden the whole approach and to disseminate the idea of incommensurability. With astonishing and admirable literary skill, Ruth Benedict sketched the profiles of three different societies — the Pueblos of New Mexico; the Dobu Islanders who live off the southern shore of eastern New Guinea; and the Kwakiutl of Vancouver island. She showed that in each culture there were different values; that these values were incompatible with each other; and that, since inside each system every value made sense and functioned well, these cultures were incommensurable. Her book was the grand and absolute statement of moral relativism.

From Malinowski and Ruth Benedict the road led straight to our modern ethnomethodologists. If one treats every society or culture as a closed circle and explains its several parts as functions of the central paradigm, one must always be best advised – and both Malinowski and Ruth Benedict had always insisted on this – to inquire from the people inside the circle what they considered to be the central paradigm. This course was not mandatory, but it was rightly considered foolhardy to eschew it. Modern ethnomethodology has now come up with the suggestion that that course ought to be made mandatory and that any attempt to locate the central paradigm of any closed circle outside the minds and the testimony of the people who are inside the circle amounts to a distortion and a falsehood about the closed circle. In making this extreme claim, ethnomethodology has the one great advantage over its ancestors: it glaringly exhibits the weakness of the model. It is one thing to insist that one take into account what the members of any circle are saying about themselves; but quite another thing to maintain that the only truth about a circle is the truth held about it by the members of that circle. Ethnomethodology has at long last glaringly exposed the great weakness of the closed-circle model by elevating a side-effect ('study the meaning of the paradigm by listening to the members of the circle in which the paradigm is upheld') into the central dogma.

After the Second World War, when the power of both Malinowski and Benedict seemed a little spent, not to mention the tarnished Germanic reputation of Spengler, the idea received in Britain a new lease of life from a totally unexpected quarter. The philosophy of the late Wittgenstein consisted largely in the contention that the meaning of a sentence consists in its 'use'. If 'use' equals 'meaning' then 'meaning' equals 'use'.[3] Since all knowledge is a linguistic phenomenon or something expressed in language, Wittgenstein argued, it has to be assessed for validity in the same way in which we assess language. Since there can be no private language – a private language would be a contradiction in terms – all language is a rule-following activity; and the conception 'rule' implies that one is behaving in harmony with, and according to, the consensus of other people who form something like a speech community. Wittgenstein summed up this doctrine in his epigram that there is no private language. Though it may seem superficially that this declaration is a declaration in favour of outside reference and against closed circles, it turns out to be the opposite. The easiest way to establish outside reference is by appeal to observation. But since all observation must initially and in the first instance be a private experience and give rise, linguistically, to personal-report sentences, observation must somehow be linked to 'private language'. The denial that there is such a thing as a private language amounts, therefore, to a denial that one can break out of a closed circle by 'observing' what goes on outside. The people who are inside that community are playing a language game. The notion of 'rule' rules out the possibility that one is following instructions just once and once only. If one did, one would clearly not be following a 'rule'. Again, in thus establishing the meaning of a 'rule', Wittgenstein is not saying anything of substance, open to a critical test; he is merely drawing our attention to the fact that a 'rule' means what the use of the word has in our community and that the meaning of the word 'rule' is how the word 'rule' is used. There is a vicious circle here, for we find that Wittgenstein's justification of his declaration that there is no private language depends, in turn, on his insistence that one determines the meaning of words by their use. The validity of the whole argument depends on the validity of the argument. Supposing that the argument is valid, we are then told that when we grasp that there is something which makes a statement true, we derive this grasp from our *use* of certain basic forms of statement as reports of observation. This situation in which a report is not a report but merely considered a report because there is a rule that it should be, is echoed in a funny scene in Tom Stoppard's play *Jumpers*. The hero is conversing with a psychiatrist while his wife in the next room is being interviewed by a detective who is trying to rape her. She cries 'help!' and the husband is understandably alarmed. The psychiatrist, however, calms him by saying it means nothing: 'In the profession, we interpret this sort of cry as a call for help.'[4]

Here, in the guise of philosophy, the systemic thinking of Voltaire and Herder, of Spengler and Malinowski, was revived in a powerful way, for Wittgenstein had all sorts of appeals which ranged from his stance as a deep and incomprehensible thinker to his reputation as a profound philosopher who was far in advance of traditional philosophical thought about the mind–body problem and ordinary epistemology and ethics and similar allegedly outmoded philosophical conundrums. As far as social science was concerned, the Wittgenstein revival of the method of the closed system and its incommensurability with other closed systems received its most poignant and pointed expression in the well-known essay by Peter Winch, *The Idea of a Social Science*.[5] Here was genuinely old wine in seemingly new bottles. To understand a society, Winch says, is to *participate* in the form of life exhibited in its pattern of social relationships.

The role – or ought we to say, the shadow? – of Wittgenstein in the consolidation of these methodologies of relativism and incommensurability cannot be exaggerated. No matter how much the various interpreters of Wittgenstein disagree as to what he had taught and said, and whether the *Tractatus* is or is not compatible with the *Philosophical Investigations*, there is one issue on which they are all agreed. Wittgenstein, they maintain, was completely original and ushered in a new phase in the history of thought. Given the fact that there is so much disagreement as to what he had meant, it is hard to say how there can be so much agreement that, whatever he said, he started a new epoch in the history of thought. I would have thought that one cannot be certain as to whether he did unless one is certain as to what he said. This curious worship of Wittgenstein, based on the admission that no matter what he said, he started a new epoch in the history of thought, must derive, then, not from his teaching but from his personality, the quasi-charismatic spell he bound his listeners with.[6] A younger generation of readers is still being brought up by teachers who have been under his personal spell. But one must wonder whether a third generation of readers, who will have been taught by people who never felt the personal spell, will keep nurturing the Wittgenstein myth, for there is certainly nothing in the written word to warrant the conviction that he had anything new to say.

Wittgenstein's later philosophy was nothing more than a radical presentation of the philosophy of closed circles. 'A blunder,' Wittgenstein said, 'is always a blunder in a particular system; just as a blunder in a game is always a blunder in a particular game and not in another.'[7] In a recent and widely acclaimed book, one of his apostles maintains that Wittgenstein, at least the later Wittgenstein, had shown how we can carry on philosophical talk after we have realised that philosophy can teach nothing about knowledge and how we have come to know anything. After the demise of mirror philosophy, of foundational and representational epistemology, the argument goes, there came the great saviour who taught us to play language games and showed us that the truth of whatever we say is always a truth or a blunder, as the case may be, in a closed system or a particular game. My reading of the history of philosophy is very different. It seems to me that Wittgenstein merely dotted the philosophical 'i' and provided a theoretical argument to justify the age-old practice of closed-system thinking. Seen in this way, Wittgenstein, far from standing at the beginning of a new epoch, is the last in a long line of closed-system philosophers and should be classified with Voltaire and Herder, Spengler and Malinowski. For that matter, Ruth Benedict's book is infinitely better reading than Wittgenstein's *Philosophical Investigations*. This may, of course, be a matter of taste. But there is no doubt that both teach exactly the same thing. Ruth Benedict, Peter Winch, Wittgenstein, Malinowski, Spengler and the ethnomethodologists are all trying to wipe out the all-important distinction made by Weber, the distinction between *verstehen* (understanding) and *erklären* (explaining), a distinction which corresponds to the distinction, made in chapter 2, between knowing what *actually* happened and what *really* happened. What *actually* happened is what appears to have happened to the people inside the circle; what *really* happened is what is judged to have happened by the people outside the circle.

Strikingly, in France, the philosophy of the closed system was revived and given a new lease of life by Michel Foucault. While philosophers in France were debating the relative merits of structuralism and existentialism, Foucault, cutting the ground from under both sides in his *Les mots et les choses,*[8] revived the system methodology and its concept of the incommensurability of systems. One could not imagine two stranger bed-fellows than Foucault and Wittgenstein. And yet, between them – each in his own way, each relying on totally different arguments – they conspired to keep this strange approach to man and society afloat. Foucault argued historically. He divided the history of Western man into three epochs. Each epoch – the medieval, the Age of Reason and the nineteenth century – formed a closed system, governed by a central *episteme*. The *episteme* of the first system was 'Resemblance'; that of the second system 'Representation'; and that of the third system, 'Evolution'. Foucault also argued that in the twentieth century there had emerged a fourth system with a new *episteme,* which he described as 'Masks' (i.e. nothing was held to be what it seemed to be). Each *episteme* was capable of giving rise to a complete system of knowledge and no *episteme* could be tested, discussed or assessed in terms of any other *episteme*. Had Wittgenstein ever been confronted with Foucault he would have turned away uncomprehending and probably given way to one of his outbursts of intemperate impatience. But to the neutral observer, the connection between Foucault and Wittgenstein is clear. If one believes that 'use' equals 'meaning' one is not far from the idea that the medieval use of 'Resemblance' was *sui generis* and could neither be criticised nor understood in terms of the twentieth-century use of the notion of 'Masks' or in terms of the nineteenth-century theory that everything has to be explained in terms of 'Evolution'.

All these thinkers share one common premiss: all understanding is organised around a central core which is not available for criticism from outside the system and which, from within the system, makes perfectly sound sense. The cores, in all cases, are incommensurable with one another.

This, in sum, is the position in intellectual history of the closed-circle philosophy. Kuhn has simply revived the notion that the human intellect is a function of the system. Each system is dominated by a paradigm, and inside each system the pursuit of knowledge is called normal science because it does not question the truth of the central paradigm. As to why systems emerge and why they fade away, Kuhn has nothing more substantial to offer than Voltaire, Herder, Spengler, Malinowski, Wittgenstein or Foucault.

Reasons for the Retreat to Historism

The various retreats to the closed-circle model have different sources. The idea of the closed circle commended itself to Voltaire because, looking back into the past, he saw uniform darkness and superstition. He was thus obliged to see the emergence of his peaks as 'catastrophes' and treat each peak as a closed, self-contained system. Herder's reason was different. Herder thought that any understanding of literature, art or religion which presumed that all men were more or less alike, was shallow and would fail to probe the real depths of the human spirit. Where Voltaire had tried to isolate certain spaces – the age of Louis XIV, for example – from their temporal surroundings and had been forced to treat what he had isolated as a system, Herder tried to isolate specific temporal sequences – the history of a nation – from their spatial surroundings. Ranke had followed Herder into the closed-circle model because he, too, considered it shallow to assume that all human beings are alike and added to his wish to avoid shallowness a dislike of progress. By considering systems in isolation, he managed to establish that each system was equidistant from God, and therefore managed to snuff out any thought of progress – be it a progress in one system or a progress of one system relative to another. When, towards the end of his life, he tried to write a universal history, he found the going very hard because he was, on his own premisses, quite unable to relate one system to another. Spengler went into the closed-system method because he wanted to warn his contemporaries that all progress was strictly limited and that all systems – the system of occidental culture included – must come to an end. The case of Malinowski and Wittgenstein is different again and deserves fuller consideration, for Kuhn's variation on the closed-circle theme is directly indebted to Wittgenstein's version. It is notoriously difficult to show how one thing, be it a language or a set of social relations or a set of symbols can refer to something else, i.e. to something other than itself. We can look upon Positivism and historicism as valiant attempts to establish such references and to explain them.

Positivism sought to account for the fact that theories expressed in language can refer to events in the world by the operation of protocol sentences or observational reports. These special sentences, it was argued, were like bridges which connect a linguistic statement – a theory, for instance – with events in the world. This theory of protocol statements as bridges is ingenious and intriguing, but it does not stand up to criticism. For a protocol statement is itself yet again a linguistic expression and can therefore not function as a genuine bridge. A real bridge, one must suppose, would have to be something which is neither language nor world. It has proved impossible to find such an entity.

Historicism sought to account for the fact that at any moment every social organisation refers to its own past. That past condition is noticeably different from the present condition. Changes must have taken place. But how exactly can one account for the fact that an earlier condition has changed into, or transformed itself into, the present condition of that organism? Historicism had the answer. There are, historicists maintained, developmental laws which determined and controlled these transformations. This theory was ingenious and intriguing but it could not stand up to criticism either. A developmental law is a non-event. Any law states that under certain conditions an event will be followed by another event. The conception of such a law requires the regularities of these certain conditions. If they are absent (i.e. if the initial conditions are singular instead of identical) the law will not operate. Whatever changes we can observe, they cannot be explained as the result of a law. A developmental law, as distinct from an ordinary law, however, maintains that a singular condition must change into another singular condition. A state of religious belief must change into a state of rational enlightenment (Comte), a state of feudalism must change into a bourgeois society (Marx), and so forth. Laws which express that singular changes of this kind will occur are misconceptions. However, one can see that if there were developmental laws, they would constitute bridges between any present state of a society and its past states.

Given the untenability of these bridges – protocol statements are as questionable as developmental laws – the easiest strategy and the way of least resistance is to beat a complete retreat and to argue that developmental laws are unnecessary because one can explain any condition of any society as a closed system which does not refer to its own past. The system, Malinowski said, contains no fossils. Similarly, one can argue that protocol sentences, or whatever might take their place, are unnecessary because one can understand any system of knowledge simply as a closed circle inside of which statements are acceptable if they conform to the rules obtaining inside the circle. A troublesome reference to anything outside the circle, be it the world or a critic who is not himself a member of the closed circle, is unnecessary. Anti-Positivists like the later Wittgenstein and anti-historicists like Malinowski could combine and reject all attempts at bridge-building literally as pontifications. It was pontifical, they would appear to have agreed, to make a bridge by using protocol statements; and it was pontifical to make a bridge by using developmental laws.

The Limited Usefulness of Historism in Social Science

This thumb-nail sketch of the history and of the appeal and power of a method of analysis may not have done justice to some of its sources of strength and some of its great merits. There are obvious merits in this method, especially when one is dealing with the human or social sciences in which every piece of knowledge put forward becomes immediately part of the subject-matter to be studied. Science is very different. A new theory never becomes part of magnetism or a molecule. It does not add to the sum total of phenomena to be studied. In the social sciences, everything that is asserted about man and man's activities is in a very real sense yet another activity and has to be studied as such. If one conceives the whole of the subject-matter as a closed system, then it becomes easier and more convenient to regard every theory about any part of the system as yet another part of the system, to be discussed, appreciated and criticised in terms of that system. In the social sciences, this approach is convenient and useful even though it ought never to be considered exhaustive.

Moreover, in cases where the knowledge one is thinking of is knowledge about other people who can think and have knowledge of their own about themselves, one cannot simply brush their own knowledge aside, no matter how much it might differ from the knowledge the outside inquirer has about them. For a start, therefore, when one is dealing with human beings, it is always helpful and advisable to consider the knowledge they have of themselves before one makes up one's own mind about them. In social science, the closed-circle method has therefore an inherent plausibility and usefulness which it does not have when the subject-matter is atoms and molecules. When the behaviour of atoms does not bear out what a physicist asserts about them, the physicist will have to change his mind; but he can never be confronted by an atom which has a theory of its own about itself. The social scientist has no such luck. Almost every subject he touches upon will sooner or later advance a hypothesis of its own about itself.

Kuhn's originality lies in his proposal to apply the closed-circle method to the study of our knowledge of nature. As indicated, the method has a clear merit in the study of human and social subjects. It can have no comparable merit in the study of inanimate nature. As far as natural science is concerned, the object of the endeavour is to produce explanations and predictions. In the social sciences, the object is the same, but it cannot be achieved unless one also takes into consideration what the subjects to be explained are saying about themselves: in the social sciences, any 'truth' has to encompass not only what makes explanations plausible to the inquirer, but also the sort of explanations which seem plausible to the subject itself. In the social sciences, the subject's own 'truth' is an integral part of the truth. In the social and human sciences, it therefore makes good sense to consider the people one is studying as part of a closed system and to seek the paradigm which they think presides over that system. At any rate, this must be the first step even though it should not be the last step. In this sense, the social and human sciences are not autonomous for there is a difference between the way other people appear to themselves and how they appear to us or between how they appear to us and how they *are* in themselves. In the natural sciences, such a distinction would be spurious for there is no difference between how atoms appear to us (provided we get it right) and how they *are* in themselves. Hence, whatever merits the closed-circle method has in the social and human sciences, it cannot have corresponding merits in the natural sciences.

However, one ought to consider borderline examples. There are social organisations, manned by human beings, which serve the purpose of explaining natural phenomena. In this category, we find universities and research institutions and hospitals. Such societies are social phenomena, but their value cannot be assessed entirely in terms of their social functioning. The value of a laboratory must ultimately be assessed in terms of its contribution to the knowledge of nature, not in terms of its social structure. Schools are even more marginal, because their value consists in their contribution to other social structures rather than in their contribution to knowledge of nature; and schools of social science are specially marginal, because their contribution consists not in their own social structure but in their contribution to our knowledge of the social structure of other social structures. In short, there are social institutions which refer to something outside themselves and which are clearly different from, say, the Trobriand Islanders, who do not refer to anything outside themselves.

Let us consider an example. A hospital is a large institution governed by certain rules. There is clear merit in considering it a closed system and in understanding its functioning as a social organisation. People come in and people come out. Some are on stretchers, others are in white coats. Some go there to earn money; others, to pay money. Some are being taken care of; others are taking care. However, such a system approach to a hospital, while enlightening, misses the point. The main question we ought to ask is whether the people who are sick in the hospital are getting better and whether they are being made better efficiently. In other words, the hospital, though a system, has a point of reference which lies *outside* the system and which enables us and entitles us to compare it to other, similar systems. To treat any one hospital as an incommensurable system would make complete nonsense of the art of healing and the science of medicine. However, Kuhn's proposal to treat the pursuit of science as a series of closed and incommensurable systems which cannot be judged with reference to a point outside themselves, makes similar nonsense of the pursuit of science. We must, therefore, come to the ultimate conclusion that that part of Kuhn which is original, is, at the same time, the part which is least tenable!

Incommensurability

Now that we have demonstrated the place of Kuhn's model of knowledge in history and disputed its novelty, we must consider its viability. For it does not follow that it is not viable just because it is not original but a recrudescence of an old strategy.

Its viability is impugned by the claim that paradigms are incommensurable and that all knowledge informed by a given paradigm is incommensurable with all knowledge informed by a different paradigm. With this claim, Kuhn's model is a strong form of historism, for these claims are identical with the claims made by Herder and Ranke for their closed circles. Kuhn has now extended this claim to the closed circles inside which 'normal science' is carried out.

In principle, the claim that paradigms and the knowledge derived from them are incommensurable with all other paradigms and the knowledge derived from them, follows directly from the by now well-established recognition that all observation is theory-laden.[9] By this, one means that one cannot simply 'observe': always one can observe only what a certain theory suggests one should observe, or observe what a certain theory leads one to expect to find. Clearly, an observation made and confirmed under one theory cannot be used, without a lot of explanation, to falsify a different theory. In short, there are no neutral and absolute observations which float around aimlessly and which can be used for purposes conceived *after* the observation had been made.

While the view that all observation is theory-laden is nowadays widely accepted and has, as such, no necessary connection with the closed-circle model, it is instructive to note that its conceptual ancestry is to be found in the long tradition of closed-circle thinking. Herder believed that the language of every nation was a unique institution and not comparable to the language of any other nation, except perhaps in the most superficial of senses (i.e. they all are noisy). Ranke founded a whole school of historical methodology on his contention that in every nation the political and legal institutions are unique and cannot be compared to, or explained by, the way similar institutions function elsewhere. A Parliament in Britain is a totally unique and individual institution which can be understood only by reference to the uniqueness of British history; the fact that there are other institutions in other countries which are called by the same name is accidental and, at best, misleading. Spengler drew attention to the fact that the term 'God' had one meaning in Greek culture; a different meaning in Magian culture; and a third meaning in occidental culture. Moreover, he added, people reared in one culture cannot understand the meaning the word has in another culture, so that all cultures are incommensurable with each other and their members forever enclosed in the circle of that culture. Malinowski was not quite so dogmatic in protesting the incommensurability of the institutions of beliefs of one society with those of any other society. But their incommensurability follows from his anthropological practice. The bartering habits of the Trobriand Islanders, he said, are to be understood as a function of their mythology, or the other way round; but never, he added, in terms of the utility or practice of barter as such. Once one looks upon barter in this fashion, one makes any particular barter into something unique which can be explained only as a function of something which is going on inside the circle in which the barter in question is practised. Ruth Benedict was more outspoken. She maintained that the ethical values enshrined in the structure of each of her three societies were a unique set of values to be understood by reference to the other institutions in each of the societies, but not to be compared or evaluated by reference to anything that was happening outside each society studied. Wittgenstein was equally adamant: 'a blunder,' he used to say, 'is only a blunder in a particular language game; never outside that particular game.'

In its extreme form, the claim that there is incommensurability amounts to the statement that it is impossible to step outside our skins – the traditions, linguistic and other, in which we do our thinking – and compare ourselves with the absolute. Quine has formulated the claim in an elegant fashion: reference, he writes, is inscrutable and nonsense, except relative to a co-ordinate system.[10] I do not think anybody would quarrel with these statements. However, it does not follow from the insight that there is no such thing as *absolute* reference that all reference must be specific to one and only one set of co-ordinates, and that co-ordinates themselves cannot be compared with each other provided one has a set of second-order co-ordinates, and so forth.

By itself, the denial of meaning-invariance has a long history. Its origins have been fully investigated and documented in Meinecke's classic work, *Historism,* first published in German in 1936. Though Meinecke's investigation linked the doctrine to historism, one can clearly see that in the form in which Quine presents it, it has no such necessary connection with the model of closed circles. For that matter, the case for the view that all observations are theory-laden was vigorously argued by Karl Popper in his *Logic of Scientific Discovery* (1934) and again taken up by Paul Feyerabend in a famous paper entitled 'Explanation, Reduction and Empiricism' (1962). Neither Popper nor Feyerabend linked the view to the closed-circle model. However, since the ascent of Kuhn and the new lease he has given to the closed-circle model, the denial of meaning-invariance has become specifically linked to the closed circles. Kuhn himself has endorsed the doctrine explicitly by stating that unless one can produce a language which will permit the translation of a statement made under one paradigm into a statement made under a different paradigm – by the nature of the case, such a language would be impossible to find – the two statements must be considered incommensurable. This follows directly from the fact that the two paradigms are incommensurable. We therefore have to consider the validity of the denial of meaning-invariance very carefully. If that denial is absolute, it would count as a strong recommendation of the closed-circle model. In fact, if it is absolute, it amounts to a demonstration that all knowledge comes in closed circles.

There are two different considerations which provide reasons for thinking that there is both limited and general commensurability in almost everything we know. Let us take the argument for limited commensurability first. In order to establish the case for complete meaning-variation and incommensurability, we are invited to consider the following example. There is no way in which we can compare Greek archaic art with the more naturalistic style of classical Greece because we know of no 'neutral' figure of a man in terms of which such a comparison could be carried out. It is indeed true that we know of no 'neutral' representation of a man; but it does not follow that no comparisons between archaic and naturalistic representation can be made. A comparison can be made because we can compare the two styles in question to a third style – say, impressionism. Impressionism offers a basis for a comparison of the other two styles not because it is 'neutral' (or 'absolute'), but because it is neither archaic nor naturalistic.

In stating that a comparison is possible only if there were a *neutral* conception of what a man looks like, the opponents of meaning-invariance demand not only too much, but more than is necessary. One can certainly compare a man painted by Manet with a man sculpted by Phidias and with one sculpted by an archaic artist. This is not due to the fact that we have a *neutral* man in front of our eyes, or an *absolute* concept 'man' at the back of our mind; it is due to the fact that we know of a system of co-ordinates which makes the reference of 'man' to something real – something transcending Manet, Phidias and the archaic sculptor – anything but inscrutable. The system of co-ordinates comes from biology. We are able to recognise men as men and are able to make sure we do not mistake them for elephants because human beings have evolved. Evolution depends on reproduction and on the comparative maintenance of species. Such reproduction would not be possible if human beings habitually mistook mice or elephants for human beings and attempted sexual intercourse with them. Only those human beings have survived whose cognitive apparatus allows them to discern human lineaments and to distinguish them from non-human lineaments. The process of natural selection has seen to the evolution of this ability. Thus, though our images of 'man' are neither neutral nor absolute, they enable us to make the reference of the image 'man' scrutable because of biological evolution and the system of co-ordinates it provides.

Turning from artistic style to physics we can look at other

examples. If there really were no meaning invariance it would have been impossible for Max Planck to invent the Quantum discontinuity. When Planck started to consider the problem of Black-Body Radiation, he began by considering an experimentally determined distribution of this radiation expressed by the formula $\rho(\nu,T)$. How, he began, was this distribution to be explained? There had been several attempts at an explanation in terms of classical theories. Planck, however, changed the paradigm by introducing the idea of what has become known as 'Planck's constant' and provided the now famous solution $\rho(\nu,T) = h\nu^3/(\exp(-h\nu/kT) - 1)$. One will notice that in spite of the paradigm shift involved in the discovery of the *constant*, his solution is not a solution of a new observation, but a solution of the old observation $\rho(\nu,T)$ made long before the shift in fundamental concepts took place. Obviously, the initial observation expressed as $\rho(\nu,T)$ was made with the help of some theories. It was theory-laden. But the theories depended on were third theories – that is, not theories involved in the introduction of the concept of the *constant*.

It had been possible to suggest other forms for $\rho(\nu,T)$ in which Planck's constant did not occur. Thus, for example, Wien's equation: $\rho(\nu,T) = a\nu^3\exp(-b\nu/T)$ with a and b as experimentally determined constants. Now a die-hard incommensurabilist might argue that this is all very well, but that the observation $\rho(\nu,T)$ changes meaning every time it appears in a different equation: it has one meaning in Josef Stefan's equation, another in Wien's earlier equation of 1893, a third in Wien's later equation of 1896, and a fourth meaning in Planck's equation. However, if this way out and if this argument in favour of meaning invariance and incommensurability were to be accepted, one would have to grant that there is no reason why one can choose between Stefan's equations and Wien's equations and Planck's equation; and no reason why one should have preferred, in the end, Planck's equation. Here then, we have an example of genuine meaning invariance, at least over a limited field.

Larry Laudan provides a good example of meaning invariance over a very large field:

> Since antiquity, scientists have been concerned to explain why light is reflected off a mirror or other polished surface according to a regular pattern. Relating the incident to the reflected angle, the problem of reflection, thus characterised, involved many

> quasi-theoretical assumptions, e.g. that light moves in straight lines, that certain obstacles can change the direction of a ray of light, that visible light does not continuously fill every empty medium, etc. Does the existence of these theoretical assumptions entail that no two theories can be said to solve the problem of reflections? The answer is clearly negative, provided that the theories which solve the problem are not inconsistent with those relatively low level theoretical assumptions required to state the problem. Throughout the late seventeenth century, for example, numerous conflicting theories of light (including those of Descartes, Hobbes, Hooke, Barrow, Newton and Huygens) addressed themselves to the problem of reflection. The various optical theories were all regarded as solving the problem of reflection, because that problem could be characterised in a way which was *independent* of any of the theories which sought to solve it.[11]

Or look at the example provided by the history of the theory of heat. In the early part of the nineteenth century, there were two rival theories of heat. One held that heat was a material substance called 'caloric' which could be shifted from one substance to another. The other theory linked heat to vibration and was based on several observations which indicated that since rubbing or friction could produce heat, it could not be caloric. Where, in friction, was the caloric before it was in the heated substance? The matter was eventually settled in favour of the vibration theory through an understanding of the atomic composition of matter. If one thinks of the movement of molecules, one can understand that heat is a vibrational phenomenon. If there had been no meaning-invariance, the atomic theory of matter could not have settled the debate between caloricists and vibrationists. Atoms come from a totally different theory. But there is sufficient meaning-invariance in 'atom' for atoms to be used in the vibration theory of heat. We have the co-ordinates of the caloric theory and the co-ordinates of the vibration theory; and we have a third set of co-ordinates which make the concept of atom scrutable enough to be inserted into the vibration-theory co-ordinates.

Or consider a different example. If there were no meaning-invariance, the Michelson–Morley experiment could never have played a crucial role in the development of modern physics. The experiment was originally carried out to determine which of two competing theories about the ether were correct. On one side, there was Fresnel's theory that ether is fixed in space (1818); on the other side, there was Stokes's view that ether is dragged along by moving bodies (1845). In the event, it turned out that both theories were false and this led, in turn, to the Special Theory of Relativity which dispensed with the ether and was able to deduce from this dispensation several observations which had been made on the assumption that there was an ether. Thus, there is quite a lot of meaning-invariance in at least two different ether theories and in the Special Theory of Relativity. If there were not, one could not have interpreted the Michelson–Morley experiment to have falsified ether theories of all complexions. So while we can admit that there are no neutral facts as such because all facts are theory-laden, we can see that some facts are relatively neutral – i.e. neutral to two theories because they are theory-laden by a third theory.

In order to forestall such considerations, Feyerabend has appealed to ethnographic data and to history in order to show that there are incommensurable theories. He considers this contention, at times, as a historical contention rather than as a logical reflection.[12] But here again, he is on uncertain ground. For if the arguments of chapter 2 are correct, one cannot write history without a paradigm and one cannot therefore appeal to historical facts in order to prove that all historical facts are paradigm-bound. If one thinks they are, one will certainly be able to produce historical facts which show that they are. But for those of us who are not convinced that all facts are incommensurable with each other, this demonstration will fail to win us over. Take Spengler, for example. All the stories he produces for ancient Greece will appear to be incommensurable with all the stories he produces for Faustian culture. But this does not prove that they are. It merely proves that they were compiled with the help of the idea that ancient Greece is a closed circle which is incommensurable with the closed circle of Faustian culture.

Now consider the more general question, the question of general commensurability. If one takes evolution into account, one will find that there is indeed a set of co-ordinates (in Quine's sense) which all living organisms share. The perceptions of every living organism are theory-laden, since every organism has a species-specific genetic endowment which is ontogenetically, though not phylogenetically, *a priori*. An outside observer who knows what that genetic endowment is, and who knows what the environment in which that organism is surviving is, could ideally predict what that organism's *Umwelt* (Uexküll's term) will be. Each of that organism's perceptions is so theory-laden that it remains meaningful and true only relative to that organism. Nevertheless, there is quite a lot of meaning-invariance because one can compare two organisms of different species and their theories, for their different *Umwelten* are always part of the same environment – at least in so far as it is observed by a third organism with a more developed cognitive apparatus which can take the *Umwelten* of the other organisms into account. In short, the fact that all cognitive apparatuses have evolved in the same environment provides ground for commensurability. It is therefore wrong to say that there is no commensurability because there is no underlying substance. There is an underlying substance in the form of the environment offered by the planet earth. This may not be an underlying substance in the absolute or the metaphysical sense. But it is an underlying substance in the biological sense on which our ability to perceive anything must be understood. Fish are adapted to water and birds to air. Parts of these adaptations are comparable because both water and air form part of the same environment and must be presumed to be compatible with each other.

It is useful to recall here that Lévi-Strauss's major contribution to the social sciences has been his argument that there is structural commensurability between the most diverse cultures. He has shown that the relativism enshrined in ethnographical observations is purely relative to the purpose to which the data are put. It may look as if a culture presided over by a mother-goddess is incommensurable with a culture presided over by a father-deity and as if no comparison can be made between the laws and taboos which prevail in these two cultures. But as soon as one looks at social structure rather than ethnology, one can see that two disparate and contrary myths can, in appropriately different settings, perform exactly the same job and can be compared. He has shown that in every cultural context there are meanings which transcend their use in the context they occupy, and he has taught us the method of 'structural analysis' which exhibits those meanings which transcend meaning-variance. Thus, for example, a father-deity and a mother-goddess can have the same structural meaning; or, for that matter, two seemingly identical father-gods can have different structural meanings.

The question of commensurability is crucial. If one insists on incommensurability and denies any kind of meaning-invariance, one cannot write an intelligible history of paradigm shifts or of the succession of alternative theories. Take the transition from Ptolemy to Copernicus. In order to make the shift from Ptolemy to Copernicus intelligible, one has to assume that there is a certain invariance of meaning which attaches to 'earth'. One can then assess that Copernicus's system was a progress as against Ptolemy's system because it opened the way for the more universal calculations of Kepler and, eventually, of Newton. If, on the other hand, one denies meaning-invariance, one will be left with a simple comparison between Ptolemy and Copernicus. The only thing then to be said in favour of Copernicus is that he simplified the calculations involved in determining the movements of the planets and the sun. Kuhn himself, on page 156 of *The Structure of Scientific Revolutions,* reminds us that even Copernicus's calculations were so complicated that they represented very little advance over Ptolemy. If we deny meaning-invariance, we cannot explain the shift from Ptolemy to Copernicus as rational progress. The denial of commensurability of any kind is intimately linked to Kuhn's argument that paradigm shifts are irrational and revolutionary occurrences which defy explanation. In order to counter this argument, we have to insist on a certain meaning-invariance and we can do this by reminding ourselves that that invariance does not have to be *absolute* to permit us to provide a rational explanation of paradigm shifts. One does not have to have absolute, theory-free, neutral knowledge of the earth in order to provide a rational and intelligible history of the transition from Ptolemy to Copernicus. In demanding too much, Kuhn, Feyerabend and their followers are weighting the dice in their favour.

The denial of meaning-invariance must therefore be rejected, even though it is admitted that there are no absolute meanings. Incommensurability does exist, but it is not absolute and not insuperable. If this is so, the closed-circle model of human knowledge turns out to be of very limited use, for the denial of meaning-invariance is at the heart of that model.

If there were no meaning-invariance, we would have to remain content with the model of closed circles. In this case, we could not distinguish witchcraft from natural science or chemistry from alchemy. For the closed-circle method says that in all cases knowledge depends on a paradigm and that the paradigms in question are incommensurable – or, as Ranke put it, all paradigms are equidistant from God and there is no reason why we should prefer one to another. One would have thought that this consequence of the Kuhn model would weaken its hold over rational and critical minds. But this is not so. Strange as it may sound, this consequence has made it doubly attractive. Both Mary Douglas and Paul Feyerabend appear convinced that there is little to choose between witchcraft and science, and they consider the denial of meaning-invariance attractive because it supports this view. One ought not, however, saddle Kuhn with the responsibility for this view. He is merely the last in a long line of advocates of the closed-circle model. From Herder to Ranke to Malinowski and Wittgenstein, people have argued against meaning-invariance and they all bear combined responsibility for the growing view that all knowledge is relative and that we are no better off with General Relativity than with demonology, or with Quantum Mechanics rather than Taoism. One would, of course, dearly like to know whether the doctrine of incommensurability and the denial of meaning-invariance has been responsible for the closed-circle method; or whether the closed-circle method has been responsible for the doctrine of incommensurability. One would have to examine this matter from case to case. For Ranke, the denial of meaning-invariance came first: *individuum est ineffabile*. For Malinowski, closed circles came first and the denial of meaning-invariance was a consequence. In Spengler, the two doctrines went hand in hand. When we come to Wittgenstein, one is hard put – but I would surmise that the closed-circle model came first and the denial of meaning-invariance was seen by him as a consequence. With Feyerabend, the denial of meaning-invariance occupies the whole centre of the stage. Feyerabend rejoices so much in his Dadaistic intellectual anarchy that he does not even consider himself committed to closed circles as a result of his denial of meaning-invariance. Kuhn's case is probably similar to that of Wittgenstein: incommensurability and closed circles go hand in hand. Whichever the order of precedence, the upshot is in all cases a strong commitment to relativism.[13] In fact, as I will show in the following chapter, the relativism which has grown out of the denial of meaning-invariance has led thinkers like Richard Rorty to question the value of all knowledge.[14]

Relativism and Irrationality

The epistemological relativism which is implied by the closed-circle model also affects our understanding of the growth of knowledge. I have argued in chapter 1 that there is a negative sociology of knowledge which enables us to distinguish between societies in which knowledge is used to cement the social bond and societies which are neutrally bonded so that knowledge can be entertained regardless of the social structure. Only in the latter kind of society can there be a growth of knowledge, for when knowledge is used as a social bond, one cannot permit criticism and trial and error of knowledge. If one uses the closed-circle model, one is committed to the view that all societies are alike in that they are constructed around a paradigm. One is then unable to distinguish those societies in which the paradigm is part of the social bond from those societies in which it is not. And with that failure to distinguish between the two societies, the purpose and value of the negative sociology of knowledge disappears. The really important distinction ought to be between societies in which the paradigm is the bonding cement, and societies in which such paradigms as are held, are not part of the bonding cement. The reason why witchcraft has flourished in certain societies is that it has been used as part of the social bond. In certain societies, people simply believe in it and people who share the belief, even though they might dislike and fear witchcraft, are defined by their belief as members of that society. Since witchcraft is in such societies not open to trial-and-error experiment, it maintains its hold. In short, the fruitful distinction between paradigms concerns the uses to which they are put in different societies, not their content. A paradigm used to bond people together – all people who subscribe to it are members of the society – can never be questioned; it is transformed automatically into a catechism, whether its content is witchcraft or Quantum Mechanics. A paradigm which floats freely in a society as a kite flies in the sky – the people forming that society are members by virtue of some other quality, such as geographical contiguity – is not a catechism and competes freely with alternative paradigms. If the belief in witchcraft serves such an important founding and bonding role in the structure of a society, it cannot be examined in the light of 'reason' – that is, it cannot be subject to trial and error without endangering the very survival of the society itself. Now if one holds that all theories — be they theories about galaxies based on experiment and observation and exposed to trial and error, or be they theories that there are witches – are all much of a muchness because they operate each in a given society (the one, in a society of scientists; the other, in a primitive tribe or a late-medieval village), one loses one's ability to explain why science has flourished only intermittently and why it is therefore different from all other forms of belief and theory. Science can be practised only when it is possible to entertain alternative theories. In places and times where such alternative theories are not available because their presence would cause social disintegration and disorientation, science cannot be practised. But if one starts with the assumption that a theory is a theory and that it always functions inside a system, one forgoes one's ability to distinguish between science (knowledge which can be pursued through the consideration of alternatives) and non-science (knowledge which is simply the beliefs current in any one social system). The explanatory power of the closed-circle method is therefore poorer than the explanatory power of an open approach. The closed-circle method fails to explain why science is present in the seventeenth century, especially in England, and absent among the pygmies of the Kalahari Desert at any time.

If one advocates a philosophy of knowledge which makes it impossible to distinguish between witchcraft and 'scientific' knowledge, one is wide open to the charge of irrationalism. Kuhn is open to this charge because he can distinguish one paradigm from another only according to its content. He can see that there is a difference between witchcraft and Quantum Mechanics, but he must consider them to be on the same level because in both cases there is a paradigm surrounded by the practice of normal science. In order to make a genuine and substantial distinction between them, he would have to be able to distinguish them according to the uses to which the two paradigms are put in the societies in which they are upheld. But if one looks upon all knowledge as a paradigm surrounded by normal science, then Quantum Mechanics qualifies as readily as witchcraft.

However, it is important to locate the precise nature of Kuhn's irrationality. He is often charged with irrationality because, in his model, the paradigm is to a very large extent immune from criticism, let alone from experiment and observation. A paradigm, in his model, cannot be falsified because anything that would falsify it must be informed by a different paradigm and is therefore ruled out. Any observation that would falsify the paradigm in force is at best an illusion or hallucination because the paradigm in force obliges people to believe that such an observation cannot be possible.

The total or relative immunity of paradigms is not irrational. Positivists were the only people who ever believed that no theory can be immune from observation. Everybody else has always been aware that all theories enjoy a certain immunity from observation and that in many cases observations, rather than theories, are dismissed and discarded. To all non-Positivists, the relationship between theory and observation is never an easy one and a certain protective attitude to a theory is not a mark of irrationality. Only people who hold that general theories are statements about the world – that is, classes of sentences which can be verified – have considered that part of the Kuhn model which bestows an immunity on paradigms as irrational. As soon as one recognises that Kuhn himself uses the concept 'paradigm' quite loosely in order to make sure that it includes theoretical and imaginative terms which cannot be reduced to or treated as 'statements' open to verification or test, one sees that there is nothing irrational in the doctrine of immunity.

The real irrationality to which Kuhn is committed lies elsewhere. It lies in his contention that paradigms are given up and switched for no good or relevant reason and that paradigms succeed one another haphazardly. This view comes from his refusal to examine paradigms according to the roles they play in societies and in terms of the attitudes people have towards them. Instead, he distinguishes paradigms entirely by their content. Given the content, he says, they all play identical parts. They all inform theories, the pursuit of which is 'normal science'. He is thus left with an endless and never-ending succession of paradigms all behaving in a similar manner – 'one damned thing after another', as the French film director Jean-Luc Godard once put it. And speaking of Godard, one is reminded of the similarity between Kuhn's philosophy of science and the philosophy which inspired countless French films and the French *roman nouveau*. The *roman nouveau* eliminated all reference to a 'real' world of nature and of human nature from the succession of events, and was thus unable to distinguish between dreams, hallucinations and genuine occurrences. Further, it eliminated the so-called 'romantic heart of things' from the narrative by a studied refusal to consider the effect of character and subjective life on the sequence of events and, finally, it constructed the sequence of events entirely according to correspondences and analogies by using the so-called 'Baudelairean rhetoric'. One would find it instructive to compare Kuhn's description of scientific activity with Robbe-Grillet's most famous novel, *La maison de rendez-vous*. Though all the ingredients of life are present in that novel, dreams, real events, wishes, day-dreams, delusions, or theatrical enactments of any of these, all occupy the same ontological status. This reference to the modern school of French literature is justified because both Kuhn and that school are guided by the same neglect of, and disregard for, the role of the outside world in the construction of our knowledge. The French school of literature has decided to discount the outside world. In the absence of that world, any distinction between dream and occurrence, between wish and illusion, is capricious. Hence, practitioners of the method refuse to make such distinctions. Kuhn, too, discounts the outside world and, in consequence, considers all knowledge exclusively in terms of a paradigm and the paradigm, in turn, in terms of nothing at all.[15]

Let us return, however, to Kuhn's irrationality. It is perfectly true, as he says, that there is no pre-ordained critical level at which a theory *has* to be discarded, regardless of whether there is a new one in the offing or not. It is equally true, as he says, that no theory is dropped unless there is a new one available which is believed to make better sense of one's experience. But it is, thirdly, also true – and this is something Kuhn does *not* say – that the switch will not be made unless the new theory is more universal than its predecessor. Bearing the third point in mind, one can see that paradigm switches are governed by a consideration other than the pure content of a paradigm. They are very largely determined, as we have seen in chapter 1, by the difference in the formal quality of the paradigms in question. For this reason, there is no likelihood that physicists will switch from Quantum Mechanics to witchcraft in spite of the fact that Quantum Mechanics and witchcraft fulfil Kuhn's minimum requirement for knowledge: paradigms surrounded by the pursuit of normal science.

We have now located the hard core of the irrationality of Kuhn's philosophy of knowledge. It consists of two related things. There is, first, his inability to distinguish between paradigms according to the *role* they play in their societies; and, second, his disregard for the notion of universality which provides a historical matrix for the succession of paradigms.

Functionalism and Structuralism

Finally, I would like to add that the foregoing analysis shows how little there is to choose between structuralism and functionalism. These two methods in the social sciences are often considered bitter opponents: many papers and entire books have been written to bring out the differences and to commend the advantages of structuralism or the advantages of functionalism. In matters of detail, there are indeed important differences. A book by Malinowski on the Trobriand Islanders makes very different reading and provides quite different knowledge and enlightenment from a book such as Mary Douglas's *Natural Symbols*. Malinowski is a functionalist and considers the Trobriand Islanders as forming a functionally integrated whole. Mary Douglas is a structuralist and shows how certain similarities in structure between the pygmies and the Bog Irish lead to similarities in their cosmological beliefs. Kuhn, however, brings the whole thing down to a common denominator. He is a structuralist – as the very title of his famous book declares. At the same time, he is also a functionalist, because he shows how the scientists who accept any one paradigm form a society in which everything they do is functionally related to the paradigm which is itself not open to question inside that society. If one examines the closed-circle method, one can see how unimportant the whole controversy between structuralists and functionalists really is. And if one remembers that at least in one respect – the inability to explain why science is present in some places and not in others – the closed-circle method is poorer than other approaches to the history and philosophy of science, one can also see that there is not only little to choose between structuralism and functionalism, but also that the two methods between them are very limited in their explanatory power.

In order to show how unimportant the distinction between structuralism and functionalism is, we can start by taking a look at molecular biology. The great discovery of molecular biology was the discovery of the structure of DNA. Once that structure was discovered, it turned out that it was identical with its function. For the structure of the molecules, arranged as they are in a double helix, itself determines the production of protein molecules. Their function, in other words, is not distinct from their structure but identical with it. So much by way of preface.

Let us take Michel Foucault as an example. In the centre of Foucault's analysis of knowledge stands his distinction between the classical *episteme* of the eighteenth century and the *episteme* of the nineteenth century. In the classical *episteme*, all knowledge was structured around the notions of classification and representation. In the nineteenth century, the *episteme* was structured around the notion of evolution. Each *episteme* is a closed circle with an identifiable structure. In this way, Foucault can show that eighteenth-century mercantilism in economics was related to the biological taxonomy of Linnaeus. Structure determined function. The central paradigm was classification and representation, and the validity of both Linnaeus's taxonomy and of Colbert's mercantilism depended on the fact that they were functionally related to each other. Had he considered physics as well, he would have said that the validity of the theory that 'heat' is a property depended on the fact that it was functionally related to representation and taxonomy.

When he comes to the nineteenth century, he finds a complete paradigm shift. Now the central paradigm is evolution. In biology, we get Darwin's non-taxonomic approach and his treatment of populations of living organisms as entities which form temporary and fluctuating species. In economics, we get theories about the dynamic relationship between capital and labour. But – and this is the crux of Foucault's matter – the reason why Darwin is valid is not because a population approach to living organisms is an advance over the taxonomic approach. The reason why Darwin is valid in the nineteenth century is that his evolutionary theory is functionally related to the fluidity theory of capital and labour. The 'advance' consists in the fact that evolutionary biology has greater explanatory power than taxonomic or typological biology. Foucault wilfully precludes a consideration of the *historical* relationship which exists between typological, eighteenth-century biology and evolutionary, nineteenth-century biology. Such a relationship is established if one looks beyond structure and takes the explanatory power of paradigms into consideration. In refusing to take the explanatory potential into account and in limiting his analysis to similarities in structure, Foucault deletes the historical dimension in the growth of science. For Foucault, each *espisteme* exhibits a structure and that structure determines the validity of all theories in that century. If they are functionally related to the structure, they are valid. If not, they are not valid. Foucault's method of using the closed-circle model is much more encompassing than Kuhn's method. But in the last analysis, both Kuhn and Foucault come to the same conclusion. Knowledge is something which is determined by the structure of the paradigm used; the validity of knowledge informed by the paradigm depends on the fact that it is functionally related to the paradigm in force.

The Lack of Interest in History and Progress

The most striking aspect of the closed-circle model is the total lack of interest in history exhibited by its upholders. Paradigms come and go and every upholder of the closed circle admits that there has been a plurality of paradigms. But neither Wittgenstein nor Malinowski, neither Kuhn nor Foucault nor Spengler, has ever displayed any interest in the question of whether there might be reasons for the way in which they succeed one another. Most surprising of all is the fact that none of these men is even a historicist. So complete is their lack of interest in history that they have not even had recourse to a developmental law which might have explained why, in the case of Foucault, the classical representation paradigm *preceded*, rather than succeeded, the nineteenth-century evolution paradigm. These systems, if we are to believe the proponents and practitioners of the model, come and go for no apparent reason at all. One must suppose that this lack of historical interest and the willingness to be satisfied with the constatation that these paradigms appear and disappear by happenstance, as it were, stems from the doctrine of incommensurability and from the denial of meaning-invariance. In order to find a historical connection or a reason for historical succession, one has to be able to connect the meaning of an institution or a theory in one paradigm with that of another. I think that this minimum requirement holds even for a historicist theory of succession. Any developmental law which explains why one paradigm was succeeded by another, and why it was not the other way round, would have to take into account the fact that the meaning of a practice or a belief can transcend any particular paradigm. If there is no meaning-invariance at all, one cannot even conceive of a historicist theory to explain how and why paradigms succeed one another. Perhaps the thinkers in question realise that a developmental law would, in any case, be a contradiction in terms and are therefore quite content not even to try their hand at one. They rest satisfied with the fact that the denial of meaning-invariance precludes all such attempts.

If one could distinguish paradigms according to their 'truth' or – which comes very nearly to the same thing – according to their explanatory power, one could write their history as the story of their increasing approximation to their goal: truth or explanatory power. But the upholders of closed circles make such histories impossible. Must we then accept the conclusion spelt out by some upholders of closed circles and left tacit by others, that paradigms succeed one another at random?

Randomness in the succession of paradigms is often not accepted. But since 'truth' as a criterion for making sense of the succession is excluded, we are really left with only two possibilities. The first possibility is historicism – that is, the belief that paradigms succeed one another because they are forced to do so by a developmental law. The nature of such 'force' is and remains mysterious and the historicist explanation is hardly plausible. This is not to say, though, that it has not found its adherents and practitioners. Comte's historicist explanation of the succession of paradigms – magic, religion, science – used to have countless supporters. And to the present day, there are many Marxist historians who explore and research the historicist aspects of Marx's theory of history. Marx maintained that the social paradigms which succeed one another are primitive communism, slavery, feudalism, capitalism. Once the scale of development is established, Marxist historians merely have to concern themselves with the question as to where any given society is on that scale at a certain time. Once this is determined, its past and future can be inferred.[16]

If one eschews historicism as a viable explanation of the non-randomness of the succession of paradigms, one is left with the recourse to the structure of the societies in which paradigms flourish. If one can determine a relationship between the content of a paradigm and the social structure in which the people who believe in it are living, one can then write a history of the succession of paradigms via the history of the social structures. This method has been proposed from time to time and goes back, in essence, to the work of Durkheim. Durkheim made it both plausible and necessary because he had seen through Positivism and understood that paradigms are not held because one's observation of nature or society obliges one to hold them. In rejecting observation as a legitimation of paradigms, Durkheim then asked himself: If paradigms are not constrained by observation, what are they constrained by? He then came up with the answer that they are constrained by the social structure which encompasses the people who hold them. In modern times, this conclusion has been taken up vigorously by Mary Douglas.

When the paradigms in question are paradigms about social structure, this method is moderately enlightening and bound to have a limited success. All human beings and every society have images of themselves. If one can track down that self-image, one may not have told everything there is to be said about that society – there are usually fossils, collective and private neuroses, unconscious, mythical compulsions, etc., which are not covered – but one will at least have said *something* valid about that society.

However, when one is dealing with paradigms about the forces of nature, the merits of such analysis are less obvious. Suppose a sociologist says that in a certain society, given its religious structure, there is a link between prevailing theology (e.g. predestination) and economic activity (e.g. thrift). This link may not exhaust what there is to be known, but it must correspond either negatively (it is false) or positively (it is true) with something the members of that society are believing. But when one comes to theories about the cosmos or about disease, one cannot consider that the discovery of a link between a certain cosmology and a certain social structure – as Mary Douglas does – is equally enlightening. Some people say that diseases are due to witches. Other people say that diseases are due to microbes. If one is to decide between these two paradigms, one cannot sensibly invoke the social structure in which the people who espouse them are living. And yet, this is precisely what Mary Douglas proposes to do. Whether we believe that diseases are caused by witches or by microbes does not depend, she argues, on the state of our enlightenment. To reject the witch paradigm as false would be to compare it to something other than itself and find it wanting. It depends on whether we are living in a society in which the centre is weak and the border turbulent; or in a society in which the centre is strong and the border repressed. At the border, people believe that pollution comes from the centre, if at all. In the centre, people believe that if there is pollution, the border must be cordoned off, strengthened or repressed.[17] In this way, one can write the history of successive paradigms of witchcraft or enlightenment via the history of social structures.

If the paradigm in question concerned social relations only, there would be a limited advantage in this procedure. But disease is not just a matter of social relations; it is also a matter of our relations to nature – and in this case the method proposed by Mary Douglas reduces us to greater poverty than necessary. In rejecting the detour via social structures where paradigms about nature are concerned, one has to remind oneself that the detour had become necessary because we came to see closed circles as the only alternative to accounting for, and measuring, paradigms in terms of their positive 'truth'. If one can see other alternatives – and other alternatives will be considered in chapter 6 — the detour becomes unnecessary. Given the possibility of alternatives to Positivism other than the closed circles, the self-denying ordinance which says that paradigms have to be assessed *internally* (i.e. assessed exclusively inside the circle in which they are held and assessed there by reference to the social structure of that circle) is, when the paradigms in question are about nature, an unnecessary impoverishment. There is a better strategy. It consists in realising that the traditional way of relating paradigms or referring them to nature by complete verification demanded too much and more than is necessary. If one can get oneself to see that a paradigm may refer to nature even though it cannot be exhaustively verified, the detour becomes superfluous. The stultifying recourse to sociological explanation (i.e. the presumption that paradigms refer to social structures) became necessary only when the initial demand was too great. One can be satisfied with very much less than Positivism required; and there is no need to tumble from the unrealistic heights of accuracy demanded by Positivism to the unnatural and poverty-stricken depths of sociological determinations of knowledge. It seems to me that of all the faults of the closed-circle method, its unhistorical implications are the worst feature. The great achievement of the theory of evolution consisted in the realisation that there is a connection between the passage of time and the appearance of species. More generally, evolutionary thought states that the relation between the passage of time and the changes in thought, art, institutions, species, societies, etc., are not random. In contrast to evolutionary thought, the closed-circle philosophy asserts that the relation *is* random and that it does not matter whether Ptolemy comes before Einstein or after. Indeed, Kuhn goes to considerable trouble to show, in his chapter 12, that even after Einstein one can use Ptolemy – provided one is prepared to go through the laborious mathematics required by the notion that the earth is standing still. In the closed-circle model, in short, the history of science shows no progress and is therefore not different from the history of art or literature.

Hegel

Kuhn could have quoted Collingwood in support. In his *Essay on Metaphysics* (1940) Collingwood had argued that every science proceeds by asking questions and answering them, and that all answers are based on ultimate presuppositions (Kuhn's paradigms) which are not examined and which cannot be considered true or false, for they furnish the framework in which the questions are both asked and answered. There are, therefore, no ultimate categories common to all paradigms, no progress from one presupposition to another. Each period is incommensurable with all other periods. Predictably, Collingwood showed a great interest in Spengler's closed systems[18] and none in Hegel. It was only later, in his posthumously published *The Idea of History*, that he confessed that Hegel's idea of history as a logical process developed in time and of our knowledge of it is not 'so absurd as at first sight it may seem.'[19]

Hegel must be considered as the first thinker who tried to give a coherent answer to the question of why one system was replaced by another, how they could be compared and why they are commensurable. This answer will be considered today, by most readers, specious; it has, unfortunately, found little favour. Whatever one thinks of the rest of Hegel's thought, this project ought to be taken very seriously. Even if it is found wanting, it should be appreciated as a pioneering effort in evolutionary thinking, at least as far as knowledge and consciousness are concerned. It is an evolutionary antidote or alternative to closed systems and equidistance.[20] It is a great pity that Collingwood did not live to revise his *Essay on Metaphysics* in the light of his later avowed appreciation of Hegel, expressed in *The Idea of History*.

Hegel tried to make a clean sweep of the notion that one can determine in advance what the immutable and universally valid concepts or the universal powers of the human mind are. He recognised that every attempt to account for them must be part of the presuppositions prevalent at any one time, and that all such attempts must therefore be bound to fail. Instead, he suggested that one could explain how these presuppositions were related to each other historically. He did not embark on the Quixotic quest to study history and to examine the facts in order to lay bare these relationships. He knew that our knowledge of history is itself dependent on these presuppositions and that therefore no one single account of what happened in history would be sufficiently neutral to enable us to infer from it how one presupposition had led to another. In other words, he consciously and purposefully avoided Kuhn's mistake as discussed and criticised in chapter 3.

Hegel, instead, had recourse to the nature of human thought. If we cannot infer from any one history how presuppositions give way to other presuppositions and if we cannot study history inductively by just looking at it, Hegel thought that the mechanisms of change and the order of change could be derived from an examination of our habits of thought. This led to his famous rejection of empirical history and his doctrine that one can determine the history of mankind *a priori*. His rejection of empirical history drew the fiery contempt and ridicule of Leopold von Ranke[21] and his project of reconstructing the history of mankind *a priori* has met with a mixture of scepticism, disbelief and ridicule from almost everybody else. But we should be clear as to what Hegel meant. He did not believe that we can have no empirical historical knowledge. He merely argued that we cannot base our understanding of the growth of knowledge and our explanation of the nature of knowledge on the knowledge of history. I find this part of his argument impeccable. Next, he did not argue that one can reconstruct the actual detailed course of events by *a priori* reasoning. He merely meant that one can understand how and why some presuppositions have given way to others and why this process of 'giving way' is a necessary consequence of human thought. As Collingwood remarked, the idea is not so absurd as it might seem.

Looking at human thought, Hegel maintained that it is always governed by the way in which particular facts are related to universal concepts. Unlike all his precursors in philosophy and unlike some of his successors, he did not believe that there was one single correct way and countless incorrect ways. On the contrary, he said, there are many plausible ways. At each time or in every closed system, one or the other way prevails. But since there are many plausible alternatives, no single way can be complete or entirely satisfactory. Therefore, in every closed system, there is an instability owing to the less-than-perfect or less-than-exhaustive conception of how the particulars are related to universals. Sooner or later, therefore, every closed system must crumble and one of the many alternative ways of conceiving the relationship between particulars and universals must come to the fore. The new way shows a corresponding lack of perfection and is therefore again unstable, and so forth.

I do not wish to argue that Hegel's conception of how one can explain that closed systems, though closed, are commensurable was sound or ought to be pursued. I merely want to stress that Hegel's project, even if we cannot consider it to have been a success, was a valiant and viable alternative to the laconic acceptance of the incommensurability of closed systems.

The closed-circle method is deficient for two reasons. First, as was shown in chapter 3, its truth canot be demonstrated by a study of history. Second, it impoverishes all knowledge we have. If we treat knowledge of non-conscious events as if that knowledge always came in incommensurable closed paradigms, we are pretending that it has no external reference. If we are treating knowledge of conscious events as if that knowledge always came in incommensurable closed circles, we are depriving ourselves of the opportunity of adopting a critical attitude to the self-understanding of the closed circles. If one compares the natural, non-human sciences with the human and social sciences, one concludes that the impoverishment brought about by the closed circles is considerably greater in the former than the impoverishment brought about by the closed circles in the latter. Even in the social and human sciences, the pretence that there is no external reference is a real error of judgment. But here, if we forgo the opportunity of criticism by comparing what people inside the circle are saying with what people outside the circle are saying, we are merely stultifying ourselves. In the social and human sciences, the abandonment of a look from the outside still leaves a very considerable knowledge about what is going on inside those closed circles. After all, if there are closed doors, we all want to know what is going on behind them. Such knowledge may not be sufficient, but it is better than being in the dark. Where our knowledge of non-conscious events is concerned, the situation is different. Since these events do not themselves form closed circles, it amounts to nothing less than intellectual castration when scientists consider themselves exclusively members of a closed circle formed around a prevailing paradigm.

There is a sort of *prima facie* plausibility in the view that since we 'know' that systems come and go, the best way of understanding history, including the history of knowledge, is to see it as a coming and going of systems. However, if we are all today aware of this historicity, we can still choose between treating the succession of circles as random – as Voltaire did, and as Foucault and Kuhn are doing – and treating them as commensurable and their succession as an evolutionary phenomenon.

Kuhn and Darwin

On the last two pages of his book, Kuhn compares himself to Darwin. He explains that people resisted Darwin and considered evolution a scandal, not because of the idea of evolution as such or because it suggested that men were descended from apes. All these ideas, Kuhn stresses, had been in the air before Darwin. They had aroused a certain amount of suspicion and unease but had Darwin not added something vital to them, he would not have caused offence. The thought to which people ultimately objected and which made them resist Darwinism, was the denial of teleology – the argument that there was no design, the denial that evolution was goal-directed. Kuhn points out that his philosophy of science makes exactly the same point. Science, according to Kuhn, is not goal-directed. There is no design, no plan. It moves away from primitive ignorance, but each move is simply a move without ultimate goal.

This misunderstanding of Darwinism is breath-taking. It is true that Darwin rejected teleology and the argument from design. But one of the central ideas in the theory of natural selection is the idea that design produces itself automatically, without plan. Evolution, so conceived, was a movement away from a primitive state. But the necessities for survival were brought about by the constraint exercised by the environment. Such evolution, it is true, is not designed; but it is directed towards a goal or, better, towards a variety of goals. Whichever way it works, one can tell which species is more successful than another and one can tell that those species which have not survived have not been successful at all. To aver, as Kuhn does, that Darwinism introduces relativism and denies that there is a design constrained by the environment, is a travesty of Darwinism.[22] People at first resisted Darwinism because they could not face the thought of self-generated design. But there can be no comparison with Kuhn, for there has been very little resistance to Kuhn.

The most important difference between Darwin and Kuhn consists in the fact that, unlike Kuhn, Darwin was not a relativist. The Kuhn model of closed circles – no matter in which of its guises one examines it – is always not only unhistorical, but also relativistic. Language games, cultures, primitive societies, paradigms, *epistemes* – they all stand side by side or succeed one another for no perceptible or intelligible reason; the values they enshrine, be they cognitive ones or ethical ones or linguistic ones, are 'good' relative to the particular centre of which they are 'normal science', 'normal morality', 'normal linguistic behaviour', and so forth. Now this is totally incompatible with any form of Darwinism. Darwinism is above all a theory of historical development. It makes it quite clear why the paramecium had to exist before the mammal and why non-human primates had to precede human primates, and so on. Next, no matter how un-teleological Darwinism is (its non-teleology is indeed not in dispute), it is not relativistic. One can see easily that if natural selection is governed by the struggle for survival, all those forms of life which have not survived are less 'fit' than those that have survived. The whole concept of natural selection rules out relativism, i.e. the belief that one form of life is as fit or viable as any other. The species which *have* survived are all relative to the environment. But their selection for survival was neither an accident nor irrational but the result of reasonably determined preferences by the environment of some species. There are always good reasons why the environment prefers one species to another. These preferences are determined by the 'fit' and not, as in the philosophy of closed circles, by fashion or chance. In brief, in comparing himself to Darwin and in suggesting that he has done for science what Darwin did for biology, Kuhn shows a complete misunderstanding of Darwin. If one is dissatisfied with the relativistic implications of the philosophy of closed circles, one must turn to the philosophy of Karl Popper. The growth of Popper's thought, Gerard Radnitzky wrote, is a 'systematic enlargement of the arsenal of weapons available in the fight against intellectual relativism'.[23]

Chapter 5

The Defence of Closed Circles

The Defence of Closed Circles

The methodology of closed circles has been advocated and supported by the most diverse people for very diverse reasons. One could not imagine philosophers further apart from each other than Foucault and Wittgenstein. Equally absurd is the proximity of Voltaire to Spengler. For this reason, we find that no matter how the method of closed circles is practised, its advocacy is based on very different grounds by its practitioners. Voltaire advocated it because he was a sort of cultural 'catastrophist'. Herder advocated it because he wanted to promote nationalism. Spengler favoured it because he saw it as a device for pricking the balloon of progress. Malinowski took it up because he had doubts about historicism. Wittgenstein took it up because he recognised it as a convenient alternative to Positivism. Basically, in other words, he was reacting against himself as he had presented himself in his *Tractatus*, though he never said so. Kuhn followed Wittgenstein, said so in so many words, and stated so in chapter 5 on 'The Priority of Paradigms'. Foucault, on the other hand, sought a way of analysing knowledge in terms of its structure rather than in terms of its content because, initially, he had been interested in showing how relative our treatment of criminals and lunatics is and how we persecute them or imprison them irrationally in obedience to prevailing paradigms, rather than to a rational appreciation of their difficulties when they are suffering and of our difficulties when they make us suffer.[1] Foucault, more than any other closed-circle thinker, started from the heart of the matter, which is: Where is the boundary between people who are in a closed circle and people who are not in a closed circle. In some cases, these different reasons advanced in favour of closed circles are plausible (e.g. one can certainly understand why Wittgenstein should have found fault with his *Tractatus*!), and one sympathises with Foucault's initial problem about crime and insanity. Equally, one can sympathise with Spengler, writing during the First World War, when he wanted to disabuse Europeans of the delusion of progress. But in all cases, one finds that the advocacy of the closed circle is partial and partisan. The advocacy is always a response to a particular problem. Even when the advocacy ends up by assuming the shape of a general argument – as in the case of Wittgenstein – the plausibility of the advocacy remains heavily weighed down by the initial partisan reason for the advocacy. Richard Rorty's defence of closed circles is the first and only argument for closed circles which is genuinely general.

During the last decade, the most sustained and reasoned defence of closed circles has come from Richard Rorty's *Philosophy and the Mirror of Nature*.[2] In this book, Rorty considers the whole issue in philosophical perspective and appeals to the verdict of history. He is taking stock of history, as he himself puts it, and finds that the history of philosophy shows that the road of reasoning about knowledge had to lead towards the methodology of closed circles. To be sure, Rorty is not a historicist, for he does not maintain that there is an iron developmental law which brought this result about. On the contrary, Rorty explains that this development was the result of critical reasoning about knowledge; about man's 'glassy essence'; about the mind as a mirror of nature; and about the nature of mind. There was no inner compulsion, no law of progress. The result, on the contrary, is the dictate of critical reason. An examination of the history of philosophy over the last 300 years, Rorty says, demonstrates this. The verdict of the history of philosophy is that there is no permanent and immutable framework for knowledge, and that the search for a 'permanent, neutral, ahistorical, commensurating vocabulary' is itself 'a historical phenomenon', he writes on page 391, quoting Michel Foucault.[3] If we could see this, Rorty continues quoting Foucault, 'we could see the history of philosophy less dialectically and less sentimentally than has been possible hitherto.'

Rorty's attitude to history is very different from Kuhn's attitude to history. Kuhn begins his study of the history of science with a paradigm of closed circles and then comes up with the discovery that history teaches that scientific knowledge is something practised in closed circles. Kuhn began with a major case study of the Copernican Revolution and then proceeded to argue the case of closed circles by giving an almost random assortment of historical examples to prove his case. Rorty, by contrast, takes a very broad look at the history of philosophical reasoning about knowledge and shows that it ends in the philosophy of closed circles and that there are very good reasons why it should have ended there by the middle of this century. In other words, he does not rest his case with the practice of closed circles, as Kuhn does, but bases his conclusion on the arguments which have led towards closed circles because all other arguments, history shows, have failed. If Rorty's evaluation of the history of philosophy is correct, we are committed to closed circles; or, as I would prefer to put it, we are condemned to a cul de sac. The question we therefore have to ask is whether Rorty's evaluation of history is correct.

If one bears in mind the argument of chapter 2, one will immediately see that there is no simple way of assessing whether Rorty's history of philosophy or any history is 'correct'. All histories are relative to a philosophy of history or to a paradigm. Since this does not mean that all histories are relative but only that they are all relative to a paradigm, the question as to whether a particular history is 'correct' cannot be decided *in vacuo* or absolutely, but has to be discussed in terms of the paradigm used for its composition and in terms of the possibility of alternative paradigms for that period and for that subject. The dependence of any history on the model used for constructing it cannot be criticised. However, one can criticise, first, the model itself; second, the execution of the model – that is, the manner in which the separate events have been fitted together in terms of the model (obviously, some historians are more competent than others); and, third, the fruitfulness of the model for the subject in hand. It is conceivable that somebody could use a model of international co-operation and of a certain kind of 'peace in the feud' (Max Gluckman's term) in order to write the history of Europe, 1914–18. But one can see that such a model would be very limiting because it would enable our historian to come up with nothing more crucial than the existence of the International Red Cross and the history of cosmopolitanism and pacifism during these years. Such a model for 1914–18 would leave the more crucial events out.

In order to assess whether Rorty's argument that the verdict of the history of philosophy is in favour of closed circles is correct, we will have to take a very close look at the model he has used to compose his history. Since Rorty, like so many historians, has failed to put his model before us in so many words, we first of all have to detect the model he has used. This detection is not too difficult because, in one respect, Rorty has put his cards on the table quite explicitly. We have seen in earlier chapters that the methodology of closed circles was always linked to a bias against knowledge. The practitioners of the closed-circle model all seem to be agreed that what happens outside the closed circle is somehow irrelevant or, at any rate, not the factor which determines what happens inside the closed circle. In thus excluding reference to the outside, the upholders of closed circles all seem agreed that knowledge is not a *relationship,* but a self-constituting activity carried on *inside* the circle. This devaluation of knowledge as a relationship between somebody who knows and something that is known, is characteristic of all closed-circle philosophies of knowledge. Rorty places himself firmly and squarely in this tradition. He does not like knowledge; he does not value it; and he does not consider it important. He is explicit about this bias against knowledge, and this bias provides a clue for the detective work we are about to undertake.

Rorty's bias against knowledge is couched in two different forms which are, strangely, incompatible with each other. This fact, however, makes detection all the easier because we can start from the assumption that Rorty is so firmly against knowledge that he is not too particular as to which of the many possible arguments which have been advanced against knowledge over the centuries he takes his stand with. For that matter, there are some quite powerful arguments against the value of knowledge – the moral argument that knowledge is presumptuous; the romantic argument that rational knowledge obscures the organic nature of the universe; and the psychological argument that knowledge makes a travesty of inward subjectivity – which Rorty does not even discuss, though I would suspect that he is quite sympathetic to all of them. The two arguments against the value of knowledge which come up again and again in his book are as follows. First, Rorty says that knowledge is Europocentric – a sort of presumption foisted upon us by considering Europe and its intellectual history to be at the centre of the universe. Second, Rorty says that knowledge is of little value or interest because it is nothing but a 'duplication' of what is already out there – something like a desire to have two things, when one would do. On Rorty's own argument, the second contention is untenable. For Rorty demonstrates that philosophers were mistaken when they believed that knowledge is a mirror-image of the world. In this way, he first tells us that whatever knowledge is, it is not a duplication because there cannot be a mirror-like duplication of the world. Then he ends up by dismissing knowledge because, he says, it is nothing but a mirror-image of the world. The first argument is wrong for a different reason. The first argument is wrong because knowledge, provided one understands it broadly as 'information', is not something treasured in Europe but something which lies at the heart of the whole universe. The whole evolution of the cosmos, as well as the evolution of living organisms on the planet earth, is a process of information-gathering and a process of information-exchange and transfer. The pursuit of science is merely the tail-end of this evolutionary information process and anything but a European idiosyncrasy. If it is something that has flourished in Europe more than anywhere else, there are very good reasons for this and all one can say is: so much the better for Europe or Western civilisation. Whatever its shortcomings – and they are legion – at least in this respect, Western civilisation has produced or tolerated something which is central to the whole universe. In saying this, I am not elevating a Western value to a central position. I am merely suggesting that the turbulent social conditions which have prevailed in the West and which have eroded all traditional culture have been more conducive to something that is central than the social conditions or values which have prevailed elsewhere.

The Verdict of the History of Philosophy

Keeping Rorty's initial bias against knowledge in mind, let us now have a look at the history of philosophy he has produced so that we can then detect the model he has used to compose it and, finally, criticise the model.

In broad outline, Rorty's stock-taking of the history of philosophy produces the following story. In the seventeenth century, philosophers came to be seized by a virulent attack of hubris. They conceived the idea that they ought to be the guardians of culture; in order to perform this function, they thought they knew something special about knowledge which other people did not know. In this way, they were able to criticise other people according to whether they had good knowledge or bad knowledge. This arrogant usurpation of the role of guardians of culture made philosophers develop a theory of knowledge. Indeed, they started making their philosophy of knowledge into the central activity of philosophy.

The philosophy of knowledge they put forward was the idea that knowledge is a mirror of the world and that one can have correct knowledge provided one makes sure that the mirror is well polished. They considered that having knowledge is of the essence of being human and since they knew how to polish mirrors, they were able to put themselves forward as the guardians of everything that makes us particularly and essentially human. In being the keepers of mirrors, philosophers thus became the keepers of men – or, at least, the guardians of man's culture and the critics of man's culture.

If knowledge is a sort of mirror, this is linked to the idea that knowledge is a relationship between mind and matter, or between mental events and non-mental events. The initial presumption therefore depends on a special understanding of knowledge as a relation between mind and matter and that, in turn, depends on one's belief that there are mental events as distinct from non-mental events.

For Rorty, Descartes and Kant are the two great anti-heroes in this story. Descartes's dualism between mind and matter laid the foundation for mirror philosophy; Kant continued mirror philosophy by refining the structure of mirrors to make sure that they would reflect properly. If knowledge is a mirror, then eyes and vision become important – and all knowledge is conceived as an analogue of seeing with one's eyes.

Without going into historical details, Rorty then examines closely the idea that there are mental events and that they mirror, along with the idea that vision is central to knowledge. After a close scrutiny of these ideas, he finds them wanting. No matter how much one twists and turns, Rorty says, the idea that knowledge is a mirror, a mental duplication of something that is non-mental, has to be given up. His examination of what he calls the 'ocular metaphor' plays a special part in this scrutiny, for the ocular metaphor, he says, is particularly wrong and misleading. Eyes simply do *not* play such a crucial part in knowledge and, quite apart from the dubious arguments which have been used to establish the dualism between mind and matter, vision is not a model of knowledge, even though Rorty concedes that there were tempting reasons for considering the eye important. To start with, he admits, the eye itself seems to be like a mirror – an organ in which the outside world is reflected.

If knowledge is not mirroring and if the eye is not the paragon of all senses, we are driven to the ineluctable conclusion, Rorty goes on, that knowledge is the beliefs or convictions which are harboured in a closed circle by virtue of some central paradigm or set of linguistic rules. He describes this central paradigm of the closed circle as an 'epistemic authority'. We do not have some pieces of knowledge because they are derived from observations or because we know they refer to something or because we have evidence (whatever that might be) for them, but because we have an epistemic authority for them in the form of the central paradigm or the speech rules prevalent in the community we are members of. The position to which the logic of the history of philosophy has driven us is, in fact, the position of the later Wittgenstein. (It is vital to grasp that the force that has driven us is the *logic* of the history of philosophy, not some inner-force according to which we had to reach this conclusion. If Rorty had appealed to a developmental law, he would have to be dismissed as a vulgar historicist.) Wittgenstein insisted that the 'harmony of thought and reality is to be found in the grammar of our language' and that grammars are arbitrary conventions obtaining in given circles. Thus, he rejected unrelentingly and unremittingly the notion that our ways of speaking can receive any justification from some sort of extra-linguistic awareness of the relationship between words and things.[4] Rorty does not quote this passage from Wittgenstein, but it is writ large over his conclusion about epistemic authorities. However, he does place Wittgenstein into the centre of modern philosophy and considers him as the ultimate and final outcome of all history of philosophy, even though he also takes his stand with similar views expressed by John Dewey, Quine and Sellars.

Rorty does not consider this strategy which has led to the closed circles as a retreat or something like a resignation in face of the overwhelming criticism he has levelled against mirrors and eyes. On the contrary, he considers this conclusion – the doctrine that our knowledge is something that is governed by the epistemic authority of closed circles – as triumphant liberation. Incidentally, this conclusion enables him to reject the idea that philosophers are guardians of culture in general. He states, on the contrary, that they are playing a more modest role. They are, at best and at most, guardians of the linguistic rules which obtain in any one circle. Thus, they are, far from being critics, essential parts of closed circles. They do not criticise closed circles and their rules, let alone challenge the epistemic authorities. They are merely modest policemen who will track down the transgressors of the rules and call them to order. In thus assigning such a modest and basically conservative and uncritical place to philosophers, Rorty also assures them of a good place inside each closed circle. As guardians of culture and as critics, they are constantly exposed to the hatred of the people they criticise, and such hatred might bring them into disrepute. As members of every circle and as people who are policing the rules of the circle, they are merely acting as critics of individual transgressors – but they never question the rule themselves or criticise the circles as such. They uphold them instead.

In short, with this conclusion Rorty hails *historism* as the ultimate deliverance of all philosophical wisdom. Good philosophers, Rorty argues on page 367, are dubious about progress and

> especially about the latest claims that such-and-such a discipline has at last made the nature of human knowledge so clear that reason will now spread throughout the rest of human activity. These writers have kept alive the suggestion that, even when we have justified true belief about everything we want to know, we may have no more than conformity to the norms of the day. They have kept alive the historicist sense that this century's 'superstition' was the last century's triumph of reason, as well as the relativist sense that the latest vocabulary, borrowed from the

> latest scientific achievement, may not express privileged representations of essences, but be just another of the potential infinity of vocabularies in which the world can be described.

This confession comprises the whole arsenal of the implications of the closed-circle model. It states that each closed circle is a law unto itself; that whatever is held to be true is so held relative to the paradigm prevailing inside a circle; that there is no reference to any event outside the circle; and, last not least, that circles come and go at random and that there is nothing to choose between them. These points cover the entire spectrum of historism.[5]

Historical Doubts

The story of philosophy which appears in this account is broadly familiar but exhibits certain peculiarities. In describing mirror philosophy, Rorty refers himself exclusively to Descartes and the Cartesian tradition as well as to Kant. If a mirror reproduces what comes from outside, one would have thought that he should have included Locke and the whole tradition of British empiricism, right down to Bertrand Russell. Indeed, in this tradition the mind is viewed as a receptacle into which the senses pour information. I would have thought that, by any standards, this conception of the mind and of its relation to the outside world must be classed as a mirror philosophy even though receptacles are not exactly like mirrors. But then, the expression 'mirror' in this argument is supposed to be a metaphor and not to be taken literally, just as the expression 'receptacle' as metaphorical for the mind is, literally speaking, no more a bucket than it is a mirror. One can only speculate as to the reasons for leaving out the whole line which leads from Locke to Russell. My surmise would be that the Lockean tradition has always, ever since Berkeley, been open to quite destructive criticism. For if the mind knows only what has been induced into it by the outside world, there can be no guarantee that there is an outside world: all one is aware of is the presence of the ideas or images one is aware of. This, at any rate, is the burden of Berkeley's argument and in one form or another this kind of excessive Idealism has never been far from the mainstream of empiricism as it derives from Locke and Bacon. By contrast, the mirror philosophers on the continent are less vulnerable to this kind of criticism. Had Rorty included the receptacle philosophers, his story would have taken a different turn. So he had to leave the receptacle philosophers out because he did not wish his story to take a different turn.

Turning now to Descartes and Kant, one comes up with considerations which make them look much less like mirror philosophers than Rorty would have it. Take Descartes first. Rorty's effort to make out that from Descartes onwards, all philosophers before Wittgenstein subscribed to the mirror metaphor is, to say the least, highly original. Less kindly, we might argue that it is idiosyncratic. Descartes certainly thought he had discovered something special about knowledge. But it was not that knowledge consists in the mirror-image. His discovery was that all thought can come only from thought and that, since knowledge is, in a way, a thought, it must be based on a prior thought: *omne cogitatum ex cogitato*. Had he put it this way, I would have felt happy to be a Cartesian. However this may be, only by a stretch of the utmost historical imagination can Descartes be credited with the view that knowledge is a mirror-image of nature.

In so far as Descartes speaks of knowledge in general terms, one might, stretching one's imagination, think that he thinks of 'having knowledge' as 'looking into a mirror'. But when one examines what he has actually written, one realises that no amount of stretched imagination will help to reach this conclusion about Descartes. Rereading the *Fourth Meditation,* one sees clearly that Descartes wanted to find out what knowledge was left over when all knowledge which is in the least bit doubtful has been removed. Descartes was not interested in knowledge as such, but in certainty. Descartes's certainty did not depend on the degree of accuracy with which the mind mirrors nature, but on the deducibility of knowledge from a premiss which was not open to doubt. For Descartes, the central issue was not mirroring but deduction.

One must have even greater misgivings about Rorty's portrait of Kant. Unlike Descartes, Kant did perhaps think of the mind as a sort of mirror. But he did not think that we ought to, or can, polish that mirror. He believed that that mirror had a certain shape or quality and that whatever we saw as being mirrored would be structured by that shape or those qualities. As he put it, the argument was a little fantastic. Why should the mirror have a certain shape? Kant never addressed himself to that question.

Today, with the help of evolutionary biology, we can think of a perfectly good answer. The mirror, if indeed it be a mirror, has a certain shape because it was formed, like the rest of the human nervous system, by natural selection. Of all possible shapes, *some* shapes survived in the struggle for survival because they produced a more fitting mirror-image than other shapes. They may still be a little wrong and produce a distorted image. But given the biological success of the human race as against all other animals (except perhaps the insects), the knowledge mirrored by the human mind cannot possibly be totally misleading. Hence, the very reasonable assumption that the polishing of the mirror was not done by philosophers, as Rorty alleges Kant suggested, but by nature (i.e. the environment) itself.

There is peculiar irony in Rorty's treatment of Kant. In Rorty's view, Kant believed that one had to keep on polishing the mirror to make sure it would reflect accurately. In 1973, Konrad Lorenz published a book entitled *Behind the Mirror*.[6] The book was a 'search for a natural history of human knowledge' and began with a criticism of Kant. But Lorenz's criticism of Kant was very different from Rorty's. Lorenz argued that Kant had failed to realise that the mirror is the product of evolutionary adaptations. The mirror, in Lorenz's view, reflects accurately enough, though not with complete accuracy. It does so because it has evolved and would not have evolved had it made too many mistakes. Lorenz holds that Kant was too modest about the mirror. Kant thought that the mirror could never mirror the world as it really is. Lorenz explained that, in some respects, the mirror *must* be mirroring the world as it really is, for if it did not, it could not have been the product of progressive selections by the environment – that is, by the world as it really is. It is inconceivable, as Lorenz states, that the world as it really is would have fashioned, by chance mutations and selective retention, an instrument of cognition which would grossly and consistently mislead us about that world. In order to find out how this has come about and why the mirror is broadly reliable, Lorenz suggests we take a closer look *behind* the mirror. Lorenz shares Rorty's misgivings about the mirror, but suggests that these misgivings can be dispelled if we look at the obverse of the mirror. That obverse has evolved and is the same category of objects as the objects the mirror reflects. Thus, Lorenz proceeds from Kant's transcendental idealism to a hypothetical realism. This means that he recognises that the appearances in the mirror, which Kant took to be the ultimate beyond which we cannot conceive or perceive, result from a kind of interaction between the things in themselves and ourselves.[7] In his heart of hearts, Lorenz says, Kant himself, less logical but far wiser than all Kantians, was not so completely convinced that what appeared in the mirror and the real world in itself were completely unconnected. If the heavens which aroused such sense of wonder in Kant had been a mere appearance and not the *real* heavens, they would most probably not have aroused in him a sense of wonder comparable to the sense of wonder aroused in him by the moral law. One must appreciate the difficulties Rorty has with mirrors. If, however, he had read Lorenz on mirrors, most of these difficulties would have been removed. Rorty keeps saying that philosophers want to polish the mirror to make sure it reflects more than imaginings and appearances. Lorenz tells us that if one needs an assurance that the mirror reflects more than appearances and imaginings, one need only to look behind it and grasp that the obverse of the mirror is an adaptive response to the world as it really is.

Leaving Evolutionary Epistemology's reinterpretation of Kant aside, we can still see Rorty's gross misrepresentation of Kant. Kant, if he did think of a mirror, realised that no amount of polishing it would make it into a more precise instrument for representing nature. On the contrary, Kant realised that the mirror has a distorting shape of its own and therefore sought to demonstrate that whatever we see in that mirror is not nature or the thing in itself, but the world of appearance, the phenomena (i.e. reflections in the mirror of our mind). Kant's famous demonstrations that the picture we see in the mirror *must* differ from what is out there in the world proves that Rorty's idea of Kant is quite wrong. Whatever can be said against the mirror metaphor, such strictures do not apply to Kant.

The Paradigm behind the Verdict of History

Rorty's history of philosophy is not only highly selective, but selective in a very special sense. All histories have to be selective. However, the special selectivity employed by Rorty gives his history its special edge and, taken together with his initial dislike of knowledge, leads us straight to the paradigm he used in order to construct his history. The paradigm itself is not mentioned explicitly by Rorty. Had he mentioned it in so many words, the reader would have understood that the history by itself does not present a 'verdict' and that Rorty has done much more than 'stock-taking'. The reader would have realised that Rorty's story is relative to the paradigm and that any blunder – to use Wittgenstein's phrase – is a blunder in the paradigm and not in the historical narrative itself. This would have led the reader straight to a critical examination of the paradigm and would have detracted from Rorty's contention that the liberating stance of historism is the outcome of the history of philosophy – and that all reasonable men, given three centuries of mirror philosophising, should welcome being liberated by historism. If liberation by historism had been seen to have been built into the history of philosophy by Rorty himself, the attractiveness of such a liberation would have been lessened. It could still have appeared attractive if one approved of the paradigm. But such an attractiveness would have seemed less compelling and would have had to depend entirely on the attractiveness of the paradigm. Historism would have been alluring, as it had allured thinkers from Voltaire to Malinowski and Kuhn. But it would have lacked the inevitability. As it is, Rorty can invite us to look at history and make us see for ourselves that historism is the only reasonable position we can take up. *Ducent fata volentem, nolentem trahunt.* This had been Spengler's motto and in this guise it betrays definite hallmarks of historicism. Initially, Rorty's examination of history was not at all historicist. In the end, however, I seem to be able to detect a definite historicist ring in his demonstration that historism is the only viable philosophy available to us. His silence about his paradigm is, in a way, meant to be disarming because it enables him to take stock of *res gestae* and to conceal the fact that he is really inviting us to look at a *historia rerum gestarum*. But since we know that it is impossible to look at *res gestae*, we must call his bluff and now determine the model he has used to distil from *res gestae* his particular *historia rerum gestarum*. Then and only then, can we proceed to genuine criticism.

A careful study of Rorty's book has enabled me to detect the model Rorty has used to compose his history of philosophy. He has used Wittgenstein's intellectual biography – more precisely, Wittgenstein's progress from the *Tractatus* to the *Philosophical Investigations* – as a criterion of selection and as a paradigm for the writing of the history of philosophy of the last four centuries. Among other things, this choice has the advantage of being something which many people can actually remember. It has, therefore, as a paradigmatic story, an initial plausibility. At the beginning of the present century, Wittgenstein published a masterly book entitled *Tractatus Logico-Philosophicus,* or *Tractatus* for short. This brilliantly written book presented a fabulous theory of knowledge as a picture of reality and explained how propositions picture simple events. This book was, in part, the result of Positivism and, in part, gave a new lease of life to Positivism. Above all, it propounded the idea that when we have knowledge, we have propositions; and that only those propositions which picture or mirror reality can be meaningful propositions. Wittgenstein's book was the arch-statement of the view that knowledge is a picture or portrait of the world. When the book was published, Wittgenstein withdrew for many years from active philosophy and never took part in philosophical debates. Eventually, he re-emerged a completely new man with a completely new philosophy.

Evidently, Wittgenstein had realised that his view that knowledge was a linguistic picture of reality was untenable. He never admitted that he had realised this. He simply demonstrated it by never mentioning it again.[8] Instead, he propounded a completely different philosophy. He argued that when we have knowledge, we have knowledge according to the linguistic rules which obtain in a given circle; and that the meaning and truth of that knowledge can be assessed in terms of the rules which govern the speech habits in a given circle. In this way, Wittgenstein jettisoned his earlier philosophy that knowledge is a linguistic mirror of reality and embraced the philosophy of language games. In his later philosophy, Wittgenstein said that the meaning and truth of knowledge depends on the kind of language spoken (or 'played') in a given closed circle and that reference to the outside world was irrelevant.[9]

It was remarkable that Wittgenstein should abandon his *Tractatus* without a word of regret or a confession of failure. He not so much as repudiated it. He simply ignored it. It is equally remarkable that there is a perfectly understandable psychological motivation in the new philosophy. We all know from common experience that we converse more easily when we are among like-minded friends than when we are among strangers. We also know that our friends will be less critical of what we are saying and that, while they may disagree here and there, they will share our broad assumptions and values.

The Wittgenstein philosophy of language games is therefore grounded in real experience. What is more, as if to reinforce the genuineness and conviction of that experience, Wittgenstein proceeded to found his own closed circles in Cambridge, where he had gone back to teach. His seminars became the model for the closed circle in which a certain language game was played according to the rules set down by Wittgenstein himself. In this way, he provided the living proof of the truth of his philosophy.

As I have admitted several times in earlier chapters, there is a lot to be said for the methodology of closed circles, and one can indeed understand a lot about the meaning of speech and of propositions about the world or about one's own mind when one views them as moves inside a closed circle, the rules of which determine the way sentences are formed. The real enormity of Wittgenstein's later philosophy consists in the exclusiveness of the closed circle. He did not suggest that, among other things, one ought to look at the language game played inside a closed circle as one way of understanding the meaning of propositions; rather, he maintained that it was the *only* way of understanding them.

The development of Wittgenstein from the *Tractatus*'s mirror philosophy to the closed-circle language games of his later years is something we all remember. It is Wittgenstein's biography and such a small span of the history of philosophy that one can accept it as a meaningful mini-narrative, a meaningful small unit. Theoretically, it too has been composed and has been put together and, theoretically, there are many alternative ways in which the single events of which it consists might have been assembled. But when one comes to small spans in the passage of time, it is helpful to settle for the conventional composition and to abide with it. Again theoretically, one would have to have a criterion of selection in order to isolate those events which make up the intellectual biography of Wittgenstein and which would enable one to assemble these isolated events into a coherent biography. Since in this case the time-span is short and both place and time specified, one could argue that whatever the criterion used was, the 'Postulate of Sufficient Specification' was satisfied – even though one may have doubts about the degree to which the 'Postulate of Sufficient Variety' was satisfied. Finally, since one cannot write history unless one settles for a paradigm, Rorty's choice is no worse than any other choice. We will accept it, and then try to criticise the paradigm.

Rorty has taken hold of it and treated it according to the biogenetic law. The biogenetic law says that the ontogeny of an organism is a recapitulation of the phylogeny of the species. Rorty has, in fact, gone on the assumption that Wittgenstein during his own life-time recapitulated the history of philosophy – at least, that is, the history of philosophy from Descartes to the present day. On the assumption that there was such a recapitulation by Wittgenstein, Rorty can then proceed to provide a history of philosophy in which the philosophy of mind as a mirror of nature eventually made way for the philosophy of closed circles.

There are four reasons why the choice of Wittgenstein's intellectual biography as a paradigm for the history of philosophy is a bad choice. This criticism is not directed against the fact that Rorty has chosen a paradigm; nor is it directed against the use Rorty has made of the paradigm he has chosen. Within the limits of the paradigm chosen, Rorty's history of philosophy appears plausible. The four criticisms will therefore be levelled against the paradigm itself.

(1) Wittgenstein's *Tractatus,* far from being symptomatic of mirror philosophy, is the only mirror philosophy ever put forward. Nowhere else can we find an explicit statement of the picture theory of meaning.

(2) Wittgenstein's progress from the mirror philosophy of the *Tractatus* to the closed-circle philosophy of the *Philosophical Investigations* was in reality a very short progress. In the *Tractatus,* it is assumed that knowledge cannot be knowledge unless it is justified. At that time, Wittgenstein thought that the picture theory of meaning is the best justification of knowledge. If the sentence mirrors reality, it is meaningful; if it does not, it is not. In the *Philosophical Investigations,* Wittgenstein still believes that knowledge, to be worthy of the name of knowledge, must be justified. He now thinks that the picture theory of meaning is mistaken and that knowledge has to be justified by its obedience to the speech rules obtaining in a given circle. When one is looking at the method of justification, the progress from the *Tractatus* to the *Philosophical Investigations* seems a long progress. But when one is looking at the notion of justification, one will see that Wittgenstein made practically no progress at all. The ultimate reason for this lack of progress is to be sought in the retention of the notion of justification. 'As long as one has a Deweyan conception of knowledge *as what we are justified in believing,*' Rorty wrote on page 9, 'then we will not imagine that there

are enduring constraints on what can count as knowledge, since we will see "justification" as a *social* phenomenon rather than as a transaction between the "knowing subject" and "reality".' If one is a justificationist like Dewey, Wittgenstein or Rorty, one is not making progress in substituting one kind of justification for another. Whenever I think of this supposed progress, I am reminded of what Dorothy Parker once said about Katharine Hepburn: 'Last night's play gave Miss Hepburn a wonderful opportunity to run the whole gamut of her emotions from A to B.'

(3) The proposal of the *Philosophical Investigations* – that all meaning is established by use – depends ultimately on a *petitio principii*. Wittgenstein argues that there is no private language and that all linguistic expression must follow a rule. A rule, he says, would not be called a 'rule' if it were something that happened only once. Hence, 'to follow a rule' *means* that it is being done often, for it would not make sense to say, 'This rule is a rule only once.' However, the justification of the expression 'means' in this statement presupposes what Wittgenstein set out to prove — that is, that one defines the meaning of 'rule' in terms of its 'use'. If this is not granted, the demonstration that a rule is not a rule if it refers to something that was done only once, breaks down. For this reason, one cannot consider the arguments of the *Philosophical Investigations* – excepting, of course, the good epigrams and the *bons mots* – to be sound arguments. Wittgenstein practised the philosophy of closed circles. But one cannot accept that the practice was well founded or commended itself to one's reason. The practice was more like a social institution, a historical accident. This observation by itself does not necessarily detract from its usefulness or even from its soundness. Many social institutions are perfectly sound though incapable of being established or legitimised by reason. The observation, however, detracts from the usefulness of the paradigm of which it is part. If there is no sound reason for the closed circles in the *Philosophical Investigations*, the philosophy of closed circles as established by that book and by Wittgenstein's practice of holding seminars every week in his rooms to form a closed circle, cannot be considered as the reasoned outcome of the rejection of the picture theory of meaning of the *Tractatus*. At best, it can be considered as one of many possible alternatives. And this brings us to the last criticism.

(4) Wittgenstein never criticised, let alone rejected, the picture

theory of meaning of his *Tractatus*. He simply dropped it like a hot brick, so much so that his own admirers to the present day are divided among themselves as to whether his later philosophy is compatible with his earlier philosophy or not. Wittgenstein simply moved from the *Tractatus* to something else. He propounded the view that whatever we know derives its meaning from the rules of a language game played in a given circle, and that sentences, far from deriving their meaning from the fact that they mirrored anything, derived their meaning from the fact that they were being understood and intelligibly reacted to in a defined circle. Each circle, he might have said, is governed by a linguistic paradigm and whatever is being said under that paradigm must be meaningful relative to that paradigm and meaningless in regard to, as well as incommensurable with, anything said under a different paradigm.

This philosophical stance is reminiscent of G.E. Moore's ethics. Moore argued that the good is the good and cannot be defined or described as something that is pleasurable or useful or reasonable. One is good when one is good. Wittgenstein said that one knows what one knows, and that the rules of the particular language game one is engaged in would confirm what one knows.[10] When challenged by Russell to give reasons for this stance, Wittgenstein replied that reasons would merely spoil the beauty of the argument and that he would feel as if he was dirtying a flower with muddy hands.[11]

Far from criticising his early position, Wittgenstein simply constructed a social situation in which his language-game theory would produce its own verification. He assembled a group of willing disciples and listeners at regular intervals in his rooms in Whewell Court at Trinity College, Cambridge, and there played a language game which made his pronouncements about pain and thinking eminently meaningful by the use they had in that particular circle. The proof of the pudding was in the eating. 'I do not allow tourists,' he warned people who wanted to join the group. This might have seemed innocuous enough if taken to mean that he wanted sustained attention in what was otherwise an unstable academic environment. Graduate students at that time in Cambridge did not have to pay fees for attending seminars and lectures and were, therefore, in the salutary habit of drifting in and out of sessions, using their powers of criticism as a guide to whether they wanted to come back or not. Wittgenstein was determined to prevent this kind of intellectual competition. Either you commit yourself to playing my game, he was saying, or you don't. If you don't, you cannot expect to learn the language game I am playing and if you do, you will soon see that we all understand perfectly well what is being said.

Here, then, we have a perfect progress from a mirror philosophy to the philosophy of language games. Rorty has used this progression as a criterion of selection. He has assumed that there is some kind of biogenetic law in philosophy and that the history of philosophy is Wittgenstein's progress writ large. During his own life-time, Rorty believes, Wittgenstein recapitulated the phylogenetic development of philosophy. At first – at least from the seventeenth century on – there was mirror philosophy. Then the mirror philosophy was found wanting and came to be replaced by the philosophy of language games.

The Alleged Strength of Closed Circles

The development from mirror philosophy to the philosophy of speech communities (or, to use more conventional terminology, from Positivism to historism) was not determined by a historical development law, but was the result of rational reflection upon the non-viability of mirrors and upon the viability of the idea that every speech community forms an epistemic authority. One has to examine, therefore, these non-viabilities and viabilities. They depend, first, on the argument that there is real strength in thinking of knowledge as something which is governed by the epistemic authority of a speech community; and, second, on the weakness of the notion that knowledge is a mirror-like reflection. Let us examine these strengths and weaknesses in turn.[12]

The strength of the idea that knowledge and truth and meaning all depend on the consensus of a speech community is, at first sight, very obvious and a matter of common experience. We can make ourselves understood more easily when we are among friends and when meanings can tacitly be taken for granted. It is perhaps not equally obvious why our commitments to certain truths should also be dependent on such consensus. But with a little reflection, one can see that consensus of like-minded people is an important factor in any decision about any truth. The whole strategy which leads to Wittgenstein's paramountcy of rules of language is both useful and plausible and, what is more, such consensus can readily produce an epistemological euphoria.

The corresponding rejection of 'mirroring' is not immediately equally plausible but becomes more so when one recalls that, for Rorty, a mirror is something mental and the rest of the world, something non-mental. Once one sees it in this way, one can agree with Rorty that 'mirroring' is not a good model for knowledge because it amounts to a form of philosophical Manicheism – a total dichotomy between mind and matter. One must agree with Rorty's rejection of this dichotomy which occurs no less than thirteen times (pages 8, 10, 35, 41, 157, 178, 209, 269, 299, 320, 368, 389 and 393). Rorty's conclusion has to be endorsed: whatever knowledge we have, cannot be *justified* by the fact that it is mirrored.

However, it does not follow that knowledge is determined by obedience to speech rules prevalent in a given community and that knowledge is not a relation. Since knowledge is not a matter of mechanical mirroring, there is a difference between input and output. This difference between input and output must be generated, for good or ill, by the nervous system of the knower. One can therefore grasp that knowledge is a relation without defining that relation as a relation between mind and matter. So appreciated, this difference points to biology. One has to ask, next, where does the nervous system come from? And why is it the way it is? How adapted is it to the world in which it functions? What is the adaptive advantage of making this contribution to the input? If this last question is asked, one will soon see that any answer is likely to show that the generation of the difference between input and output is more likely to be for good than for ill. These are questions which Rorty not only fails to put, but – as we shall see – studiously avoids. In fact, he goes to great lengths to make sure that they cannot be put.

After establishing that knowledge cannot be a relationship because it is not like 'mirroring', Rorty argues that it must be justified by something else. Here, then, is the heart of the matter. For Rorty, knowledge is not knowledge unless it is justified. If it cannot be justified as a mirror-image, it must be justified by the epistemic authority of the speech community in which it is held. In Rorty's view, the great divide in philosophy is between the upholders of mirror philosophy and the believers in the authority of speech communities. As against this, I would argue that the great divide is between justificationists of all persuasions – be they mirror philosophers or speech-community philosophers – and Popperian falsificationists, who believe that we can have knowledge but that no knowledge can ever be justified. Rorty, taking his stand with justificationism, is inviting us to put the clock back to Linnaeus and a Linnaean universe in which all speech communities are equidistant from God. The less said about their evolution and the more said about their incommensurability (allowing, however, for genus and families), the better. The value of knowledge, he concludes, must be determined exclusively by reference to the framework in which it is held.

If these speech communities are the final epistemic authorities, we have to find a way of defining their membership. How are they constituted? Who is in and who is out? Functionalist anthropologists who derive from Malinowski have always had a ready-made answer to this question. Their communities were defined automatically by tribal boundaries and/or by the fact that the members lived in a geographically self-contained area, preferably a distant island. But if speech-community authority is to be elevated to a philosophical principle, such a special answer will not do. For the epistemic authority of a speech community to be accepted as a valid philosophical principle, one has to resort to an ethical criterion for membership. But if ethics are to determine membership, the question of Heidegger's Nazism and of Wittgenstein's homosexuality become intimately relevant,[13] especially since Heidegger and Wittgenstein are the philosophical heroes whose example Rorty invites us to follow. Rorty rarely faces this question and on page 226 he contents himself by quoting Quine: 'An observation sentence is one that is not sensitive to differences in past experience within the speech community.'[14] Quine, Rorty adds, excludes the blind, the insane and a few other 'deviants' from such a speech community. I suppose one must be grateful for small mercies: one shudders to think what would happen if only those observation sentences could be called true which had the consent not only of *l'homme moyen sensuel*, but also of the blind and the insane. However, if the blind are to be excluded, why should the deaf be included and who exactly are the 'occasional deviants'? In the very early part of this century, the Swiss psychiatrist Kraepelin had no difficulty in deciding who was insane. But since then, the boundaries of insanity have become very frayed.[15]

The question of the exclusion of the insane is specially interesting in view of R.D. Laing's almost Quinean contention that since there is no independent way of determining a person's insanity, 'insanity' is nothing but a label given to some people by the 'epistemic authority' of those people who are institutionally defined as 'psychiatrists'. A better Quinean than Quine, Laing would certainly challenge Quine's categorical exclusion of the insane. Has Quine ever considered Thomas S. Szasz[16] or R.D. Laing[17] on the subject? Quine's *Ontological Relativity,* the book of essays from which the above quotation is taken, appeared in New York in 1969. There is no excuse for not taking Szasz and Laing into consideration before reprinting this passage. And even if Quine does not consider this matter, why does Rorty pass over it in silence?

The enormous difficulty one encounters in determining membership when one is seeking to derive epistemic authority from closed circles far outweighs the initial advantages and the superficial plausibility of according epistemic authority to closed circles.

The Real Merits of Mirrors

It was alleged that the second rational ground for the recourse to closed circles was the weakness of the mirror account of knowledge and the frailty of the ocular metaphor. When one now turns to examine this weakness and that frailty, one will find that they are, though weighty, not as great and by no means as decisive as Rorty alleges. If the proposal to treat knowledge as a non-relational phenomenon, the validity of which is to be assessed by reference to a paradigm in the centre of a closed circle, is to be taken seriously, one would really have to persuade onself that the relational view of knowledge stands and falls with the mind–matter dichotomy. This, however, is by no means necessary. There is a lot to be said *in favour* of mirrors and *in favour* of the ocular metaphor, and most of the things to be said in favour do not depend on the mind–matter dichotomy at all. Rorty notwithstanding, mirror philosophy is anything but absurd. True, if the mirror is conceived as a passive receptor of stimuli, it is not likely to account for perception, let alone for knowledge. But the idea that the mind is a passive mirror and that that exhausts what we mean when speaking of man's 'glassy essence' is only one of the many ideas contained in the image of mirrors, even though it is the idea that was taken up by Positivists and which must be considered mistaken. Let us instead look at the real nature of mirrors, which is revealed when one examines all the other ideas contained in the image.

Exactly six years before Rorty published his own book against mirrors, Konrad Lorenz had published a book with the suggestive title *Behind the Mirror*. Rorty blithely ignored Lorenz's idea that we ought to look behind the mirror and proceeded as if Lorenz had never existed. The key idea of Lorenz's book is that if we think of knowledge as a sort of mirror, we ought to recall that it is the kind of mirror which has been selected by evolutionary pressures to be adaptive and that it cannot be completely misleading in its ability to mirror parts of nature. If it were, it would not be here today. In view of Lorenz's argument, if one moves away from the simple mirror philosophy of the *Tractatus*, one ought not to move away from mirrors but look behind the mirrors in order to see how evolution has produced the human nervous system. In his book, Lorenz referred to Karl Popper and to Donald Campbell, who had argued along this line before him. It is bad enough that Rorty in writing a book on the nature and growth of knowledge paid no attention to Popper and Campbell; it is even more remarkable that he paid no attention to a book which used the key concept 'mirror' and which showed where one might look for a viable improvement on the plain mirror philosophy of the *Tractatus*. Like Wittgenstein himself, Popper rejected the plain mirrors of the *Tractatus*. But unlike Wittgenstein, Popper did not suggest that we ought to see a non-relational epistemology as the only possible alternative to the mirrors of the *Tractatus*.

Let us look at a concrete example. Mirrors are linked to light and to vision. The simplest mirror one can envisage where knowledge is concerned, is the retina of the human eye. It receives light signals and registers them. But the image projected on the retina is blurred and unsteady and if one were to make a photographic record of it and develop it, there would be no similarity between the hazy print with smeared lines and the crisp and sharply detailed images one actually sees with the eye. Here, Rorty would say, we have a perfectly good reason why knowledge conceived as what is mirrored is not knowledge. It would be impossible to translate these smudged lines into linguistic expressions or to formulate them as sentences. So far, we might agree with him. Rorty then would go on to say that philosophers, instead of dismissing the idea that knowledge is what is mirrored, have insisted that the mirror ought to be polished more carefully. This is where Rorty's troubles begin. Taken literally, the project of polishing that mirror makes no sense. One cannot polish the retina and any interference with the retina, far from yielding better outlines of what is 'out there', would only damage the retina and one would finish up by seeing less, not more. So the invitation to polish the mirror cannot be meant literally. It must be a metaphor for manipulating the manner in which the perceived smudges are transformed into language. Again, Rorty has no difficulty in showing that no amount of manipulation will lead from these smudges on the retina to words and sentences. Even if some language manipulation could succeed in translating the blurs and smudges into sentences, one could have no assurance that the sentences thus formed would truly describe or refer to the objects which one deems to have caused the blurs and smudges. If one comes away with such an assurance, it would have to be an act of faith – but we are not in the business of dealing with faith and are, therefore, left in the air. Our procedure has not yielded knowledge, or, if it has, a knowledge so gained is not guaranteed to be true or reliable. Rorty then gives up. He throws up his hands in despair at the idea that knowledge is linked to mirrors or that properly polished mirrors constitute an eternally valid framework for knowledge. He is quite happy at his despair because, after all, he had set out to show that knowledge has nothing to do with mirrors and now, being in despair, his next step is to seek refuge behind the epistemic authorities of a language-game circle. His despair is comforting to him because he *wants* to legitimise these peculiar epistemic authorities.

At this point, we should suggest to him to have a look *behind* the mirror, instead of throwing up his hands in despair. We can take the suggestion that we ought to look behind the mirror literally. For behind the retina there is the optic nerve and the nervous system and, finally, the brain. In the early stages of transmission of impulses from the retina to the brain, there begins a process of neural computation. Blurred contours are sharpened. Some cells register light; others register shadow. Some cells fire when horizontal bars of light hit them; others, when vertical stripes hit them. Some cells respond only to certain axes of movement – side to side or up and down. And so it goes on, until an incredibly complex pattern of neural activity is set up in one part of the brain. And then, by a process which we do not understand at all, the person of whose body that retina is a part, has a conscious image of a chair. He *sees* a chair. What we see goes far beyond what is perceived. The shifting panorama of contours and shadows and colours and movements which the retina has registered is transformed into a steady object and designated by a word. The signals have become an enduring object in a coherent three-dimensional space.

It is of the greatest importance to stress the difference between Rorty's attempt (and its failure) to explain how what is mirrored can be transformed into language, and our attempt to explain neurologically what is going on behind the mirror. Rorty's procedure, whatever linguistic expressions it leads to, cannot show whether or why the linguistic expressions are true and whether we are right in designating something we 'see' as 'chair'. Thus, Rorty's failure drives him into the arms of language games whose epistemic authority alone could legitimise the employment, on a given occasion, of the word 'chair'. By contrast, when we are looking *behind* the mirror, we are examining the role of the nervous system. That system is a product of evolutionary adaptation. If it interpreted messages from the retina in a consistently faulty manner – that is, in a manner which is consistently out of step with what is 'out there' – we would not be here to suffer the consequences. Our ancestors in the animal kingdom would long since have been eliminated in the struggle for survival, long before the human or hominid invention of culture could have devised strategies for protecting us from the terrible consequences of such simple and fundamental mistakes of wrongly identifying our retinal registration of light and movement. Therefore, we must conclude, our computation of the signals registered by the mirror cannot possibly be grossly misleading as to what is 'out there', for the evolution of the nervous system which does the computing and interpretation would not have taken place had it not been adaptive. This conclusion does not mean that the nervous system's interpretations cannot be mistaken and that no errors can occur. It merely means that they cannot be grossly and consistently mistaken and misleading to the point where we could never tell whether to sit down on an object or avoid it like a death-trap. Unlike Rorty's superficial consideration of the surface of mirrors, the effort of looking *behind* the mirror has been worth while because it has helped us to understand why our perception of steady objects and the employment of linguistic symbols for them is legitimate. The need for a recourse to language games and their epistemic authority is obviated as soon as we are prepared to look behind the mirror.

As soon as we look *behind* the mirror, we make a number of breathtaking observations. First, we find that every living organism is a sort of hypothesis about the environment made flesh – a literally incarnated theory about a part of the world. The tick or the paramecium have minimum information about their environment and if that information were wrong, neither tick nor paramecium could have survived. However, neither the whole of these organisms nor the brain of a higher organism are, in the first instance, mirrors of the world in which they are living; if they were, the theory about the world which these organisms embody would disappear at night or when the organism is removed to a different environment. In the absence of the world, if the organism or the brain were a mirror, the mirror would be blank. For no mirror stores the image it mirrors. Up to a certain level of evolution, organisms and brains are theories about the world, but not mirrors. When we come to the higher primates, however, there is a change. With the evolution of the cerebral cortex there emerged one part of the brain which has no specific function for speech, for movement, for pain or for whatever. It is more or less blank and therefore plastic. It can take in messages and interpret them. In short, it can learn. Depending on the size and structure of that cortex, it can learn one thing just once – the way some ducklings can get imprinted once and not again – or it can learn lots of things most of the time. This part of the brain though not a mirror in the mechanical sense, is very much like a mirror in the metaphorical sense. It can 'mirror' the environment and interpret it.[18]

The mirror notion is sometimes adequate to describe an essential cognitive relationship between organisms and their environment, and sometimes not. Let us examine these relationships and the real nature of mirrors systematically, from the bottom up.

(1) The hoof of the horse carries a lot of information about the soil of the steppe, and the fins of fish represent the laws of hydrodynamics. In this sense, they mirror their environment because they encode information about it: one can deduce a lot about the steppe by looking at the hoof. The information is not exhaustive; not even as exhaustive as the information carried by a key about the lock into which it fits. 'Mirroring' here is a bit of a metaphor, but a very adequate one.[19]

(2) All organisms carry an image about the world they will thrive in before they have actually 'seen' the world. Here, 'mirroring' is not a suitable expression to describe this innate knowledge, for it can make no sense to say that something is mirrored *before* it is seen or sensed. The first weasel encountered by a chicken is not a new experience, not something which is mirrored in the chicken's brain; but exactly what the chicken was programmed to expect. These expectations are ontogenetically *a priori* and are the result of a complex phylogenetic process. In this case, we should not think of mirrors but of programmes.

(3) In some organisms, one part of the brain is, to start with, plastic and can be imprinted by an experience. However, the kind of experience which can imprint itself is very limited and the organism has to be programmed for it. Here, it makes sense to speak of partial mirroring. Partial, because its operation is restricted by the fact that only some experiences are reflected and that those which are, are retained permanently and cannot be replaced when the object mirrored is gone.

(4) Next, we come to organisms with a large, plastic and very flexible cerebral neo-cortex. This part of the brain has no programmed function to make us hear or enable us to move or to speak. Therefore it is very similar to a mirror: it is plastic in regard to objects which appear before it. Such mirroring is like reflection in some respects, it is not at all like reflection in other senses – for there is no straight reflection. The energy transfer goes through the most diverse neural processes and the input and the output (our consciousness of whatever is noticed?) are qualitatively and quantitatively different, even though there is – as in really good mirrors – genuine correspondence between input and output. Moreover, this correspondence is not suddenly established nor does it produce itself. On the contrary – and here we are again getting away from real mirrors – it has to be established and checked very laboriously by pattern matching. With the help of innate expectations the mind makes a proposal, so to speak, of how incoming stimuli are to be interpreted. Then the proposal pattern is established and compared with the pattern abstracted from the input. After several attempts and the dismissal of patterns which do not match, a 'correct' match is retained by selection.[20] Mirrors, by contrast, reflect without such pattern matching.

The mind, therefore, is in many different senses a mirror, though in no single sense completely like a mirror and in some of its functions – the operation of innate expectations – not at all like a mirror. Therefore, the notion that the mind is a mirror of nature cannot be simply dismissed. It has to be qualified by a careful consideration of the nature of mirrors.

When we take a closer look at the much despised ocular metaphor, we will again find that modern biology tells us that there is less reason for contempt than Rorty admits. Of all the human senses, the sense of vision has a very special significance. Unlike other animals, we depend more on vision than on smell, feel, touch or hearing. There are well-known neurological reasons for this and it has something to do with our bipedal, upright posture. Hence also, our common speech habits. When we want to say that we understand we say, 'I see!' but not, 'I hear!' or, 'I smell!' For that matter, Jews and Muslims shrink from making God visible, but have no qualms about claiming to have 'heard' him. Whether these speech habits are fully justified or not is hard to say, but the fact that they are widespread and deeply ingrained points to the very special position occupied by the human eye. These and similar English idioms are not wholly misguided: physiologists have indeed shown that the human eye is a very special cognitive apparatus. Rorty is inclined to argue that the preference for ocular metaphors when we are talking of knowledge is prejudicial because it reminds us of the eye's steady gaze and makes us think that the eye, more than any other sense, perceives what is immutable. In fact, biologists have shown that this is not so. The eye is a marvellously complex organ capable of perceiving the most intricate kind of movements and of using part of the nervous system to produce an illusory image of steadiness in what is being taken in through the eye while we are constantly moving our heads, as well as our eye-balls inside those heads, in order to make sure we do not suffer from continual optical vertigo. Finally, though I grant that this is not a real argument, two philosophical jokers have recently published a book under the title *The Mind's I*, thus drawing attention to the peculiar relationship which seems to exist between 'seeing' and 'being conscious' and to the fact that the English language appears more capable than any other language of emphasising this extraordinary human peculiarity.

If metaphor and Hofstadter's pun on the metaphor are not arguments, some reflection on modern theories of vision will show how wrong Rorty's objection to the ocular metaphor is. Rorty thinks that the ocular metaphor has been ingrained and maintained itself because philosophers imagine that knowledge must be knowledge of something immutable and that knowledge is contemplation. Now, the activity of the eye is more like contemplation than any other activity, or so it might have seemed to the Greeks and possibly even to C.D. Broad, whose *Scientific Thought* (1923) Rorty quotes on page 39 to support his contention that philosophers get their belief in the mind's eye from their conviction that the eye's steady gaze can be fixed on something immutable. More recent literature would have been more helpful. C.F.v. Weizsäcker's *Der Garten des Menschlichen*[21] (1978) has an enlightening chapter on the unity of movement and visual perception, and the whole of chapter 7 of R. Gregory's *Eye and Brain*[22] is a very detailed explanation of the subtle complexity which makes the eye, more than any other organ, capable of taking in movement. Rorty might also have looked at Holst's 'Active Function of Human Visual Perception'[23] to learn that to 'gaze' is to take in movement and change. In so far as Rorty's objection to the ocular metaphor is based on the idea that it is linked to the eye's 'steady gaze' at immutability and that once we give up the notion that knowledge is perception of immutability, the ocular metaphor ceases to be justified, Rorty is quite simply wrong. The ocular metaphor may have had its origins among the Greeks, who did not know much about optics and neurology. But if it is to be abandoned, there must be better reasons than a reference to Greek ignorance and to an example used by Broad in 1923.

A truly 'steady gaze' and real immobility of the eye, far from leading us to the idea of contemplation, would result in blindness. Moreover, we have come to understand that our perception of space depends on our understanding of space as the medium in which our bodies move. This, in turn, depends on our perception of our body in relating to other objects and thus shows itself to be an *optical* phenomenon.[24] Moreover, spatial perception or distal knowing[25] is fundamentally different from any other kind of perception by direct bodily contact. In order to make distal knowing possible, time must elapse between the origin of light in the object seen and the registration of the light stimulus in the relevant part of the brain. When we act or move in response to a direct stimulus of bodily contact, we do not have to 'think'. But when there is a time-interval between origin of stimulus and registration of stimulus and when we link this interval to our notion of space, we gain a breathing-space which eventually encourages thought, even abstract thought. Here, we can detect how, in a very roundabout manner, vision is linked not only to our knowledge of spatial relations, but also to our eventual ability to think and to contemplate. Theoretical contemplation, which Rorty assumed to have been derived from a mistaken perception of retinal steady vision, is, in reality, linked to vision because vision is the very opposite of steady gaze.[26] All in all, when one is taking a really close look at biology, evolution and physiology, one sees that mirrors and ocular metaphors are not nearly as inappropriate as Rorty makes out.

The Relevance of Biology

If one considers all these arguments in cold blood, one can hardly come to the conclusion that it is reasonable to proceed from the demise of the *Tractatus* or of Positivism or of mirror philosophies to the methodology of closed circles and to the epistemic authority of speech communities. No matter how plausible such a recourse is on first acquaintance, the attractiveness of closed circles and the weakness of mirror philosophy is not sufficiently great to commend such a progress. And if one is not prepared to invoke a developmental law which could compel one to make that particular progress, one will be well advised to look elsewhere. The obvious place to look is biology and evolution. At every turn of the argument, we have seen that it is imperative to look in that direction and it was these looks at biology and evolution which have shown that the progress to closed circles is highly questionable and far from reasonable. There is at least one other alternative.

Rorty, with the clairvoyance of a real somnambulist takes careful and well-measured steps to make sure he does not have to consider that other alternative. A consideration of biology would have to be based on the understanding that man is not unique and that we must consider his biological ancestry and evolution. Next, it would have to allow that man's knowledge is all of a piece with the knowledge and information which plays such a critical role in evolution. Finally, it would have to account for the fact that there is a link between the regularities which exist in nature and the fact that all living organisms are sensitive to them and that man, above all, is capable of conceptualising them in the shape of 'universals'. Although Rorty never addresses himself explicitly to these three questions, he takes great care throughout his book to bring forward arguments which make a consideration of biology impossible. In this way, he is able to create the impression that the progress towards closed circles and speech communities is in fact the only alternative available. He affirms again and again that man is unique; he alleges explicitly that there are no 'universals' and that it was a major error of judgment when Plato and Aristotle introduced them to our awareness; last, not least, he is convinced that our interest in 'knowledge' is something like an obsession. Let us examine the validity of these points in turn.

In no less than ten places, widely dispersed throughout the book,[27] Rorty takes pains to claim that human beings are completely unique and totally different from animals and all other organisms. In a sense this is patently true. But when one is considering knowledge, one cannot write as if we were living before Darwin and before ethology. Nor can one pretend that our whole knowledge of biology does not show us that there are very striking and remarkable continuities between human beings and pre-hominid animals and other organisms. And yet, the argument that human beings are totally separate and unique occurs in Rorty's book on pages 35, 38, 43, 44, 183, 184, 186, 189, 190–1 and 232. Why does Rorty protest so much?

He not only asserts that man is unique, but also offers arguments to establish the uniqueness of man which are downright false. On pages 183–4, Rorty claims, for example, that the difference between a child's ability to have pain and a photoelectric cell's sensitivity to a stimulus is absolute. This is incorrect. The cell has a discriminative response to a stimulus. The child, in gradually learning a language about its sensitivity to a stimulus, starts, like the cell, from a discriminative response and then proceeds to learn a descriptive response which involves language. Discriminative response and descriptive response are linked in an evolutionary way. Discrimination leads by selection to an ability to have expectations. Then follows an advantage in the ability to make verbal abstractions of such expectations, and this leads, again through selection, to an ability to make descriptive responses. Organisms with a descriptive as well as a discriminative response are better adapted than organisms with a discriminative response only. But there is no reason for thinking that there is an absolute discontinuity between discriminative and descriptive response or that the child and the cell are 'set apart'. All this is well explained by Konrad Lorenz in chapter 1 of his *Behind the Mirror*, 'Life as a Process of Learning'.[28]

Next, we turn to the allegations that there are no universals and that it is an error of judgment to believe that there are or that we have knowledge of them. On page 38, Rorty writes that we would have been much better-off had we confined ourselves to 'pointing out particular states of affairs' and refrained from going into the business of speaking poetically about birth and death as such and if mathematics had never prided itself 'on overlooking individual details'. Rorty here brings up the old nominalist strategy and then goes on to explain the genesis of this error of judgment. It all goes back, he says, to the notion that knowledge is contemplation and, in particular, contemplation of universals. Knowledge conceived as contemplation, in turn, stems from the ocular metaphor and from mistaking the eye of the mind as the model of knowledge. If there is such a glaring error of judgment, one might ask, why have people not seen the light and corrected it? Rorty has an answer for this. He says on page 43 that 'to suggest that there are no universals – that they are *flatus vocis* – is to endanger our uniqueness.' Rorty sees the persistent belief that there are universals and that their presence in our 'minds' has to be explained as a sort of anthropocentric predicament. Since he has other reasons for establishing the uniqueness of man, he is willing to let go of this one. In reality, it seems to be the other way round. If man had no knowledge of universals, as Rorty thinks, he would be totally unique in the whole realm of living organisms. For, in common with all organisms, even the simple paramecium[29] is ratiomorphous: it survives because of its 'knowledge' of a dependable relationship between carbon dioxide and the bacteria on which it, the paramecium, feeds. It is not equipped to detect bacteria; but it can respond to the presence of carbon dioxide. It can grasp only one single piece of information. But since it expects this information to be information about a regularity in nature, it survives. In a dim way, the paramecium has 'knowledge' of a universal. If Rorty is right in saying that human beings have no knowledge of universals, human beings would be *truly* unique. Rorty must, therefore, be wrong in thinking that philosophers have resisted giving up the idea that we have knowledge of universals lest such lack of knowledge would make us like animals and put an end to our uniqueness. Given the biological background to our knowledge of universals, his case would be better served by saying that philosophers have clung to universals because they *fail* to appreciate that man is unique.

If one views the growth of knowledge as an evolutionary process in which knowledge grows, either in the shape of organisms or in the shape of theories, by random mutation and selective retention, one must pay special attention to the selected retention in all organisms of the ability to expect regularities in their environments. If one alleges that there are no regularities and that our knowledge of universals is an error of judgment, one is compelled to drop the idea of evolution altogether or replace its mechanism by something other than random mutation and selective retention. With an uncanny and almost unconscious sense of direction, Rorty makes sure (on page 38) that the question of regularities, and of the knowledge of universals to which they might give rise, does not come up – or, at least, does not have to be faced as one of the crucial questions in philosophy. He seems to consider awareness of universals to have been the philosophical Fall from Grace – the ultimate, philosophically speaking, Original Sin. Once people thought of universals, he argues, the road was open for Plato's misconstruction of their nature and for the notion that universals are entities to be contemplated with the eye of the mind – and hence, the unfortunate ocular metaphor which is so deeply ingrained in the notion that the mind mirrors nature.

Many readers will readily agree that Plato's and Aristotle's treatment of these universals was not above reproach. The attribution of spirituality to universals seems especially questionable, for such attribution clearly derives from the fact that, as such, they are not to be seen by the eye but only by the 'eye of the mind' – or should we take up Douglas Hofstadter's appropriate pun and say that they are to be seen only by 'the mind's I', thus drawing attention to the close connection between personhood and awareness of universals. I doubt very much whether the ubiquity of the ocular metaphor and our habit of treating 'I understand' and 'I see' as synonymous really stems exclusively from Plato's recognition that universals play some role in our knowledge. However this may be, it is significant that Rorty thinks the world would have been a better place if universals had never been heard of. He, for his part, obviously seems to find no great difficulty in orienting himself in his environment without abstract universals or general concepts. One must wonder how he could have managed to master the English language sufficiently well to write a 400-page book and the mind boggles when it tries to fathom what Rorty's private environment might look like or be like if he thinks he could find his way from A to B without the help of abstract universals. The real point is that Rorty is here putting up an old nominalist argument and thus unwittingly barricading any road which might lead to thoughts of evolution.

How Valuable is Knowledge?

Last, we come to Rorty's conviction that our interest in knowledge is an obsession rather than a virtue.

The argument begins with a bland statement that knowledge is not worth having. Rorty says on page 370 that knowledge is merely (*sic*) an accurate representation of what is already there – a sort of mental duplicate. He insinuates that only people who are greedy to have two things instead of one, seek knowledge. With this jejune idea of knowledge in mind, Rorty maintains that our Western culture has been unique in using *knowing* as a paradigm and that, in successive phases of our culture, philosophers have tried to show that the rest of culture can profit from following their example. Thus, philosophers have set themselves up as guardians or overseers and have endeavoured to criticise culture and to model behaviour on whatever knowledge they pretended to possess. As Rorty states on pages 366–7:

> Successive philosophical revolutions within the mainstream have been produced by philosophers excited by new cognitive feats – e.g. the rediscovery of Aristotle, Galilean mechanics, the development of self-conscious historiography in the nineteenth-century, Darwinian biology, mathematical logic. Thomas's use of Aristotle to conciliate the Fathers, Descartes's and Hobbes's criticism of scholasticism, the Enlightenment's notion that reading Newton leads naturally to the downfall of tyrants, Spencer's evolutionism, Carnap's attempt to overcome metaphysics through logic, are so many attempts to refashion the rest of culture on the model of the latest cognitive achievement.

There is a lot to be said for this view of Western history – or, at least, for the history of Western culture. But why the acid note? Why the contempt for the worthy men who sought knowledge and somehow failed to envisage all the time their own limitations and their own fallibility?

The dislike of knowledge goes deep with Rorty and is surprising in a philosopher who uses historical knowledge to show that the closed language circles with their cognitive relativism must replace the idea that we can search for knowledge and the idea that knowledge can grow. We have found that the knowledge to which Rorty appealed is not as 'raw' as he thought. But, as knowledge goes, it was historical knowledge even when composed on the assumption that Wittgenstein's intellectual progress was a recapitulation of the history of philosophy from Descartes onwards. It is curious that Rorty, when he holds knowledge so cheap, should attribute so much importance to historical knowledge and base his argument on the verdict of historical knowledge. For historical knowledge is not only knowledge, but, compared with our knowledge of physics and astronomy and chemistry, much less reliable and, if anything, more transparent. In all historical knowledge, the model or the philosophy or the general meta-historical theory on which it is based, is more manifest than in almost any other kind of knowledge. For a man who does not set much store by knowledge, Rorty spends a lot of time with historical knowledge and places a heavy burden of proof on it. One must insist that Western or not, the effort to use knowledge as a central paradigm is neither wrong-headed nor perverse. On the contrary. It is perfectly in tune with our knowledge of the universe in general and of biological evolution in particular. All evolution is a progression of knowledge in which the environment selects what is compatible with it so that one can see that the later stages always contain knowledge about the earlier stages. This progression of knowledge far transcends the limited case in which a 'mind' knows something about the rest of the world. I shall return to this point in my last chapter. Here, I merely wish to point out that Rorty is wrong in thinking that the mainstream of the Western philosophical tradition has shown itself to be idiosyncratic. Far from it. It has been exactly on the right track. Knowledge is central. But in Rorty's view, people who talk about the Roman Revolution or about time warps or about the wave equations of Quantum Mechanics are simply dull and greedy people who want to have two things when one would do. Armed with this grotesque idea of knowledge as a duplication of reality, Rorty explains that in every reflective culture people single out one or other human practice as the paradigm of all human activity. Bad luck had it, he continues, that in Western culture 'having knowledge' has been singled out. Here, we not only have a misleading description of knowledge as a mere doubling-up, but the explicit declaration that the Western preoccupation with knowledge is idiosyncratic. There is no need to go into the question of culture and its paradigms. But it is important to stress that a preoccupation with knowledge is not idiosyncratic. Conceptual or propositional knowledge is merely a special case of having information. The transfer of information from environment to organism by natural selection and the passing on of adaptive information, either by genes or by education, is one of the fundamental mechanisms of evolution. True, in human culture there are things other than knowledge. Moreover, knowledge can be inhibited by culture and it can lead to the destruction of culture. But none of these insights supports Rorty's contention that preoccupation with knowledge is idiosyncratic and ought to be stopped because it is a Western prejudice.

If these arguments are not sufficient, one can also see the centrality of knowledge by taking a closer look at the biology of cells. The origin of the first living cells ever is ultimately linked to the way in which some molecules surrounded themselves with a membrane and separated themselves from the rest of the world. No matter what changes have been brought about by evolution, this device of isolation by the formation of a boundary-like skin has been so efficient and so good that no living organism has ever been able to manage without it. The isolation, however, had to be selective. Every cell maintains itself by metabolism and needs parts of the environment which have to be allowed to cross the membrane. However, and this is crucial, the membrane has to be highly selective in what it lets cross its boundary. Only by 'knowing' what can and what cannot pass is the cell able to maintain its own orderly structure *vis-à-vis* the relative chaos of its environment. With the emergence of this skin, the molecules on the inside are able to set themselves up as an orderly system separate from the objectively existing world on the other side of the skin. The skin has to be able to distinguish the different parts of the outside world to make sure only those are allowed to pass across the boundary which will help to maintain the orderly arrangement of the molecules inside. This means that most of the outside world has to remain excluded. The skin must be able to tell the difference and to recognise the parts which may cross.[30] The distinction between the inside and the outside is thus of the essence of living organisms and so is the ability to recognise those parts of the environment which may cross the boundary between inside and outside.[31] All human knowledge is an extension of the elemental discriminatory power or an extrapolation from it. Preoccupation with knowledge is therefore not idiosyncratic nor accidental.

This chapter began with a discussion of the value of knowledge and has ended with a discussion of the value of knowledge. One's assessment of the value of knowledge is at the centre of the whole argument about closed circles. The argument started from Rorty's bias against knowledge and ended with his studied attempt to isolate knowledge from biology and from evolution, so that it could be stigmatised as something idiosyncratic. The plausibility of the closed-circle argument depends on the value one places on knowledge. If one does not rate knowledge highly, there is no compelling reason why one should not seek shelter in closed circles and hide behind their epistemic authorities. If, on the other hand, one places a high value on knowledge, such shelter will remain cold comfort.

Nobody would argue that knowlege is self-constituting. Knowledge has to understand the world and to understand how and why we understand the world and how the knower is related to what he knows even though he is part of the world known: a truly formidable complexity which is not simplified by *ex priori* attempts to isolate 'mind' or define 'self'. If the knower *could* pull himself up by his own bootstraps and if knowledge *were* self-constituting, it would be the only phenomenon in the universe which is not linked to or derived from another phenomenon. Every person who has ever probed his knowledge has faced up to the fact that knowledge has its roots and origins outside its own rational realm of thinking. It is one of the great ironies of philosophy that the only people who thought that knowledge was self-constituting were those tough-minded Positivists, people who would stand no nonsense from metaphysics and other idle speculation. They beheld knowledge as if it were an Olympian stance, a god-like privileged position totally outside the universe, a place from which one could survey the world as one might from Mount Olympus – something like the still point at the centre of the wheel. All other people, more modest than Positivists and more realistic than those Olympian metaphysicists, have gone somewhere to explain knowledge. However, there were differences in the lengths to which people were prepared to go. Those who valued knowledge highly, have sought those roots and origins in biology and evolution – that is, in those realms in which our very existence is rooted. Those who valued knowledge not at all, have gone no further than language because all thoughts are expressed in language. Given the fact that all distinction between thought and language is tenuous and really undefinable – to 'define' it, one would have to use language – the excursion into language is no excursion at all. In between, there are the people who placed a low value on knowledge. They were willing to go a little way, but remained readily content in finding those roots and origins in social organisation or sociability. Sociability is, in every respect, a secondary phenomenon. It, too, has its roots in biology and evolution even though biology can by no means account for it completely. But there is a great difference between seeking the roots of knowledge in sociability and seeking the roots of knowledge in biology. If one is content with finding those roots in sociability, as all closed-circle advocates are, one shows oneself easily satisfied and prepared to settle for less than one can get. Such self-denying modesty is, in all cases, the direct expression of the low value one places on knowledge. If knowledge is something that is neither edifying nor important, there is no reason why one should not be satisfied in considering it a function of man's sociability. If, on the other hand, one considers it to be edifying and important, one will go further afield and seek to link it to biology. The link to biology, as we have seen, does not by-pass or ignore the connection to sociability; it merely puts that connection in its proper place and realises that it is, in turn, derivative rather than final.

Chapter 6

Evolutionary Epistemology

Popper's Philosophy of Knowledge

Let us return to the beginning of the whole argument in chapter 1. We require a philosophy of science which has a number of characteristics. First, it must not legitimise itself by an appeal to the history of science because we have shown that the history of science is dependent on a philosophy of science. Second, it must account for the fact that in science there has been progress, because, as we have argued, the history of science is notably different from the history of art and literature. Third, it must be capable of explaining the remarkable discontinuity in the history of science: it must be able to account for the fact that the pursuit of science and progress in scientific knowledge is rare, sporadic and exceptional. Fourth – and this requirement follows directly from the second requirement – it must allow that scientific theories are commensurable and that there are reasons other than fashions and whims for replacing one theory by another theory. Finally, last not least, the philosophy of science we require must allow for the fact that all genuine knowledge has to be confronted with the environment and must not be permitted to be retained by the fiat of a subjective will or the consensus of an elite, no matter how carefully institutionalised in the shape of an Academy or Royal Society. Since conscious knowledge about the world is a continuation of pre-conscious knowledge enshrined in organisms which are adapted to an environment, exposition of knowledge to the environment for criticism and eventual elimination is an essential requirement for every philosophy of science. If the retention of knowledge depends, according to a philosophy of science, on 'acceptance' by a designated body of people rather than on toleration by the environment, that philosophy of science breaks the continuity between evolution and the growth of knowledge and sets up an artificial, qualitative barrier between the 'fit' involved in successful evolution and the 'fit' involved in true knowledge. However, one qualification is needed. We said that genuine knowledge must be tolerated by the environment. Toleration is indeed all that is possible and necessary. Neither organisms nor conscious knowledge are *determined* by the environment. Both organisms and conscious knowledge are, in fact, underdetermined by the environment. An adapted organism is simply an organism which survives and is not eliminated by the environment. It is not an organism which fits the environment like a hand in a glove. The organism will survive as long as it is compatible with the environment. The same applies to knowledge. Conscious knowledge always says more than the environment warrants. It is therefore underdetermined. In saying more, it can still be considered a 'fit' – or an *adaequatio rei et intellectus,* to use a medieval, scholastic term – as long as what it asserts is compatible with the environment.

Given these requirements, we can see that Kuhn's philosophy of science does not qualify. In the first instance, it clearly does not stand on its own feet but claims to be derived from the history of science. Since such a history presupposes a philosophy of science, it cannot legitimise one – least of all not the philosophy of science which has been used as the general framework for composing it. Next, Kuhn's philosophy of science is unhistorical in that it avowedly fails to explain why one paradigm preceded another and why one paradigm was earlier or later than another. It cannot see any connection between the growth of knowledge and the succession of paradigms. What is more, by making any one paradigm incommensurable with any other paradigm, it makes all knowledge (i.e. normal science) relative to the paradigm which happens to be fashionable and thus makes it impossible to weigh the relative merits of the paradigms themselves. As I have argued above, there is something to be said for the profession of such incommensurability when one is dealing with art or with social institutions. There may indeed be no obvious reason why one should compare the institutions of the Trobriand Islanders with those of the Andaman Islanders. But when one is dealing with knowledge, the absence of commensurability is a fatal flaw, for the growth of knowledge is a historical phenomenon – an approximation to a goal – in a sense in which the history of art and literature or the successive emergences of social institutions are not. Again, since 'language games' are, partly, ends in themselves (i.e. forms of social exchange and communication used only obliquely to convey information) nobody need blame Wittgenstein for maintaining that one cannot measure the relative merits of one game against another. But scientific knowledge is different. It is neither a closed system nor a game. It is therefore essential that one theory or paradigm should be capable of being compared with any other; any philosophy of scientific knowledge which expressly precludes such comparison is constructed in such a way as not to be relevant. The account it gives of scientific knowledge is so wide off the mark as to be well-nigh unrecognisable.

By contrast, Karl Popper's philosophy of science qualifies by all the requirements listed. It is now almost half a century since Popper first proposed that the chief characteristic of scientific knowledge is its falsifiability. To start with, this philosophy of science is based on the uncontestable consideration that a general theory can never be verified because observations in its favour must, by necessity, be limited in number. This philosophy does not depend on the observation of the history of science. Its truth depends on nothing but a logical argument. Not even Carnap, who found Popper's scepticism in regard to induction unacceptable, doubted Popper's logic. He merely maintained that, in spite of this logic, it made perfectly good sense to say of a certain hypothesis that it was positively confirmed. Psychologically speaking, Carnap is right. Repeated observation of a phenomenon countenances a guess that we have here a law of nature. Nobody would deny this. What is to be denied, however, is the claim that repeated observation justifies rather than countenances the guess and that such justification proves the truth of the guess.

In summary fashion, this philosophy of knowledge explains that the search for knowledge begins with guesses and conjectures which must be framed in such a way that they are at least in theory falsifiable. Their falsifiability assures them of an 'empirical content' – that is, when falsifiable, we know that they are *about* a real world and different from mere imaginings which do not refer to anything objective and are, therefore, not falsifiable. The advance of knowledge depends to a large extent on the boldness of these conjectures. When these conjectures are falsifiable, but not yet falsified, they are said to be provisionally true. In this account of knowledge, there can be no certain knowledge, no certain method for acquiring it, no guarantee that acquired knowledge (i.e. unfalsified knowledge) is true by virtue of having been acquired according to a 'correct' method. The rationality of knowledge consists in its exposure to criticism and falsification; not in the presence of a 'rational' method for obtaining it, as observation and induction were alleged to be. In short, Popper stood the old Positivism on its head: instead of starting with the collection of observation and working forward by induction to generalisations, Popper maintained that we start with general conjectures, make deductions from them and end up by trying to falsify the deductions.

In rejecting verification as a legitimate basis of knowledge, Popper rejected all forms of Positivism and the assumption – or ought one to call it a presumption? – that meaningful statements *must* be equivalent to some logical construction upon terms which refer to immediate experience. In order to hold fast to the distinction between metaphysics or superstition and genuine knowledge, a distinction which had been so important for Positivism, Popper suggested that the distinction can be based upon a consideration other than verification. Since, logically, one single falsifying observation falsifies the general theory or law which suggested that the observation be made, Popper held up falsifiability as the criterion by which one can distinguish phoney knowledge from genuine knowledge. If knowledge can, ideally, be falsified and if one can point to the observation which would falsify it, it must be knowledge about the world. In giving up the requirement of verification and substituting the demand for falsification, he did not give up the demarcation between knowledge and non-knowledge. He merely rejected the notion that knowledge is built up piecemeal, by careful collection of observations and by summation of separate observations, from the bottom up. He proposed, instead – without surrendering the possibility of distinguishing meaningful knowledge from meaningless knowledge – that we think of knowledge as something proposed by the mind and then exposed to falsification. One starts with a general theory, deduces particular statements from it and then seeks to discover whether these statements can be falsified by observation. Having a general theory right at the beginning of the growth of knowledge, one knows what one can deduce from it and learns what one ought to observe – that is, where one ought to look. In this position, the 'knower' is in an infinitely more advantageous position than the 'knower' envisaged by Positivism. The 'knower' of the Positivists is supposed to start with observations and he is supposed to make them without the assistance or guidance of presuppositions. Presuppositions, on the contrary, in the view of Positivism, are a distorting and disabling element. Supposedly starting with observations, the 'knower' is in an impossible and completely unreal situation. Imagine what one might do in response to an invitation to 'observe'! Confronted by such an invitation, ought one simply to stare straight ahead or gaze at the nearest object in front of one's eyes? Or should one watch, instead, the space between one's eyes and the nearest object? When asked to 'observe', as the Positivists would have it, people usually and understandably do a double-take and ask, rightly: 'Observe what?'

Moreover, with falsificationism, one can also initially distinguish between theories. If one is comparing two different theories, one will find the one which has easier, more obvious and more frequent possibilities for falsification preferable.

In its original form, there is a clear difficulty in Popper's falsificationism. While the logic of the argument upon which it is based cannot possibly be impugned, it is very difficult to find actual examples in the history of science which show that theories are abandoned when they are falsified. Popper does give historical examples. Examples, however, are not a history of science and the *Logic of Scientific Discovery* is not only not a work of history but completely unhistorical. Its argument is entirely theoretical. In almost all cases where Popper gives examples, it has been found that the history of science can also be told in a different way so that the abandonment of an old theory appears not necessarily due to its actual falsification. The most striking story, of course, is the story about Einstein and the Michelson–Morley experiment. It would make a good Popperian chapter in the history of science if one could show that the experiment falsified the ether theory and that Einstein, aware of this falsification, then proceeded to make a different conjecture. Most histories of science indicate, however, that Einstein had not even heard of the famous experiment and that, whatever the reasons he had for his new theory, the falsification of the old theory was not one of them. The Michelson–Morley experiment, according to many histories of science, was not designed to test the ether theory, let alone to falsify it. It was designed to decide between two competing ether theories and, initially, its results were not even considered a falsification of any ether theory.

In *The Logic of Scientific Discovery* (first published as *Die Logik der Forschung* in 1934), Popper gave some brief examples of what he then thought the history of science was. These snippets of the history of science were composed with the help of simple falsificationism. Popper then said that 'what compels the theorist to search for a better theory . . . is almost always the experimental *falsification* of a theory, so far accepted and corroborated . . . Famous examples are the Michelson–Morley experiment which led to the theory of relativity . . .'[1] Since Popper wrote this, it has been established beyond reasonable doubt[2] that Einstein did not know of the Michelson–Morley experiment when he proposed the Special Theory of Relativity and that therefore one cannot consider the history of science as a progression determined by falsification of accepted theories and the subsequent invention of new theories.

It seems, therefore, that the history of science, however it is composed, does not really bear out Popper's original account of the process of scientific reasoning or scientific progress. It is not that the account as such is false, but that it seems incomplete. Something was missing. The missing part has something to do with the fact that falsifying observations as such are very difficult, if not impossible. Every observation, as Popper himself keeps insisting, is 'theory-laden'. If one makes an observation to test, for instance, a prediction made by the General Theory of Relativity, one has to rely on theories about the photosensitivity of certain plates, about the behaviour of the human retina, about the constitution of the measuring instruments – to mention only the most obvious examples. While in pure logic, one falsification renders a universal proposition false, in practice it is almost impossible to make any such simple falsifying observation, for in making it one always depends on other theories and this fact makes it always possible to put the blame for any falsification on those other theories. If one wishes, one can thus avoid falsification endlessly.

There seems to be a large number of difficulties in the concept of falsification, despite its logical impeccability. A falsifying proposition, to start with, has to occupy a privileged epistemological status. Unless such privilege is conceded, one can endlessly wonder whether the proposition which falsified a theory is true. If there is no privilege, the truth of such a proposition can be questioned in spite of the fact that such truth would have to depend on nothing more than a particular observation. Next, in an important sense, all theories which have ever been held have also been falsified because every observation relevant to the theory shows up anomalies. No water ever boils at exactly 100 degrees centigrade – but nobody would take any such anomaly as a falsification of the theory that water boils at 100 degrees centigrade. Moreover, all falsifications are themselves fallible and many practising scientists, though appreciative of the theory of falsificationism, have expressed doubts as to whether it is practically helpful in a problem situation.[3]

One could also ask whether the requirement that beliefs about the world be falsifiable is naturally compelling to rational men.[4] On the face of it and out of context, one could not really say that it is 'compelling'. But if one puts it into a biological context, one can see that falsification is related to elimination and, in such a context, it appears plausible as a mechanism of selection. The reason why it is not naturally compelling outside a biological context is that it depends on observation and that observation, in turn, is dependent on concepts. Hence, there can be errors and delusions and one can say no more than that falsification is accepted by convention as a standard of veracity or empirical content and that the errors, delusions, illusions, misunderstandings and ambiguities which must creep into concepts and words describing the falsifying observation are not minimised or kept at bay by conventions but are standardised by conventional language rules. Thus, everybody makes the same errors and nobody can identify the errors as errors. Errors which are not thus out of step cease to be errors. Alternatively, one can imagine that conventions set up social solidarity and co-operation among men who thus protect themselves indefinitely from the disastrous consequences of holding false beliefs. For example, a pastoral society could cling to the belief that its animals need to be fed only once a month. Under non-social circumstances, any man who held such a belief would cause the animal to be very lean and he would therefore lack food. However, in a social situation, he could make up for his false belief by banding together with twenty other men, stage a military campaign at regular intervals, and steal food from another tribe. Thus, the consequences of error are postponed and the process of falsification is nullified.

However, in a biological context, falsification appears in a different light. In that context, falsification becomes naturally compelling because it is the analogue of elimination in the struggle for survival. An animal of the prairie with weak legs is unlikely to leave many offspring. There is physical elimination. Concepts and their potential errors do not enter into this situation. When one comes to consciously held theories (i.e. disembodied organisms instead of incarnated theories), one must try to simulate such physical elimination as much as possible. Instead of seeking evasive action by running for shelter in conventions or solidarity, one ought to seek to expose one's theories and beliefs as much as possible to falsification. For sure, concepts and words come into all observations, even into falsifying observations. But one has a choice. One can either assimilate such observations to the struggle for physical survival in biological evolution and correct the concepts that intrude in the light of one's knowledge that the senses which make observations are adaptive and therefore not totally misleading all the time; or one can draw away from biology and assimilate observations to the protective shelter of social institutions and correct them in the light of one's knowledge that all human communication, be it for thought or for action, must be based on rules. There can be no doubt that when one is aware of that choice, the reasonable man must opt for the first alternative.

There are other doubts in regard to falsification. Falsificationism by itself is not rich enough as a philosophy of science to enable one to write a history of science. It represents a sort of timeless ideal of rationality,[5] a 'timeless and universal rational organon'. The history of science, however, has to include all sorts of irrational moments of inventiveness, of psychological and sociological determinants of inspiration so that, at best, the sequence of events which would emerge if one used refutation events as the sole criterion of selection, would show very little similarity to the actual history of science. This last consideration is not an argument against falsificationism; nor can one invoke 'what actually happened' in the history of science because, without a criterion of selection, one does not know what actually happened. This last argument merely casts some doubts upon the fruitfulness of falsificationism for the composition of a history of science.

Popper's Selectionism

Perhaps for this reason and perhaps for other reasons – the history of the development of Popper's thought has not yet been written – Popper himself enlarged his account of scientific progress. From the mid-1960s on, in all his writings, though falsification as such was not dropped, it came to be absorbed in a wider concept. Popper began to speak of 'error elimination'. Logically, 'error elimination' is not really different from falsification. But in practice, it is a looser procedure and describes the actual progression of scientific knowledge in a more realistic way. Finally, in his *Objective Knowledge*[6] Popper showed that progressive error elimination is not only the method by which conscious scientific thought proceeds towards truth, but also the method by which all evolution of organisms, from the amoeba to *Homo sapiens*, progressed. Using 'P' for problem, 'TS' for tentative solutions, 'EE' for error elimination, Popper described the fundamental evolutionary sequence of events as follows:

$$P \rightarrow TS \rightarrow EE \rightarrow P$$

The sequence, he argued, is not a cycle. The second problem is different from the first because it is a problem in a new situation which has arisen because of the tentative solutions which have been tried out and because of the error elimination which controls them. With this formula, one can write the history of the rejection of the ether theory and the emergence of Einstein's theories without having to maintain that Einstein invented his new conjecture because an old conjecture had actually been falsified and because he knew of this falsification.

Not the least merit of the formula is that it accounts for the negative sociology of science mentioned in chapter 1. In regarding the growth of knowledge as the result of progressive error elimination, Popper must imply that there can be no growth of knowledge under those social conditions in which knowledge is artificially protected from competition with other knowledge because it is used as a social bond. When it is used as a social bond, it must be protected dogmatically. Alternatives cannot be entertained and therefore selection cannot take place. Alternatives are entertained only in those societies in which bonding is neutral and does not have to rely on particular pieces of knowledge. Moreover, the availability of alternatives depends also largely upon the creation of alternatives. Alternative pieces of knowledge are human creations. The more creative people are, the more alternatives will be available for competition. Creativity, in turn – though nobody quite knows what it ultimately depends on – is favoured when people can 'bisociate', in Koestler's sense as explained in his *The Act of Creation*. It is favoured when people are capable of taking apart ideas that are conventionally associated with one another and of reassembling the bits in a new way – a sort of *bricolage*, if one prefers Lévi-Strauss's terminology. Bisociation and *bricolage* are more likely to occur under these conditions of loose social bonding – in open societies, to use a good old Popperian term. Societies are never wholly open or wholly closed, but there are degrees of openness. The greater the openness, the better the chance for *bricolage*. Here, then, we have an explanation of the negative sociology of knowledge and can understand how social conditions encourage or discourage the growth of knowledge.

The concept of error elimination likens the growth of knowledge to evolution. Just as in ordinary evolution, organisms are naturally selected, so in the growth of knowledge, certain theories are selected. They are the theories which survive the process of error elimination. As in evolution, there is neither finality nor certainty in such survival: either a change in the environment or a novel observation can eliminate a species or a theory which has so far been selected.

In order to make selectionism viable, one has to show that biological evolution and the growth of articulated knowledge, or of knowledge articulated as general theories, have something in common. The factor they have in common is the fact that both biological evolution and articulated universal theories embody a store of knowledge. This knowledge is the information about the environment which remains after error elimination has taken place. In organisms, this knowledge is stored in the gene pool of a given population; in theories, it is the information encoded in those general theories which survive error elimination. Every organism which has ever appeared on earth is a sort of conjecture; if the information it contains about its environment is compatible with that environment, the organism survives because it will breed faster than organisms which contain information less compatible with the environment. The same is true of conscious theories. Every theory is a conjecture, a proposal. Once made, it is compared to the environment and, if compatible, it survives error elimination. Such information, be it in the gene pools of populations or in the minds of men, is never a portrait of the environment or a mirror-image induced in the organism or the mind *by* the environment. The proposals are not made in response to the environment. They are thrown up freely, by chance, and are unpredictable and undetermined.

It would not seem an exaggeration to say that organisms are embodied theories about the environment, and that theories held by conscious human beings are disembodied organisms. Consider the following example of knowledge stored in a surviving organism:

> Infusoria . . . by means of their phobic and topic responses . . . seek an environment containing *inter alia* a particular concentration of H-ions. The commonest acid found in nature is carbonic acid, the highest concentration of which is found in waters in which paramecia flourish, especially in the vicinity of rotting vegetable matter, because the bacteria that live on this matter give off carbon dioxide. This relationship is so dependable, and the occurrence of other acids, let alone toxic ones, is so rare, that the paramecium manages admirably with one single item of information, which put into words would say that a certain acid concentration signifies the presence of a mass of bacteria on which to feed.[7]

With this representation, Konrad Lorenz clearly likens organisms to theories and we can thus see the similarity between selection and falsification. In its original narrow sense, falsifiability was a measure of empirical content. A falsifiable theory obviously had a greater measure of reference to something real in the world than a theory which was not falsifiable and from which one could not deduce statements which, if false, would make the theory untrue. It is essential to bear in mind that, in the narrow sense, falsificationism was designed as a measure of empirical content and not as an instruction for deciding when theories had to be rejected. The real reason for discarding theories is not intimately linked to falsification at all. One rejects some theories and prefers others because one prefers theories which are more universal to theories which are less universal. The less universal a theory, the less its explanatory power. Hence, comparative degrees of universality rather than falsity determine the succession of theories. Being initially concerned with the demarcation problem and the measure of empirical content, the falsification criterion cannot automatically be extended to become the basis for a history of science in which theories are discarded because they are false. The temptation to apply it to the history of science is great and even Popper himself has at times given way to it. But in its narrow form, the falsification criterion should be used to measure degrees of empirical content, and not to write the history of how and why theories succeed one another. However, the great value of the falsification criterion lies in the fact that it can be blown up into selectionism and *then* used to compose a history of science.

Strictly speaking, narrow falsificationism obscured our understanding of the history of science and of the growth of knowledge. For example – and this example is frequently used by Popper himself – Einstein did not falsify Newtonian Mechanics. Nevertheless, the General Theory of Relativity superseded Newtonian Mechanics because it had greater universality. For that matter, the General Theory of Relativity does not discard Newtonian Mechanics. The latter remains as an alternative for certain kinds of calculations. For this reason, when we come to consider the growth of knowledge, we should amend falsificationism and transform it into selectionism. In doing so, we are drawing attention to the fact that the dismissal of a falsified theory is never mandatory. Falsifiability is an important consideration because it enables us to distinguish between theories according to their empirical content. This is doubly important after the disappearance of verification as a criterion of empirical content or reference to reality. But falsifiability must be qualified and expanded.

In saying that a theory need not be discarded even though it has been falsified, we are not asserting that it is immune from experience. On the contrary. Falsification has shown that it is anything but immune and that it has empirical content. But there may be other considerations for shoring it up with, for instance, an *ad hoc* hypothesis or whatever. Since the theory is not immune, one has to make a special decision not to discard it, even though one is now permitted to discard it. A theory which is not, in principle, falsifiable, is different from one which is falsifiable, falsified and nevertheless kept. Only a theory which is not, in principle, falsifiable is truly immune. A refusal to discard in the face of falsification is therefore not tantamount to a declaration of immunity.

The entire question as to whether theories which are falsifiable and, when falsified, not discarded, are immune or not, arises *only* when one takes falsification to be absolute. If one takes falsification to be a command to discard, then a falsified, non-discarded theory must appear immune. But if one takes falsification merely as a measure of content and as a permission to discard, a falsified, non-discarded theory is not immune. Such a theory is not kept because it is immune, but because one has reasons for not availing oneself of the falsification. The question, really, is whether one takes falsification to be a command or a permission to discard. It seems that if one is taking it as a command, one is acting like an inductivist or a Positivist who does not go by his own decision, but claims to be guided by the 'instruction' he has received from the 'outside'. If one discards a theory in response to falsification alone, one is really acting like an old-fashioned Positivist who is discarding a theory because nature has induced him to do so, or because he has slavishly induced from nature that it must be discarded. In short, while falsifiability is a *sine qua non* of empirical content and reference, it is not the factor which explains the dynamics of theories and the manner in which they succeed one another.

It is uncertain whether Popper himself and most Popperians would be prepared to accept this re-evaluation of the role of falsification. It must retain its important place. But when one is concerned with the growth of knowledge and with the dynamics of theories, it is more fruitful to place selectionism (i.e. an expanded falsificationism) into the centre of the stage. The preoccupation with the growth of knowledge is, as we have seen, not idiosyncratic. On the contrary. When one is concerned with knowledge and cannot explain it the way the old and naive Positivists were wont to, the growth of knowledge becomes a central part of knowledge itself. Popper himself has declared that the growth of knowledge is his main concern[8] but it may seem, to judge from many of his more recent works, that he thinks that the best service is rendered to our understanding of that growth by his theory about Worlds 1, 2 and 3 and the relationship in which he says they stand to each other. Popper distinguishes three worlds. First there is the objective world of material things – World 1; then there is a subjective world of minds – World 2; and a world of objective structures which are the products, though not necessarily the intentional products, of minds or living creatures – World 3. World 3 is a creation of emergence through the interaction of World 1 with World 2. But once World 3 is created, it exists independently. Popper takes such independence very literally. The knowledge which is in World 3 is knowledge written on paper or stored in computers, not events in minds. That knowledge includes as its forerunners, so to speak, the nests built by birds or the webs built by spiders. Although Popper never said so, World 3 is very similar to what Hegel used to call 'objective spirit'. World 3 is the world of ideas, science, language, ethics and institutions – all creations of the mind. Once created, these creations create their own problems which we have to discover and for which we have to discover solutions.

It comes, then, to the question of the interpretation of Popper's thought. Should that interpretation veer towards the Worlds 1, 2 and 3 theory? Or towards selectionism and evolution? I do not think that these two interpretations are incompatible, but it does seem to be a question of emphasis. Both directions follow upon falsificationism – but the second, I think, more cogently than the first. In my view, the concern with evolution is more fruitful when one comes to an understanding of the growth of knowledge than the concern with Worlds 1, 2 and 3. At any rate, I would remind the reader that Popper himself declares that there is more to good theories than their authors have put into them; one may therefore feel free in one's attempts to steer the momentum of Popperian thinking towards evolution rather than towards the problems involved in the distinctions between Worlds 1, 2 and 3. Popperian thought – and this is one of its major merits – is concerned with openness and indeterminism. It must of necessity, therefore, remain open towards the possibility of an evolutionary interpretation regardless of whether Popper himself treats this particular interpretation as his main concern or not. Equally important is another tenet of Popperian thought. One need not, he says, logically define every concept or idea until one is certain of it and knows that it is incapable of refutation. The concept of selectionism, in the way we have expanded it from falsificationism, should be regarded in the light of this openness. Popper himself and many of his followers have not always heeded this openness and have frequently aimed at a certainty and finality about indeterminism and uncertainty which is both unobtainable and unnecessary. As I remarked in an earlier chapter, we must remain as uncertain about our knowledge of knowledge as we are about knowledge itself.

Objectivity without Evolution

Selectionism is enlarged falsificationism. In linking the philosophy of science to evolution and in thus making epistemology evolutionary, Popper has also established his philosophical realism on a more secure basis. Ordinarily, realism is very difficult to establish. We can never compare a proposition about the world with the world. We always have to compare it with another proposition, so that we never really come face to face with 'reality'.

The early philosophy of Popper – his falsificationism – sought support for philosophical realism in the correspondence theory of truth, especially in the form in which it was put by Tarski. Tarski's truth definition shows how the internal structure of complex sentences can contribute to their meaning and he hoped to show how semantic notions, including a semantic notion of truth, can be part of a physicalist (read: philosophical realist) scheme. Language expressions, he hoped, would support physicalism. The young Popper was worried by the fact that the correspondence theory of truth was hard to prove – for instance, what could actually correspond to a statement of fact? Tarski was a revelation for him. Tarski, he thought, had finally shown that true statements are really true about reality and that propositions (linguistic expressions) can correspond to facts (non-linguistic phenomena). This revelation made a deep and lasting impression on Popper and he has never wavered from Tarski. In *Objective Knowledge* there is a moving account of the day on which Tarski[9] explained his theory of truth, while he and Popper sat on a bench in Vienna's Volksgarten.

Tarski's theory, however, is of very doubtful value. It is very hard to see how a mere semantic argument can help to establish philosophical realism. The semantic difficulty apart, a simple correspondence theory of truth, whether in the Tarski form or any other, would have, for example, great difficulty with the phenomenon of light. If the proposition 'light is a wave' is true if and only if light is a wave, how can that proposition be 'true' when we know that light is not only a wave but also a particle? In so far as Tarski's analysis is a purely formal or semantic one, it is not affected by the peculiar 'logic' of Quantum Mechanics and its uncertainties. But these uncertainties and that peculiar logic show that any concept of truth which is based on a straight either/or distinction between truth and falsehood is irrelevant and not applicable. Quine said that this kind of attribution of truth to statements does not presuppose any notions other than those already used inside the statement itself. We understand no more when we claim that a statement is true, than we do when we understand that statement itself.[10] Popper himself was and always had been aware of these difficulties but he has never ceased to stress the importance of Tarski's definition of truth for his own philosophical or 'metaphysical' realism. If science is the search for truth, then one has to believe that the truth sought is truth about the *real* world. Tarski seemed to provide the necessary support. However, as we shall see, there are biological considerations in favour of at least hypothetical realism which obviate reliance on Tarksi's correspondence definition of truth.[11]

Support was indeed necessary. We are entitled to know whether what we know really corresponds to a world or whether what we know is a sort of figment of our mind, a figment which is so fictitious that it also protects us against the possibility of ever finding out that it is a figment by fictitiously providing those answers to any tests and attempted falsifications which confirm us in the belief that there is a real world apart from our knowledge. This is a very old philosophical problem and, in spite of innumerable attempts, it has not been possible to provide a viably conclusive solution.

Broadly speaking, and leaving strict philosophical logic aside, one could assume that knowledge is 'objective' to the degree to which one can demonstrate that the observer's standpoint has no part in it and is excluded from it. This sounds seductive, but cannot stand up to criticism. In order to ascertain whether the observer has been excluded, one has to know what the stuff he has to be excluded from is like. In other words, the implementation of this requirement of objectivity presupposes knowledge of an objective world. And so we come across the age-old hermeneutic circle; in order to know 'objectively' and in order to be sure that what one knows is knowledge of an objective world, one has to know beforehand what one wants to know. This circularity has bedevilled all epistemologies from Plato to the present time. Any epistemology which requires a clear distinction between knower and known so that it can make sure the one does not intrude into the other, has to assume that both the knower and the known are known so that they can be distinguished. Or, at least, either the knower or the known have to be known in advance – in which case, one can consider that the other is what is not included in the one, or the other way round. Experience has shown that even this reduced demand is impossible to meet. Compare, for example, the two great competing ontologies of the seventeenth century, the ontology of Newton and the ontology of Huygens. It will be completely apparent from such a comparison that each ontology is intimately linked to a specific epistemology and that there is no way in which one can separate either ontology from its epistemology. Newton postulated a world in which there were bodies inside an empty isotropic space and a time which is the same for all points in that space. In this world, causal connections between bodies depend on their position in space at a certain time. The simplest conception of causal efficacy must be the assumption of instantaneous causal action at a distance. This ontology also controls the conception of light as transport of corpuscles or particles, for one cannot conceive of processes other than the transport of particles. By contrast, in Huygen's ontology, processes are the results of pushes and pulls. Hence, there has to be a medium which transmits these impulses – a continuum which makes this kind of causal efficacy possible. If there is a continuum, light could be waves transmitted in that continuum. Alternatively, if one assumes that light is a wave, one is committed to an ontology in which there is a medium in which waves can travel.[12] Both ontologies are clearly mind-dependent (i.e. they owe a lot to the theories about light and causality). In short, we cannot achieve objectivity by separating the world from the mind. In order to do so, we would have to separate our knowledge of the world (mind) from the world. This cannot be done because we cannot have knowledge of the world without having knowledge of the world.

In the past, philosophers have reacted in different ways to this circularity. Some, from Plato onwards, have been dogmatic about ontology. They have simply assumed that they know what the world was like and then proceeded to construct an epistemology that would do justice to that ontology. They have thought that there are two questions when in reality there is only one. They have thought that there is, first, the question: What is the world like? Second, there comes the question: How can we know it? There is, however, only one question – the first. Once it is answered, the second question is automatically answered. In other words, the dogmatism about ontology makes the search for a suitable epistemology redundant.

The next strategy is reductionism. From Aristotle onwards, philosophers have tried to assume that our sensations and consciousness can be reduced to events in the real world. They must assume, one can only suppose, that there is some direct causal operation which works upon the mind and causes the mind to have certain awarenesses which can be formulated as sentences – or, possibly, the other way round. Although this strategy for vindicating that our knowledge is knowledge of a really objective world seems based on all manner of superstitions about causality, it has enjoyed a very wide support, right down to the present day. Looked at in the cold light of reason, there can be no conceivable justification for thinking that such reductions are possible, let alone exhaustive. In all its varieties of sensationalism, phenomenalism, presentationism, representationalism, it always comes to the same thing. A sense experience is evidence about the mind or person who has it; it can by no stretch of the reasonable imagination be considered evidence about an objective world, alleged to have 'caused' it.

Next, we come to the sceptics, whose most convincing modern representative is Quine. There is no real ground for believing that there is an objective world to which our knowledge refers; and, similarly, one cannot really make an ultimate distinction between true knowledge and false knowledge, between superstition and science. But, he adds, you 'should not venture farther from sensory evidence than you need to'[13] and one ought to have an ontic preference, but no more than a preference, for observations. How far, one ought to ask, 'need' one venture from sensory evidence? Quite a lot, Quine seems to be saying, and, if one does not 'need' to, at least, one may:

> Physical objects are conceptually imported into the situation as convenient intermediaries – not by definition in terms of experience, but simply as irreducible points comparable epistemologically to the gods of Homer. I believe in physical objects, and not in Homer's gods. But in point of epistemological footing the objects and the gods differ only in degree.[14]

After the sceptics, we come to the sociologisers. Here, we meet a very broad spectrum of opinions which are, however, all agreed on one point. Since we seemingly have no access to standards which enable us to distinguish absolutely the knower from the known and which would thus enable us to exclude the mind from the world and to recognise what is objectively there, we must apply, in our search for an objective world, the standards of a social group and defer to the epistemic authority of a speech community, however defined. Accepting that our ways of speaking about the world cannot receive any justification from some sort of non-linguistic knowledge about the way words and things are related to each other, these people ground the harmony of thought and reality on the rules of our grammar. In the face of the certainty that we can have no knowledge of the presence of something by virtue of which a sentence can be true or meaningful, this strategy may seem radical – but it has a lot to commend it. In the hands of Wittgenstein, it always seemed eminently reasonable because Wittgenstein steadfastly refused to examine its social and political implications. In the hands or minds of his innumerable followers, this strategy appears neither innocent nor reasonable. For once one's attention is drawn to the fact that our knowledge of the objective world depends on our membership of a community and on obedience to the rules prevailing there, one has necessarily to examine the ethics of the community, the justice of its organisation, the political goals it pursues, and similar questions. And from there it is only a short step to the observation made so cogently in this context by Michel Foucault – that all questions of knowledge are really questions of power,[15] for the composition and governance (even the intellectual governance) and epistemic authority of any community must, in the last analysis, boil down to an investigation of the power that controls it. At one end of the spectrum, our sociologisers follow Wittgenstein and show wise resignation. In the middle of the spectrum, they embark upon the search for the sociological determinants of our knowledge and the social reasons for the construction of reality; in doing so, they display a total epistemic narcissism. Knowledge, they are saying, is nothing but a reflection of my society in my mind. At the far end of the spectrum, they are into politics and power. Richard Rorty gently reminds us of the politics involved in considering koala bears for membership of these communities; and Michel Foucault, less gently, glories in being able to show that questions of knowledge turn out to be questions of power. Rorty wonders whether we should exercise our power and include koala bears but exclude pigs from these intellectual edict-making communities. Foucault hints openly at the possibility that the proletariat may seize power in order to force us to accept its edicts as the basis for knowledge.

If it is so difficult to establish that there is an objective world from which one could exclude the mind of the observer, some have argued, one might try to proceed in the opposite direction and establish what the mind of the observer is like. Then, so the argument goes, one can know what to subtract from knowledge. After all, if one wants to separate two things – mind and world – it is enough to separate out either one and take what is left to be the other. Having failed in our attempt to separate an ontology, let us look at the possibility of separating the mind.

The chances of success are equally unpromising. They are made specially unpromising by a phenomenon which is playing a major part in modern knowledge. Both in Quantum Mechanics and in Thermodynamics, there is a well-known phenomenon which makes it look as if the processes of nature were actually controlled by the human mind and by our knowledge of these processes. This is not just a matter of a well-known distortion effect which simply shows that when an observer is intruding into a room of observed subjects, the subjects are affected by the intrusion. The phenomenon I am referring to is infinitely more complex and does not depend just on a simple intrusion. It *looks* as if an intrusion may have taken place when in reality there may have been none. There is no telling at the moment what the correct answer might be; but whatever it will be, the phenomena in question show how difficult it is to be sure what is an intrusion of the mind into a natural process. All we can see is that there are physical processes which *look* as if a mind had intruded and which appear indistinguishable from processes into which no mind has intruded.

I am referring, of course, to the Uncertainty Principle in Quantum Mechanics and to the Second Law of Thermodynamics. As far as Quantum Mechanics is concerned, there is an uncertainty about the location of, say, electrons. It looks as if that uncertainty results from the fact that in order to locate the electron, it has to be hit by a sub-atomic particle and, in being so hit, it is deflected from the path it was occupying. Now, electrons may just be the sort of 'entities' which behave in this seemingly peculiar fashion. On the other hand, their behaviour may be due to the intrusion of an observer. Whichever way this matter may one day be resolved, the appearance of an observer's intrusion will always be there – which shows how difficult it is to separate the mind out of nature. The laws of Quantum Mechanics may be *objective*; but they look, at the same time, as if they are not.

Or take the Second Law of Thermodynamics. Since the increase in entropy stipulated by the Second Law is an increase in disorder and randomness, it looks as if the increase in entropy is not objective but merely the result of our ignorance, of our inability to keep track of ever-more *seemingly* random movements of molecules. The faster and more randomly they move, the greater our ignorance of the system. Hence, it looks as if there is no increase in entropy at all; but merely an increase in our ignorance. On the other hand, the increase in entropy could be perfectly objective and real. Nevertheless, it is indistinguishable from an increase in our ignorance in regard to the system. Again, there is no telling how this matter may be resolved one day. If it is resolved in favour of objectivity, it will nevertheless continue to look as if it were a matter of our ignorance. This example shows again how tricky it is to disentangle mind from the world, the knower from the known. The known may be out there, objectively and in itself; but it is so cussed that it looks as if a knower had intruded into it even when he has not!

Leaving nature's cussedness aside, one can take a sweeping glance at attempts to separate out the mind of the knower, rather than an ontology. However, a glance at the major traditional philosophers who have attempted such a description of the human mind will not be encouraging. Plato sought to determine the features of the mind from his observation that we have only uncertain knowledge of reality and its objects. The mind, therefore, must be something which adds the required certainty. Descartes determined the features of the mind from his observation that he had certain knowledge of one single fact – that is, of the fact that in thinking he *was* thinking. Kant determined the features of the mind from his observation that we have certain knowledge of Newton's Mechanics. He determined what the mind was by showing what it must be like to have that kind of knowledge. Hegel derived the features of the mind from his observation that the knowledge the mind has of itself not only changes, but has grown.

In the twentieth century, these grand strategies for the discovery of a mind which knows reality have been replaced by more refined analysis of how words refer to things and what has to be satisfied for this reference to be unequivocal. This, in turn, has led to discussions of whether we know things or processes, as well as to discussions of whether we know things and baptise them or whether we choose names in accordance with our knowledge of things. In attending the numberless conferences devoted to this question and in perusing countless books and papers about it, I have never yet found a sensible discussion as to how the notion of reference would fare when seen in the context of, say, Quantum Mechanics. It would be a sobering experience for the participants and antagonists in this debate to reflect upon the physicists who do not get a picture of the atom or of Quantum processes from their new matrix mechanics, i.e. who do not have anything these words like 'atom' and 'Quantum process' *refer* to. On the contrary, matrix mechanics was invented precisely to avoid making a statement which could refer to anything physical. Waves, in Quantum Mechanics, are not material events and the word 'wave' therefore does not *refer* to something that is happening, but to a 'wave of probability'. Our knowledge of Quantum Mechanics shows that one can have quite a lot of knowledge, even though one's knowledge does not have a precise focus of reference. That knowledge can be couched in such a way that it does not refer at all to specifically locatable events or objects. If this is so, does it matter whether 'referring' is a kind of christening or a summing up of observations?[16]

Next, we keep discussing whether our thoughts represent judgments or whether they are our judgments. Are language-users guided by mental fact or are they simply and mindlessly following a rule for the use of language? Are they doing, in speaking, two things or, as Wittgenstein maintains, one thing? Alternatively, are we in speaking expressing a private language or does 'using a language' simply mean 'following a rule?' And then, there always comes the question as to whether our concepts, no matter how they are related to judgments, are mental or not. If mental, one has to provide a description of what is non-mental and this leads back to the older controversies about the nature of mind and this, in turn, leads back to a consideration of whether what is special to mentality is the power to abstract and go beyond the observation of physical particulars.[17] Though these contemporary discussions have the air of being precise and the appearance of being promising, they have as yet not led to a single view which goes in any important way beyond the results or non-results of the earlier grand strategies. The volume of these discussions is inversely proportional to the lack of results. 'If only we could get it right!' the participants in the discussion seem to be saying. 'If we could get the relationship between objects and words, between concepts and judgments right, we would know how objective our knowledge is.' Unfortunately, one cannot even tell what 'getting it right', in this context, would mean. Would it mean consensus? If so, then whose consensus? They all talk as if, with a little more effort, the problem could be solved. But where precisely is the problem? And supposing there is a problem, would one not be obliged to conclude from the impossibility of agreement that it is spurious? If there were a problem, one or the other view would eventually gain support and compel agreement. The impossibility of reaching agreement seems to indicate that there is no standard by which the cogency of any of these views could be assessed, for if there were agreement on what the problem was, one could judge which of the many answers about reference, individuals, translation or concept could be considered the best answer. These arguments either make sense or they don't – 'sense' not meaning 'meaning' but 'logically cogent'. If they did, they would compel assent; if they didn't, there would be no point in putting them forward. The fact that they have not compelled assent should be taken as a demonstration that they *do not* make much sense. The argument about private language is very similar to the medieval debate about the number of angels who could dance on the point of a needle. The debate depended entirely on the definition of an angel as a non-extended substance. The debate about private language depends entirely on one's definition of language. The other debate about reference is not even in the same class. Its resolution depends on absolutely nothing. There is no logical point which has been overlooked and which might decide it one way or the other; there is no evidence at which one might point which, if produced, would settle the matter. It is sensible and understandable to have conflicting opinions on such interesting topics as politics and art, ethics and religion. But it is very difficult to see the reason why people should carry on having different opinions on so unedifying a subject as reference when there clearly is no conceivable way in which the debate could be advanced or improved and when one cannot even imagine what sort of argument would count as an advance or what could be gained by a settlement.

If, on the other hand, one takes one's stand upon the alleged empirical basis of scientific theory, one seems to be committed to an endless string of problems in cognitive psychology. The fact is, however, that we *have* scientific knowledge. What we are lacking is an explanation of this fact. Most philosophers go about their business seeking to justify that knowledge. Seeing that it exists, there seems to be little point in seeking to justify it. The real question we ought to answer is how it has come into being. Knowledge, like life itself, is its own justification. What we want to know is how it has grown. If one looks at the relationship between mind and reality in the first instance by looking at the mind which is supposed to be doing the knowing of reality, one obviously cannot produce any arguments in support of the supposition that what we know is knowledge of something out there, called reality.

When the debate has reached this conclusion, it is now a very prevalent strategy to invite the participants to form a closed circle – a speech community or a language game or accept some other framework or paradigm – and allow that circle to exercise epistemic authority. Obviously, arguments of this kind can lead nowhere, but the cultivation of speech habits within the fixed precincts of a framework is viable. For inside the circle, one *can* do something one cannot do outside the circle. One can decide who conforms to the habits of the circle and who does not. This invitation to form circles and to close them by making the prisoners submit to the epistemic authority of the circle was an approach favoured not only by Wittgenstein himself, but also by Quine, Sellars and Kuhn; it solves nothing, however. But it does inject law and order into the debate. In any case, with the voluntary submission to the framework, one can now be confident that such knowledge as is held by the prisoners is knowledge justified by the framework. There is no longer any need for any of the *prisoners* to go hungry for knowledge, though there seems to be no end to the starvation of free citizens.

For people who think that knowledge is only knowledge if and when it is justified, it becomes very attractive to accept an invitation to join one or the other of such closed circles. In refusing the status of knowledge to guesses, conjectures and hypotheses, these people are bound, sooner or later, to be left high and dry – the only thing which amazes is that it took so long for them to realise that the justified and legitimate emperor had no clothes on; and that if one cannot get oneself to be a democrat and live with conjectures, one would indeed have to submit to the epistemic authority of one or the other closed circle and use that authority to legitimise and justify such knowledge one would be allowed to have. After all, it is better to submit to a prevailing norm than to go hungry.

Nevertheless, this strategy and the invitation which results from it has to be rejected. The participants in the debate find the invitation attractive because they cling to the conviction that nothing can qualify as knowledge which is not justified. Having failed to find justification by defining reality, mind, reference, meaning, speech acts, etc., they now are tempted to seek more modest justification by hiding behind the authority of a closed circle. This temptation ought, however, to be resisted because the disease can be cured in a different way. But even if it could not, I myself would rather die than say 'yes'.

In view of all these difficulties and doubtful strategies for the resolution of these difficulties, it cannot be an exaggeration to say that philosophy has shown itself quite unequal to the task. Philosophically, the problem of defining either mind or an objective world has always been, and remains, untractable.

Objectivity with Evolution

The development of modern biology and of the Darwinian theory of evolution by natural selection shows a way out of this impasse. Where philosophy has been powerless, biology can help. It provides the missing link in the arguments about objectivity. The great merit of Popper's philosophy of knowledge is that it avails itself of this opportunity offered by biology.

Popper's philosophy of knowledge does not solve the problem of objectivity, but it shows that it need not be solved and that it can be by-passed. It is able to do so because of its use of Darwinian evolution. If we accept that we are here in the world, we must accept that the world is the sort of world which has brought about our existence. Our presence, therefore, is not only a guarantee of an objective reality as the result of which we are; it is also evidence of the fact that that objective reality must be of a certain kind, for if it were different, we would not be here. There may well be other worlds, and they may well all be totally different from our wildest dreams. But there must be at least one world which has made our evolution possible. In a different world, the evolution of *Homo sapiens* would not have been possible. Being here implies not only those billions of years which have preceded the emergence of life on earth, but also the particular interaction between life and environment which is envisaged in the theory of natural selection. If there were no objective environment, there would have been nothing to do the selecting as a result of which we are here the way we are. In basing his philosophy of knowledge on evolution, Popper can simply afford to disregard the quest for objectivity and avoid all the pointless efforts which have been made by philosophers to show that when we know, our knowledge corresponds to something objectively present. With the theory of evolution, we simply take the presence of an objective world for granted. Its presence cannot be proved 'objectively'; it must, however, be presumed, for the emergence of life is the result of the selective pressures of that objective reality. For this reason, we speak of 'hypothetical realism'.[18] Feyerabend states categorically – and, incidentally, uses this statement to justify his cognitive anarchism – that 'the world which we want to explore is a largely unknown entity.'[19] In the light of evolution, this statement appears to be simply false. The world we want to explore is not 'largely unknown' at all. It is the sort of world which has produced the sort of beings who want to explore it.

At first glance, it might look as if with this argument we are back with the old circularity which surrounds the problem of ontology. In order to devise a correct method for knowing and in order to form an intelligent opinion as to whether anything discovered by this method is 'objective', we would have to know in advance what we are setting out to discover. In short, we have to have an ontology. But we cannot get an ontology unless we have knowledge of the world or, at least, of the sort of thing the world is. We have encountered this circular problem already in chapter 1, when we were looking for a substantive conception of rationality. If we could have an ontology, we realised then, we could call the method best designed to discover the world our ontology alleges to exist, a rational method. We realised then that this kind of circularity prevents us from having a substantive conception of rationality (i.e. a conception of the *right* method which will lead us to a desired end). However, in the present context, we might have a second string to our bow. Let us try again by formulating the problem in a different way. Instead of concerning ourselves with rationality, let us concern ourselves with the relation between knower and known.

It has always been supposed that the real philosophical problem is to find out what kind of mind we ought to have (i.e. what kind of method we ought to use) in order to find out something about the world. If one starts by asking about mind and method required, one seems to presuppose that one knows what sort of thing the world is – that is, that one has an ontology up one's sleeve. Here, we are back with the circularity involved in all attempts to discover an ontology. The classic case is Kant. He took it that Newton was right and that the world is the sort of world Newton said it was – a box of space with lots of masses moving in that box. Kant then realised that the problem left for the philosopher was to explain what kind of mind a man would have to have in order to get to know this Newtonian world.[20]

In the past, philosophers have shown great self-assurance in making assertions about the stuff the world was made of. They may have been backward in knowledge and science, but they have always been confident about ontology. Some said the world was made of atoms; others maintained that it had been hand-crafted by God and that man, in particular, had originally been made of clay; others maintained that it consisted of sentient monads; some asserted that it consisted of nothing but processes. In the present century, philosophers have become more self-conscious about their ontologies. Let us look at some more recent attempts and list them in ascending order of plausibility, where 'plausibility' means 'least strain' on our credulity. Obviously, that system of thought is best which needs least ontology.

At the very bottom of such a list, we must place the recent attempt by P.Smith to establish 'realism'.[21] A statement refers to black holes, Smith says, if there are black holes; to atoms, if there are atoms. In this scheme, there is obviously a very heavy burden placed on ontology.[22] This kind of ontology requires a lot of knowledge in advance and its plausibility must, therefore, be zero. Next, we place the formal attempts at an ontology by Gustav Bergmann. Here, it is asserted that what exists in the full sense are universals or characters, be they relational or non-relational. Then we need individuators and some entities like 'exemplification ties' which are said to subsist. If we want to make an attempt at the ontology of 'two yellow spots', we would need at least the universal 'yellowness'; a conception of singularity (i.e. in this case 'two' singulars, for there are two spots in nature); and a tie of exemplification, for each existing spot exemplifies the universal 'yellowness'. This is a very rough summary and does not do justice to Bergmann's logical acumen. The attempt is to be rated above that of Smith, but is not all that plausible because it requires a fairly clear knowledge of the number of yellow spots in nature and amounts to little more than a logical categorisation of what we know.

A little higher on the list we place a recent attempt by Roy Bhaskar in his *A Realist Theory of Science*.[23] Bhaskar tries to provide an ontology of transcendental realism. His efforts look promising because he is aware of what he calls the 'epistemic fallacy'[24] which reduces 'being' to knowledge. But in order to avoid this fallacy, he has to postulate that there be 'closures', i.e. only what is inside an experimental situation is causal.[25] Then he goes on to postulate 'atomic' facts so that he can separate causal laws from patterns of events because, ontologically, patterns should not be reduced to laws.[26] He also has to separate the fact from its causal efficacy[27] and then he lapses into Aristotelian terminology: 'once a tendency is set in motion it is fulfilled unless it is prevented'[28] and 'only things and materials and people have powers.'[29] He also distinguishes between the actuality of causal laws and the facts themselves.[30] The attempt is courageous and valiant. But with so many postulates and assumptions, one feels betwixt and between. Assumptions and postulates are not 'knowledge' and one concedes that thus the epistemic fallacy is indeed avoided. But the making of assumptions must be guided by hidden knowledge and must correspond to something which Bhaskar knows and we do not know.

Next in ascending order comes the attempt of Keith Lehrer.[31] 'Scientific theories and descriptions that are simple, precise, comprehensive, coherent and predictively fecund have a better chance of being true than those that lack these virtues.'[32] If this statement were taken out of context, one would have to assign a low place to Lehrer on our list because the statement seems to postulate that the world is the sort of thing of which statements with the above qualities are correct. But in context, the statement is very disarming, for Lehrer continues that his confidence in the virtue of these qualities is not dependent on an ontology but derives from a 'subjective' commitment and that one could not demonstrate that an assertion that theological description is better, is false. 'Here we arrive,' he says, 'at the bottom rock of subjectivity on which all else rests.' He then goes on to consider the two fashionable and popular objections to subjectivism – a recourse to 'empirical evidence' and a recourse to the epistemic authority of a speech community – and rejects both. He is thus left with his total bottom rock of subjectivity. Although Lehrer has an ontology, he admits that it is a subjective act of faith; since he rejects the two popular strategies for grounding such an act of faith on Positivism or speech communities, we must rate his ontology above Bhaskar's ontology because it has less content on account of its avowed subjectivity. There is content, but since it is undogmatic and subjective, it is totally disarming.

Next in order of ascent let us place, for argument's sake, the ontology of Popper. There is no real ontology in Popper at all. It is extremely modest and Popper has at times referred to it as nothing more than a 'manner of speaking'.[33] However, we can reconstruct a sort of minimum ontology for Popper. If it is said that theories must be framed in such a way as to be falsifiable, one must assume that the world is the sort of world which would falsify untrue statements. This means that one supposes that the world is not the sort of world in which, for example, the voice of God could falsify anything. This kind of ontology makes a minimal strain on our credulity and must therefore rate high on our list.

From Popper's ontology, it is a very short step to the 'Anthropic Principle' which tops our list because it imposes no strain at all on our credulity. The 'Anthropic Principle' states[34] no more than that the world must be the sort of thing which has produced us by evolution so that we can sit here and talk or think about it and perceive it. Instead of starting by asking what sort of mind is required to know the world – a question which invariably leads on to a search for an ontology because one cannot know what mind is required unless one knows what kind of world it is supposed to know – the 'Anthropic Principle' tells us that we take it the other way round. We do not ask a question about the mind or about method; we ask what kind of world the world must be to have been able to produce the sort of mind we have. In thus completely reversing the order of questions, the 'Anthropic Principle' does away with the need for an ontology. It simply realises that we would not have a mind to know, let alone a method for acquiring knowledge, unless we had evolved. The only question, therefore, is the question about the nature of the world – the question which scientists of all shades and complexions have always asked. By taking evolution seriously, the 'Anthropic Principle' shows us that what we took to be the problem of ontology is really the problem of what the world is like.

There is only one question to be asked, not two questions: one about the nature of the world, and the other about the nature of ontology. Knowledge and ontology, with evolution, become one and the same thing. There is no ontology here at all and the 'Anthropic Principle' not only tops our list, but eliminates the reason for all attempts at ontology. The 'Anthropic Principle' is totally plausible because it does not strain our credulity since it does away with all ontology. The evolving world, it states, has evolved in such a way as to produce, among other things, the mind we have. The realism involved in the 'Anthropic Principle' is 'hypothetical' because, since we have a mind, it is a reasonable hypothesis that there must be a real world which, by a process of evolutionary selection, has produced our mind.

Ironically, hypothetical realism provides an answer to one of Wittgenstein's many aphorisms. 'The most difficult thing in philosophy,' he wrote in his *Remarks on the Foundations of Mathematics*, VI, 23, 'is to maintain realism without empiricism.' Wittgenstein started on the assumption that we know that there is a real world *because* we experience it empirically. Realising, however, that there is no way in which we can accumulate perceptions and declare that their sum total is *evidence* for the existence of a real world which somehow *corresponds* to our perceptions, he concluded that it must be very difficult to be a 'realist'. Hypothetical realism has solved the problem. It says that we are realists because we are here. If there had not been a real world to select us for survival by providing the selective pressures, we would not be here to wonder about it. Hypothetical realism is realism without empiricism, realism without sense experience as a foundation of knowledge.[35]

The whole matter hinges on the role of perception. If one means by perception the sort of gathering of observations which are gradually incorporated into one's mind and retained by learning and summed up as knowledge, one remains involved in all the countless difficulties and quandaries discussed in the preceding section. Empiricism, we have seen there, cannot be a foundation of knowledge of an objective world. If, however, one takes it the other way round, the problem disappears. If what we call knowledge is the result of selective pressures, we can be sure that what we know is the result of the world which has done the selecting. Darwinism and Popperian philosophy of knowledge have a common denominator. In both theories, we find that proposals are made to the environment and that the false or non-adaptive proposals are eliminated. The common denominator is: approximation to the truth by error elimination. Darwin discovered that this mechanism is at work in the evolution of living organisms; and Popper, that it is at work in the evolution of knowledge. If Darwin had known of Popperian terminology, he might have formulated his theory of evolution by saying that it consists of conjectures and refutations. With this theory, neither Darwin nor Popper need to occupy themselves with fruitless attempts to show how we can learn by piecemeal observations; how we can inductively sum up these piecemeal observations to tell us something which limited experiences cannot tell us; and how, by painful memory work, we can learn to incorporate these summations into our store of knowledge or into the structure of our living cells. Least of all, they do not have to worry whether and how what is thus laboriously built up can have veracity and represent an objective world. In both theories, experience plays a negative, eliminating role: it falsifies wrong conjectures.

When one is comparing neo-Darwinian theories of evolution with Popper's philosophy of knowledge and is seeking the common denominator, there is room for argument. One could argue, for example, that the common denominator consists simply in the possibility of thinking of theories as disembodied organisms, and of organisms as embodied theories. In this case, *falsification* appears as the common denominator. Popper himself goes further than this. He explains that there is a similarity between the mechanism in genetic adaptation, in adaptive behaviour and in scientific discovery: the common denominator here is *problem-solving*.[36] This common denominator appears very attractive when one accepts that

> evolution proceeds like a tinkerer who, during millions of years, has slowly modified his products, retouching, cutting, lengthening, using all opportunities to transform and create . . . Making a lung with a piece of oesophagus sounds very much like making a skirt with a piece of granny's curtain.[37]

I prefer, however, yet a different common denominator. F. Jacob writes:

> Evolution is built on accidents, on chance events, on errors. The very thing that would lead an inert system to destruction becomes a source of novelty and complexity in a living system. An accident can be transformed into an innovation, an error into a success.[38]

This passage reads as if it had been written by Popper, for Popper shows that we learn from our errors. Once a theory is falsified and an error eliminated, we are nearer a correct theory with greater verisimilitude. The more errors we make, the greater the progress. Unconscious organisms take ages to benefit from their errors and yield more adaptive organisms because they have to wait to be physically eliminated and for offspring to try out variations. Human beings, capable of consciously formulating theories, can achieve a tremendously fast turnover because they can abandon false theories and do not have to wait for coming generations to test the 'adaptiveness' of theories by physical trial and error in actual survival of organisms. Conscious human beings can even make errors on purpose and do not have to wait for a chance error to happen. Here, then, we find that the common denominator is *error-making*.

Errors are eliminated or corrected by experience and, in the last analysis, 'experience' must mean 'observation' or 'interpretation of observation'; and, in this sense, Popperian philosophy of knowledge is a form of empiricism. But there are empiricisms and empiricisms. When we recognise the crucial role of observation in Popperian philosophy of knowledge, we are not thinking of the sort of observation which conventional empiricists believe to be constitutive of knowledge or the inductive summation of which they hold to be knowledge. In short, in Popperian philosophy observation is the end of the process, not the beginning.

Nevertheless, though negative and some kind of end game or final move, it does play a crucial part – like an ultimate court of appeal. Though not primary and though it is not the starting-point in our acquisition of knowledge, it is essential. For most conventional and traditional empiricists, observation even in this negative role presents a formidable problem. Why, one might legitimately ask, should one accord such a privileged status to observation and allow it to falsify? What is so special about observation and/or sense experience? An empiricist like Ayer is simply dogmatic:

> We say that a sentence is factually significant to any given person, if, and only if, he knows how to verify the proposition which it purports to express – that is, if he knows what observations would lead him, under certain conditions, to accept the proposition as being true, or reject it as being false.[39]

In this formulation Ayer does not link observation to inductivism. His requirement as to what would make an observation valid applies equally to a falsifying observation. Why, then, is observation the ultimate test of falsity? Why not revelation or authority or intuition? It has been argued that one ought to give preference to observation because observations tend to be inter-subjective and can be shared by many people. This argument cannot hold. The inter-subjectivity of observation is highly questionable when one considers such things as optical illusions; and when we come to the possibility that an observation may have to be interpreted, we are on even more uncertain ground. For that matter, there are many illusions which are perfectly well inter-subjective. Moreover, both revelation and intuition, not to speak of authority, are inter-subjective because of the power of both suggestiveness and auto-suggestiveness. On the other side, alchemists used to appeal to observations as evidence of the truth of their procedures to produce gold. But since their observations consisted often of as many as 700 different steps or reactions of chemicals under heat, their observations have notoriously proved *not* to be inter-subjectively testable.

Quine, as we have seen above, is less dogmatic than Ayer. He suggests nothing more than that we should give a slight preference to observation. Why should we? All demands that we ought to pay attention to observation seem to be without foundation. Observation merely tells us, after all, that something is happening to or in our nervous system.

There is, nevertheless, a perfectly good reason why we should pay attention to observation and give it more than just slight preference over other methods of falsifying statements. Evolution conjectures that the nervous system, complete with its sense organs, is adapted to the environment. Thus, we know that experience by observation is not just an event inside our nervous system. The theory of evolution and that theory alone puts teeth into the demand for falsification by observation. Without evolution, there could be no reason why we should prefer observation to authority or intuition or revelation as a standard for falsification. Evolution transforms the appeal to observation from a dogma into a reasoned criterion or test when and when not we come into contact with the outside world, i.e. with something that is not just an event inside our nervous system. A modern philosophical St Paul might therefore say that observation may be faith and hope; but without evolution, it is of no avail. In this way, observation for falsification purposes is vindicated by evolution. There are good reasons why it should be preferred to other methods. There is no need for Ayer's dogmatism and no ground for Quine's scepticism. None of these arguments, however, can or should be construed to mean that we should *begin* with observation and with nothing but observation and insist that all we know should be reduced to observation. The theory of evolution can only vindicate the primary importance of observation in regard to falsification; it cannot establish it as a source of knowledge. If one regards observation as a source of knowledge one cannot appeal to evolution, for evolution tells us that such knowledge as is embodied in organisms is the result of selective retention of adaptive proposals, not the result of accumulated learning by observation.[40]

In Evolutionary Epistemology, knowledge is compatible with reality – that is, the knowledge which has survived error elimination. It does not have to represent reality or tell us what reality is like and does not have to be a complete 'fit' to reality. All that is required is that it should be compatible with reality. Nevertheless, we know that there is a 'real' world other than our knowledge of it because what we 'know' has been selected by it and is tolerated by it. Our knowledge of a 'real' world has been left standing by that world because the two are not incompatible, even though that knowledge is neither objectively nor certainly known. For all that is required for the selection of either organisms or theories is that they should be compatible with reality. Organisms as well as knowledge are merely minimum adaptations to reality. Neither an organism fit to survive, nor a theory which has escaped the process of error elimination, tell us what that reality is exactly like. But they tell us what is compatible with it. For this reason, the correspondence theory ceases to be crucial for philosophical realism. Popper would not agree; but his own arguments in favour of Evolutionary Epistemology make it superfluous.

The idea of 'compatibility' has to be used with discernment. Contradictions are compatible with any proposition. This, indeed, is the formal definition of 'compatibility'. But it would clearly be wrong to say that a contradictory theory is a good theory just because it is compatible with everything. A theory which is compatible with reality in the present sense, must make *some* assertions or have some implications which are not compatible with reality. An organism which is compatible with its environment is not compatible with all environments. Reality, like Kant's *Ding an sich,* cannot be known. But unlike the *Ding an sich,* it makes itself felt. It selects. It weeds out the non-fits and thus cannot but bend the growth of knowledge towards itself. In this view, the mind is part of reality and, in principle, not different in its relation to reality from the relation of every organism to reality.

Evolutionary Epistemology also throws light on another problem which has been troublesome in Popperian thought. In order to explain the growth of knowledge and to show how new theories supersede old theories by explaining new facts *as well* as old facts explained in the earlier theory, Popper has introduced the concept of verisimilitude. This concept is logically not an easy concept. A theory can be either true or false or plausible or unfalsified. But it is very hard to accept that it can be verisimilitudinous (i.e. that it can be like the truth) without being actually true. If this is hard to grasp, then the notion that there are degrees of verisimilitude is even harder to grasp. We can give good reasons for thinking that the General Theory of Relativity is nearer the truth than Newton's Mechanics; but we cannot easily demonstrate that this is so.

Evolutionary Epistemology cannot provide such a demonstration, either. But it can shed light on the meaning of the concept of verisimilitude and thus explain it without providing a precise logical status for it. A comparison with the notion of verisimilitude in biology can shed considerable light on this matter. A tick is dependent on its ability to detect the presence of mammals. It is programmed to let itself fall from a twig when it 'smells' butyric acid and to cling to an object it encounters, provided that object has a temperature of 37 degrees Celsius. It so happens that the odour of butyric acid and the specific temperature to which the tick reacts is the minimum definition of a mammal.[41] We say, therefore, that the tick, though its picture of mammals is very incomplete, has knowledge which has some verisimilitude to mammals. But this knowledge has less verisimilitude than our own knowledge about mammals. This difference in the degrees of verisimilitude can be illustrated best in a negative way. It is easier to simulate a mammal to mislead a tick than it is to simulate a mammal to mislead a human being. In this example, the degree of verisimilitude is not determined by a degree of verisimilitude in representation. The tick has no representation of a mammal. It merely has some basic information. For that matter, a human being's knowledge of a mammal is, strictly speaking, not a representation of a mammal, but knowledge of a large number of qualities of mammals which is brought into operation for the purposes of response every time a sufficient number of these qualities are detected to be present. It would not make much sense to describe the list of qualities as a pictorial representation of the mammal. If one had to rely on pictures of mammals, one would have to have not only a separate picture for each species and sub-species, but literally a picture of every single member of every single species. Since human knowledge of mammals has greater verisimilitude than a tick's knowledge, human knowledge is better. But it is so not in terms of its better representational power. The biological analogy helps us to detach the notion of verisimilitude from the notion of representation. As long as we think of verisimilitude in terms of representation, all inquiries about degrees of verisimilitude will lead to inquiries about accuracy of depiction. Accuracy of depiction or of pictorial reproduction are irrelevant. It is important to salvage the notion of verisimilitude because it helps us to sharpen our concept of progress. When we compare two theories, we should prefer the theory which has a greater verisimilitude – provided we do not mean by verisimilitude, verisimilitude of pictorial representation.

The difficulties which have arisen in regard to the concept of verisimilitude all stem, predictably, from the fact that a non-representational and non-inductive theory of knowledge cannot really claim that one can compare theories by comparing the degree to which they 'represent'. All attempts to formalise the concept of verisimilitude cannot hide this initial conceptual contradiction between non-representational knowledge and verisimilitude. A non-formal, intuitive approach will help; and it will confirm that the notion of degrees of verisimilitude is essential.

Verisimilitude is the epistemological analogue of adaptation in evolution. Adaptations are fits to the environment, but never perfect fits. A good adaptation is one that is compatible with the environment which includes, of course, competitors. It need not be more and is more only in rare cases. Hence, the notion of verisimilitude in knowledge. A theory is never perfect, never wholly true, never the whole truth and, what is more, even if it is, one cannot prove that it is: thus a theory is a verisimilitude. Just as there are degrees of compatibility with the environment, there are degrees of verisimilitude. Whatever the logical difficulties in the concept, it is conceived in the spirit of Evolutionary Epistemology and derives its fruitfulness from evolutionism. Neither organisms nor theories are induced or determined by the environment. They are free and undetermined proposals or conjectures. Those that have no verisimilitude at all, do not survive. A conjecture which is dead right and therefore either a complete fit or *totally* true, is against all chances. Even then, one means no more than that it is compatible with all parts of the environment, but not that it accurately pictures the whole environment. All in all, Evolutionary Epistemology shifts our attention from preoccupation with accuracy of depiction to degrees of compatibility (i.e. to verisimilitude).

Most conjectures, be they organisms or theories, are merely verisimilitudinous. They say more than the environment warrants.[42] They are underdetermined.[43] A mallard duckling 'knows' that it must follow the first quacking object it sees, whereas the environment merely justifies that it should follow it if it is its mother. All humans 'know' that the sun will rise tomorrow, whereas the environment we have experienced does not justify such a theory. It merely tolerates such a theory. All knowledge, even the knowledge encoded in the body of a paramecium, consists of unjustified expectations and transcends experience. The environment tolerates mallard ducklings prepared to follow any object which quacks with the right call-note in front of them because, in practically all cases (unless Konrad Lorenz is present and does the quacking), that object will be its mother. Both our mallard ducklings and our human scientist jump to a conclusion which is not warranted by the environment. If they jump to a conclusion which is incompatible with the environment, the mallard ducklings will be eliminated and the scientist must eliminate his theory. There is no mechanism known to us which would allow the environment to determine the knowledge held by the mallard ducklings or by the scientist in exactly the right way. The environment cannot directly produce a replica or a mirror-image of itself in living matter, not even when that living matter has a conscious mind. For this to happen, unconscious living matter would have to be able to encode whatever it 'learns' in its gene pool. We know now that this form of Lamarckism cannot take place.[44] Conscious living matter would have to possess some kind of clairvoyance which produces information about non-observable and non-observed events such as future events.[45] Knowledge about the world, in all cases, depends on universals: in non-conscious beings, upon genetically programmed expectations of regularities; in conscious beings, upon conjectured predictions of regularities. But in neither case can we expect living matter to pick up the *exactly* correct instructions about these regularities from the environment because there is no mechanism available to do it.

When we are thinking of non-representational verisimilitude we are reminded of the idea of J.v. Uexküll[46] that every organism cuts out a special part of the environment which part then becomes its reality. The rest of the environment simply does not exist for that organism. A frog's eye announces only changes in illumination and the outlines of curved objects in movement. Nothing else is of interest or concern to the frog. A dog's world is largely a *smelt* world; a bat's world is a *heard* world; and man's world is, to a very large degree, a *seen* world.[47] In the world of a paramecium there are fewer events than in our world. But those few events which take place are just as real as those which take place in our world.[48]

As far as metaphysical realism is concerned, the absence of such a mechanism of instruction by the environment or direct transfer of information is a positive advantage. If there were such a mechanism, it would be very difficult to know whether all details had been accurately reproduced or encoded in organisms and/or theories; for if there were such a mechanism, nothing less than complete accuracy of information would be acceptable. But since we know that there is no such mechanism, we are left to conclude that the organism and the theory which have survived have been selected for survival or retention because they are compatible with reality. This conclusion is a very solid argument in favour of the presence of such a reality – for without it, there would have been nothing to do the selecting. From this perspective, Kant appears both right and wrong. Right, because he knew that the thing in itself, the noumenal world, is not accurately portrayed in our knowledge. Wrong, because he did not and could not, living as he did before Darwin, grasp that through natural selection the categories of our understanding have been selected for survival by the things in themselves, so that we can be confident that whatever we know is not as unrelated and as uninformative about the things in themselves as his total dichotomy between phenomena and the noumenal world would suggest. It was one of the many merits of Hegel to have spotted this weakness in Kant and to have argued that in evolutionary perspective (even though his evolutionary perspective was pre-Darwinian and un-Darwinian), there cannot be such a complete dichotomy and that all our knowledge reflects at least indirectly some real information about the noumenal world.[49]

The nature of the environment constrains the sort of adaptations which are possible. An adaptation which is a minimum compatibility is one which contains the absolute minimum of information about the environment required by the organism in question. This information has, epistemologically speaking, a very low degree of verisimilitude and, since it is compatible with a very large number of features of the environment, is very hard to falsify. The better the adaptation and the tighter the fit, the more verisimilitudinous the information it represents. Hence, it is easier to falsify. Its empirical content grows and it is more readily subject to error elimination because there are fewer features of the environment which are compatible with it. Some human organisms are capable of putting forward conjectures and theories about their environment which are more than *minimally* compatible with that environment. They therefore show a high level of verisimilitude and, by that token, have a high empirical content which makes them more subject to error elimination and criticism by that environment than the information stored, say, in the gene pool of a population of paramecia which contains only the absolute minimum information necessary for survival. There are lots of things a paramecium can do without being eliminated by the environment as an error: it has very low verisimilitude. For example, it does not have to make a bee-line for that part of the water which contains its food. It is sufficient for a majority of the members of the population to get there sooner or later. It can, for example, afford to ignore the oxygen in the water and the water's transparency as long as it is informed about its penetrability. By contrast, Quantum Mechanics or the DNA theory have a very high verisimilitude: almost everything remotely relevant to them will eliminate them if either theory makes one or two false predictions.

Selectionism, in short, is an enlargement of falsificationism. Falsificationism was a theory of knowledge. Its great initial strength and viability derived from the fact that it obviated the need for a specific epistemology, i.e. a correct account of how we come to know. If one has a falsificationist theory of knowledge, one asserts something about knowledge which makes it unimportant to know exactly how this knowledge is acquired. Epistemology used to be of great importance as long as people believed that there was a right way and a wrong way of acquiring knowledge. Falsificationism made knowledge of the right way superfluous. Selectionism is a theory *about* knowledge. The enlargement of Popper's philosophy from falsificationism to selectionism can be expressed in Popper's own words: 'The book [*The Logic of Scientific Discovery*] was meant to provide a theory of knowledge.'[50] Forty years later, he said of himself that he has become totally absorbed in the study of the growth of knowledge.[51] At first, he was interested in the demarcation of knowledge from non-knowledge, i.e. metaphysics. Later, the interest shifted from the demarcation of knowledge to the growth of knowledge.

Selectionism is an enlargement of falsificationism also in a different sense. Theories do not get selected because they fit or are right, but because they are not incompatible with a niche in the environment. In falsificationism, one used to say that a theory is provisionally true until it is falsified or that 'truth' is an unfalsified hypothesis. Selectionism enlarges this formulation: a true theory is a theory which is compatible with the environment. It increases in truth or becomes more verisimilitudinous if it is compatible with a larger part of the environment. In this sense, Einstein's theory is better than Newton's because it explains more; *Homo sapiens* is an improvement on a cat because man is more flexible – that is, he can maintain himself in a very large variety of different environments. A theory ceases to be compatible when the environment changes or when another theory appears which is *more* compatible in the sense of being compatible with more. Being more compatible, it competes successfully with the older theory. In this way, we arrive at the Popperian notion of preference. In this notion, theories do not have to be justified and we do not drop a theory because we can no longer justify it. Theories are abandoned because another theory is preferred. In order to make such comparisons possible, we have to assume that all theories are commensurable. They are commensurable because they are all competing in the same environment. In Popper's philosophy of science, for this reason, the commensurability of theories is of paramount importance. Any philosophy of science which holds that theories are incommensurable with one another and that preference for any one theory is determined by a mere paradigm change, seems to assume that there are different environments to which they are a fit.

In Popper's Evolutionary Epistemology, progress is seen primarily as an increase in universality. A theory is better than its competitor if it is more universal.

The proper way of understanding increase in universality is to see the increase in explanatory power of the later theory. The later theory is more universal when it explains several new phenomena as well as all the phenomena which used to be explained by the older theory. Thus, Einstein's theory is more universal than Newton's theory not because one can deduce Newton from Einstein and not vice versa, but because the phenomena explained by Newton's theory can be explained by Einstein's theory plus many phenomena which could not be explained by Newton's theory. For this to be acceptable, we have to say that theories are commensurable via the phenomena they explain, but not by a simple confrontation of one theory by another.

This whole problem arises because we have discarded representation as a criterion of truth. If we had not discarded it, we could easily argue that progress consists in a growth of accuracy of depiction. But having discarded representation as a criterion of any theory, this argument is not open. Take gases. The Boyle–Charles law for a perfect gas does not represent gases more 'accurately' than Dalton's law of partial pressures or Graham's law of diffusion. But it is more universal in that it explains the behaviour of gases in terms of tiny molecules, each one of which is subject to the laws of Newton's Mechanics. The Boyle–Charles law is a progress towards greater universality because it explains not only new phenomena, but also the phenomena explained by Graham's law and by Dalton's law.

Kuhn objects to this notion of progress in terms of greater universality. If the two theories involved in this progress are to be commensurable, he says, we have to have a language into which at least the empirical consequences of both can be translated without loss or change.[52] In other words, he insists that in all cases there is complete meaning-variance so that one can never say that a theory explains phenomena which used to be explained by another theory. In Kuhn's view, any theory which is alleged to explain some new phenomena as well as the old phenomena explained in an earlier theory, does not do so because the old phenomena have a meaning which is strictly and exclusively dependent on the older theory which explained them. If that theory is dropped, the same phenomena cannot be reproduced and therefore cannot be said to be explained by the new theory. If the new theory explains something similar, it is still only something similar, but never the same.

This argument derives its strength from the generally conceded fact that all observations are theory-laden. There is no such thing as a strictly neutral phenomenon. But its great weakness is that it forgets that though there are no phenomena which are completely neutral, there are always phenomena which are neutral relative to the two theories to be compared. These 'neutral' phenomena are not absolutely neutral, but neutral relative to the two theories. They are, of course, theory-laden by a third theory which is more or less independent of the two theories to be compared. Thus, one can compare two theories successfully *without* translating the empirical consequences of one theory into the consequences of the other. Or, by the same token, when one compares two theories, one obtains automatically a method for translating the empirical consequences of one theory into the empirical consequences of the other.

One can discern a relationship between explanatory power, degree of universality of a theory and verisimilitude. An increase in any of these will bring about an increase in the other two. Let us start with explanation. Explanation does not consist in the revelation of a mysterious force or an unmasking of hidden events.[53] Explanation, Popper says, is brought about when one can deduce a prognosis from an initial condition with the help of a general law. Ideally, one can explain the fact that I am now typing by saying that whenever I type the letters 'I t y p e' on a certain typewriter on a certain desk at a given time, I am pushing my fingers against the respective keys on that particular typewriter. Thus, one would take the writing of the letters as the initial condition, the pushing of the fingers as the prognosis, and the phrase which begins with 'whenever . . .' as the general law. This law would have very little generality and refer, in fact, to nothing but the event in question. Nevertheless, one would take the whole deduction as an explanation of 'pushing the fingers'. However, the general law invoked has a very low degree of verisimilitude because it ceases to be true a second after the time specified in it, since it refers to a particular moment of my typing. Similarly, its explanatory power is very poor, because, in referring only to one particular moment, it cannot explain why I keep pushing my fingers down a moment later. Finally, it has an almost zero degree of universality because it contains specific reference to a time and a place and could not apply to a different typewriter. As soon as the 'general' law is enlarged to become more general, the verisimilitude will increase and the explanatory power will increase. Hence, we see that in our desire to gain more knowledge, we are seeking more verisimilitude and an increase in the generality of the laws or generalisations we employ. Confronted by a choice between two laws, we must naturally prefer the more general one and thus opt automatically for the one which has more verisimilitude. In this sense, the desire for knowledge contains an inbuilt sense of direction and indicates which of two competing theories is to be preferred. The preference does not have to be made in response to a straight falsification. It is, more often, the result of a comparison between theories and a preference for the theory which has greater universality. Since the rejected theory has less verisimilitude than the preferred theory, we call the rejection an error elimination. In this sense, progressive error elimination will lead to greater verisimilitude and an increase in universality.

With the wider formula of selectionism rather than with narrow falsificationism, we establish the continuity of the growth of knowledge with the evolutionary process in a neo-Darwinian sense. Popper here offers a philosophy of science which does not depend for its truth on a study of the history of science; but which, on the contrary, makes the writing of the history of science possible. The formula takes account of the fact that the growth of knowledge is a historical phenomenon and that that growth tends towards a goal, even though it can never actually reach it. Finally, it takes account of the fact that progress is not an accumulation of knowledge. Any later theory, indebted as it is to an earlier theory, is commensurable with an earlier theory in the sense that both theories are tentative solutions of a problem and that, in the course of history, the problem itself is being transformed. There are no closed systems here and no language games which succeed one another in a higgledy-piggledy, ahistorical fashion. Science, in Popper's philosophy of science, is a historical phenomenon.[54] In the early stages, the selection of valid hypotheses is done by the environment. In the later stages, provided the social conditions are suitable, it is done by conscious criticism. The criticism is the criticism of human minds which are, in turn, the products of natural selection. Thus, there is no need to define in advance what sort of entity the human mind might be.

The final and perhaps greatest merit of the formula consists in the way in which P $\rightarrow$ TS $\rightarrow$ EE $\rightarrow$ P explains that the growth of knowledge, though undetermined and unplanned and not designed, nevertheless, by the sheer accumulation of error eliminations, moves in the direction of truth. The strategy of the argument is perhaps not new. It is certainly reminiscent of the old argument of the invisible hand which, in the absence of conscious and willed design, nevertheless leads towards an optimisation of economic returns. At any rate, in the eighteenth century this argument was first used in the field of economics when Adam Smith demonstrated that one need not follow a plan in order to bring about the achievement of a design. Darwin, too, used this argument. He was not, as he kept insisting, arguing against design. The sheer constraints of the environment upon evolving organisms were bound to produce design. He attacked, however, the argument *from* design – that is, the belief that since there was design in evolution, there must have been a plan, a divine Providence or some other kind of preconceived determination of design. Neo-Darwinists have therefore been able to characterise evolution as a process which, though lacking in intentionality and foresight, is nevertheless creative and productive of design. This results from the constraints of the environment upon chance mutations. The Popperian formula for the sequential growth of knowledge is the only description of the growth of knowledge which shows that despite the absence of the planned accumulation of sense observations (the sort of accumulation Bacon and his countless followers had envisaged), the progression moves nevertheless towards increasing truth about the world.

If there were to be a debate as to whether Kuhn (see end of chapter 4) or Popper has done for science what Darwin did for biology, Popper would win hands down. For that matter, though it was Kuhn, as we have seen, who complained about 'resistance' to his theory of science in terms which are almost reminiscent of the way in which Freud used to complain about resistance to his theory of infantile sexuality, it is Popper – not Kuhn – who has found a certain amount of resistance. Resistance to Popper can be explained in institutional terms and has nothing to do with the actual content of his theories. At the time when Popper could have been accepted, philosophers in Britain were dominated by the linguistics of Ryle and Austin; on the continent, Heidegger and Sartre occupied centre-stage. In America, they were looking either towards Britain or towards the continent or came, during the Second World War, under the influence of Carnap and the Vienna Circle's Positivism and inductivism which seemed to follow so well upon American pragmatism and operationism. Scientists, though the main beneficiaries of Popper's philosophy, are rarely interested in philosophical questions. Those who are, have acknowledged the liberating effect of Popper's philosophy of knowledge on their work.[55] With Popper's philosophy, they no longer have to wrestle with the discrepancy between their practice – in which theories are given priority and observations are seen to be theory-laden – and the philosophy of Positivism, Baconian or other, which tells them that they ought to start with observations and with nothing but observations. But the liberating effect of Popper's philosophy of philosophy-minded scientists was offset after the Second World War by the new generation's barrage of Marxism, neo-Marxism, revisionist Marxism and structural Marxism. To Marxists of all persuasions who have established a real corner in sociology and the sociology of knowledge, Popper's philosophy appears indistinguishable from Positivism because, like Positivism, it is concerned with knowledge which claims to be knowledge of a real world. Throwing Popper in with the Positivists is like saying that tablespoons are like elephants because neither can climb trees! Marxists, however, whatever their particular colour, are committed to seeing all knowledge as an ideology and confine themselves therefore to those aspects of knowledge which can usefully be explained as a function of a social structure rather than as assertions about the real world. Those aspects of knowledge which cannot be usefully so explained, are forced by them into a Procrustes bed and assimilated to knowledge which can be explained as a function of social structures. Either way, Marxists and Marx-inspired social scientists cannot afford to distinguish between Popper and Positivism because such a distinction would be too damaging to their initial commitment. Here again, Popper is meeting with enormous resistance.

The Bipartite History of Science

In the Popperian view of the growth of knowledge, the growth consists of two separate movements which interact. There are, first, chance mutations (in the case of evolving organisms) and conscious theories or conjectures about the world. Second, these tentative solutions are incessantly exposed to selective pressures by the environment. Those which are a 'fit' are selected for survival and the others are eliminated as 'errors'. These are blind conjectures and selective retentions. The element of chance and blindness is present in the mutations and the conjectures. But the selective process is not governed by chance. On the contrary, the selection by the environment of 'correct' or 'fitting' mutations is the anti-chance factor in evolution as well as in the growth of knowledge. If evolution and the growth of knowledge are continuous, then one must expect to find that the growth of knowledge, like evolution itself, is divided into two parts.

This conclusion has a bearing on the history of science and on the way in which it ought to be studied and written. It forces us to accept that there are really two histories of science. There is, first, the history of the chance mutations or conjectures and inventions; and, second, the history of the selective process. Agassi has convincingly and, I think, conclusively shown that the writing of the history of science depends on the vagaries of the philosophy of science. There are as many histories of science, he seemed to be saying, as there are philosophies of science. 'The actual critical process [of the growth of knowledge]', P.K. Feyerabend wrote, 'is very complex and has never been analysed to everyone's satisfaction. But of one thing we can be sure: *experience* plays a very fundamental role in it.'[56] The complexity of the process can now be somewhat reduced – or, at least, be divided into two parts. The first part remains, undeniably, incredibly complex. But the second part, the selective process, can be shown to be a fairly reasonable, not to say rational, story. The first part consists of the intricate by-ways of inventiveness. The second part consists of the rational reasoning which leads to error elimination and selection. When we thus divide the history of science into two parts to correspond with the chance factor and with the anti-chance factor, the story becomes less complex and less mysterious.

Broadly speaking, the distinction between the two parts corresponds to the distinction between conjectures and refutations. In the first part, there will be all the stories of how conjectures were being made. In the second part, there will be the stories of how they were refuted so that the second part will also show which conjectures survived because they failed to be refuted. I would all the same hesitate to use these labels for part one and part two. Part one must contain a great deal of general history as well as biography and will show much more than the formulation of conjectures. Part two will certainly not just be the story of attempts at refutation. It will contain stories of doubts and of the weighing-up of competing conjectures because error elimination, rather than straight falsification, will be the content of most of the stories it contains. If one has to give names to the two parts, I would suggest that part one be called the story of inventions – to correspond with the story of mutations in biology; and part two, the story of selective retentions – to correspond with the story of natural selection in biology.

The question of names apart, it is essential to realise that Popperian philosophy of science enables us to make the distinction between the two parts of the story. This is the whole of the contribution the philosophy of science makes to the history of science. Once the distinction is made, the histories in part one and in part two can be written as all histories are written. They have to depend on general laws so that single events can be located and linked together. But these general laws do not have to be general laws of scientific method or general laws about the behaviour of people labelled 'scientists'. They are judiciously collected and reasonably examined general laws and one does not need a special philosophy of science to write the stories of part one and part two. The philosophy of science one needs in order to write the history of science has taught us that the history of science must come in these two interacting parts. The distinction between the two parts is the specific and necessary contribution of Popper's philosophy of science to the writing of the history of science. Once this is established, the historian of science can avail himself of any general law or any set of general laws as his judgment thinks fit. The stories in part one and the stories in part two will themselves not be relative to any further philosophy of science, and not even to Popper's philosophy of science. It is the distinction between the two parts and the mode of their interaction which is relative to Popper's philosophy of science, not the contents of part one and part two.

The distinction between the two parts must not be confused with the well-established distinction between the internal and external history of science. The internal history of science is the story of experiments and theories and debates about theories. The scenario is fairly rational and the protagonists are always scientists. The external history of science includes the psychological and sociological background, the institutional conditions which make science possible, as well as any other factor which may or may not be relevant. Whatever the uses of such a distinction are, it clearly does not run parallel to the distinction between the two parts here proposed. Internal history would, for example, include conjectures and inventions, provided they are of a 'scientific' nature, and exclude them only when they are, for instance, hermetic, alchemical or Neoplatonic. It would also include the process of error elimination and selection. The subjects of internal history are thought-contents and their logical relations. External history, on the other hand, would include inventions only when they are of a non-scientific character, and would deal mainly with the non-scientific determinants of science and its growth such as psychological pressures, economic conditions and social institutions. It would concern itself with the sociology of science without necessarily attempting to reduce the internal history to the external history. It describes the causally related social, psychological and other non-cognitive factors which influence the development of science. The distinction between internal and external is probably useful, though perhaps a trifle scholastic. If one considers that quite important decisions to select or adopt a theory can be the result of events in external history, one must conclude that the distinction is somewhat artificial and not all that enlightening. However, it is well established. In 1970, it seemed new: E. McMullin[57] used the distinction, but used the words 'HSi' and 'HSii' for internal and external, respectively. Whittacker's book on ether, McMullin said, is HSi (internal history) and P. Williams's book on Faraday is HSii (external history). Since then, the distinction and the labels 'internal' and 'external' have become common usage.[58] However common the usage, there is a divergence of meaning in the terms as used by different authors. For Kuhn, internal history of science is concerned with the substance of science. It can be studied if the historian sets aside the science *he* knows and relies on the journals and textbooks of the period, thus leaving out the innovators who changed the direction of science. External history is concerned with the activity of scientists as a social group. Mary Hesse's use of the distinction is quite different. Lakatos[59] uses the terms in yet a different sense. Internal history, in his mind, is the *rational reconstruction* of the arguments used; external history, by contrast, is concerned with the *psychology* of invention. In his terminology, 'external' refers to the actual history of science and 'internal' to the ideal history of science. There would be no need to argue with people who find the distinction useful, were it not for the fact that it is often believed that external history is empirical while internal is not. A historical narrative, no matter what its subject is, is 'empirical' in the sense that it uses evidence. It is 'non-empirical' or transcends experience in that it employs meta-historical general laws for keeping its particular events lined up and linked. This is as true of any internal history as of any external history and whatever the distinction between the two, it does not correspond to the distinction between empirical and non-empirical.

Scholastic or not, the distinction between external history and internal history has nothing to do with the distinction which follows from Popper's Evolutionary Epistemology, between the inventive and the selective parts of the scientific enterprise. Writing the history of science in two parts, let us first indicate all those events which belong to the process of invention and conjecture. Here, we have a bewildering mass of evidence. It ranges from the psychoanalysis of scientists, of their dreams and fantasies, to the prevalence of traditional metaphors and religious myths. Kepler was devoted to sun mysticism and derived his imagery and his determination from his conviction that the sun *must* be in the centre. Harvey was obsessed by circles, circular motion, the ubiquity of cycles. At the same time, he lived in an age when pumps were being tried and used all over the place. Here, we find a technological determinant of his conjecture that the heart must be a pump. The technology, in turn, was rooted in the economics of the seventeenth century which, in turn, was linked to the politics and social developments of his age. Galileo received his training in a school of design[60] and this may have helped him to turn his mind away from the humanistic philosophy of the age of the Renaissance in order to read in the 'book of nature' – a metaphor which was also widely used by humanists who read that book in a very different way. Historians writing part one of the history of science have rightly wondered what might have caused Newton to conceive the possibility of action at a distance. According to some, his early childhood separation from his beloved mother was crucial: during the separation, he became familiar with the experience of longing for his mother who was a long way away.[61] Alternatively, it is also possible that we should here remind ourselves of the enormous power of astrological thought. Newton may well have derived the idea of attraction over a distance from his knowledge of astrology which had taught that distant stars can influence human destiny. With the causative role of early childhood, we are into psychology; with the causative influence of astrology, we are into the history of ideas. And who knows whether Virchow did not owe a debt for his theory about cells to his political convictions about self-governing republics? Maxwell was inspired, so it seems, by statistical calculations performed by a French sociologist who tried to cope with demographic problems.[62] Leonardo may have derived his courage to dissect human bodies from his observation that other people, too, had broken the limits of convention and decency. If an archbishop can conspire to murder the Medici brothers during High Mass in front of the main altar of the cathedral, why should I, he may have reasoned, refrain from dissecting dead bodies?[63] Einstein lived in an age of great social and political upheaval. One of his close friends from Zurich went back to Vienna to murder the mayor of that city.[64] Obviously, tradition was not being observed and some foreigners in Switzerland, at that time, were given to daring experiments of thought – a point charmingly made in Tom Stoppard's *Travesties*.

The history of these inventions and conjectures is limitless and irrational. There are no boundaries, no methods. One never knows what belongs to the history of science here and what does not. The history of the Hermetic tradition in the sixteenth century, though superficially part of the history of magic and obscurantism, nevertheless overlaps with the history of scientific conjectures, as Frances Yates has beautifully shown. The history of metaphysics, as Burtt has demonstrated, is part of it, though linked to an older, non-scientific system of thought. Paracelsus may not have been a scientist, but without him, as Debus has shown, the story of science would have been very different. Magic, sectarianism, mythology, alchemy – all overlap with inventions which eventually found their way into science, as is clearly recognised by Mary Hesse in her *Revolutions and Reconstructions in the Philosophy of Science*.[65] And as Koestler in his ominously entitled *The Sleepwalkers* has shown, the inhibitions and depressions of Copernicus may have been the psychological roots of his determination to show that the earth is not at the centre of the planetary system. Also belonging to part one are Merton's famous theories on the connection between sixteenth-century Puritanism and science, as well as the ideological considerations which prompted the founders of the Royal Society apologetically to espouse Bacon's inductivism as the paragon of scientific progress.[66] Part one further encompasses the stories about Malthus's influence on Darwin, Manuel's book on Newton, the stories of

Kekulé's dream and of Poincaré's streetcar, as well as the story of the peculiar personal friendships of the members of the Phage group[67] and Watson's *Double Helix*. Popper himself gave a good description of part one:

> The initial stage, the act of conceiving or inventing a theory, seems to me neither to call for logical analysis nor to be susceptible of it. The question how it happens that a new idea occurs to a man – whether it is a musical theme, a dramatic conflict, or a scientific theory – may be of great interest to empirical psychology; but it is irrelevant to the logical analysis of scientific knowledge.[68]

Popper here is saying that the 'how' of part one is distinct from the selective process described in part two, but he should not be interpreted as meaning that part one is not part of the history of science.

There is no need to multiply examples. This part of the story – the chance part, the blind conjecture part – is untidy. There is no boundary to it and one can write it only if one does not neglect the nooks and crannies of private obsessions, strange beliefs, and the wider pressure of politics, technology and sociology.

If part one is concerned with the inventions and reasons for the inventions, whatever they might be, it will in all likelihood become clear that the inventions and conjectures are not made entirely at random. First, they are more likely to be made under social conditions in which knowledge is not pre-empted for social bonding and is released from the bondage in which it is kept if it is used for social bonding. Second, in any one society, there is a great likelihood that inventions should be couched in terms of available metaphors or correspond to the deeper psychic currents in the minds of individual scientists. These correlations can be studied and classified and they force one to the conclusion that the inventions and conjectures are not absolutely random, but only random relative to the selective procedure (i.e. to part two of the story). When one is looking at part one, the conjectures are not random or not very random but tend to cluster around major themes represented by the cultural context or the psychology of the people involved. The inventions are not rational and are not made in pursuit of reason or any correct method because there is no correct method known. But this does not mean that they are arbitrary or random.

The importance of psychological and metaphysical motivation is well presented by Gerald Holton.[69] The foundations of Quantum Mechanics were laid under metaphysical auspices because Planck was fascinated by the Absolute. Einstein believed that God does not play dice; Niels Bohr was dominated by the vision of the complementarity of Yang and Yin. In Descartes's mind, inertia was somehow linked to the immutability of God,[70] Kepler was deeply immersed in solar mysticism.[71] These examples and many others show that inventiveness is not random in relation to the cultural context, even though it must be clear that this absence of randomness does not constitute a rationale for scientific discovery: for in part two of the story, this inventiveness must always appear as random.

The second part – the story of the anti-chance part, of the selective process – is much easier to write. Harvey may have been inspired by the technology of pumps and obsessed by circles and mythical formations. But the manner in which his theory was selected for retention and Galen's theory eventually crowded out, is a process of pure rationality. Here, the non-chance factor is paramount. It is inconceivable that Harvey's theory should not have been selected and that a false theory, in competition with it, should have retained the attention of scientists. Just as the environment selects for retention and survival those organisms whose populations' gene pool stores 'correct' information, so the scientific environment selects for temporary retention those theories which fit experience. The process may not always be instantaneous, but it is inevitable. This does not mean that truth will out and that one only has to sit back and wait until truth makes itself manifest and wins the day. Nothing could be further from the truth. One first needs the irrational, accidental, unplanned part of the story – the conjectures. Only conjectures which have actually been made can be selected. If they are not made, the truth will not out. But once they have been made, once conjectures are offered for competition and comparison, the truer or more verisimilitudinous ones will survive.

Popper's early falsificationism was not rich enough to be used as meta-historical theory for writing the history of science. Popper himself, before he was an evolutionist and when he was still confined to falsificationism in the narrow sense, wrote, as the above quoted remark shows, that the events of part one – the psychology of imagination and all social pressures, etc. – are not part of the history of science. *The Logic of Scientific Discovery*, first published in German in 1934, was therefore an unhistorical book or, as Lakatos once complained, 'highly ahistorical'.[72] In the context of falsificationism, this is completely justified. History cannot prove the truth of a philosophy of science – so there was no need to refer to it. The reason why history cannot be used to sustain a philosophy of science has nothing to do with the fact that one cannot derive an 'ought' from an 'is'. It is due to the fact that history itself has to be written and that one cannot write it without a philosophy of knowledge. *The Logic of Scientific Discovery* is, in this sense, a book with an infinitely better strategy of argument than Kuhn's *Structure of Scientific Revolutions*, which relies almost wholly on history. Moreover, falsificationism by itself would yield only part two of the history of science – and part two without part one is incomplete as a history of science. There was therefore every reason, *pace* Lakatos, why *The Logic of Scientific Discovery* was an unhistorical book and why, in spite of many subsequent editions, it has remained one.

Nevertheless, the distinction between parts one and two which follows from Popper's Evolutionary Epistemology is foreshadowed in falsificationism. It runs parallel to Reichenbach's distinction between the 'context of discovery' and the 'context of justification'. In Reichenbach's world, the former was of no interest. People who paid attention to it were judged guilty of 'the genetic fallacy of psychologism'. Not being an evolutionist, Reichenbach could only imagine that people who showed an interest in the genesis of scientific ideas thought that the 'how' of an idea amounted to a justification of the idea. It did not occur to him that while the 'context of discovery' might indeed be the story of how ideas come into being without, at the same time, being 'justified' just because they have come into being; and that the 'context of justification', rather than consisting in attempts at proving the truth of the ideas which have come into being, might consist of the story of eliminating the false ones.

Evolutionary Epistemology has clarified the distinction. As D.T. Campbell writes, the history of science is basically a 'descriptive epistemology'.[73] It is concerned with the question of how people proceed when they acquire knowledge. Traditionally, philosophers have taken little interest in this question because the 'how' by itself is no guarantee of correctness. But when one looks upon scientific knowledge as knowledge which is always open to criticism, the 'how' (i.e. the method of actual invention) is highly significant because it is that part of the story which provides the material upon which the selective process of part two is to be exercised. The 'how' is relevant and important, even though the question whether the actual method of invention is impeccable or not is neither here nor there. The 'how' merely shows how knowledge is invented *in order* to be exposed to the critical selective process described in part two. When we think of science as progress, we can see that its history comes in two parts: there is, first, the story of theory-formation; and, second, the story of theory-appraisal.[74]

The Consequences of the Failure to Grasp the Bipartite Nature of the History of Science

The failure to grasp the bipartite nature of the history of science has had some curious results. If there was at first a reluctance to attribute any real importance to part one and to dismiss interest in part one as 'the genetic fallacy', the pendulum seems now to have swung in the opposite direction. There are many philosophers who make the opposite mistake and consider part one the most important part of the story. Since part one, correctly understood as what Gerard Radnitzky calls 'theory-formation', does not contain the story of 'theory-appraisal', and since they know that appraisal and evaluation is an important part of the history of science, these philosophers have made many different attempts, mistaking part one for the whole of the enterprise – a sort of intellectual synecdoche, as it were – to show that part one, too, contains efforts at appraisal.

Let us start with the simplest of these attempts. It is often argued that there are rules for research methods and that the story of theory-formation should show how and whether these rules have been followed.[75] There is nothing wrong with the suggestion as such, except that it is unnecessary. Moreover, there is a wide divergence of opinion as to what 'rules' have been, or ought to have been, followed. If one consults Einstein's description of how he came by some of his best ideas, one will realise how wide off the mark the rational 'rules' suggested by other writers on the subject are:

> What precisely is 'thinking'? When at the reception of sense-impressions, memory pictures emerge, this is not yet 'thinking'. And when such pictures form series, each member of which calls forth another, this too is not yet 'thinking'. When, however, a

> certain picture turns up in many such series, then – precisely through such return – it becomes an ordering element for such a series, in that it connects series which in themselves are unconnected.[76]

Such an account of method is very different from the 'rules' culled by Noretta Koertge from Robert Pirsig's advice as to how to maintain a motorcycle in his *Zen and the Art of Motorcycle Maintenance*. These rules state that, having chosen an auspicious day, one should first look at the obvious; next, at the probable; and so forth. The point is that it does not matter whether Einstein and Pirsig agree or not and whether Noretta Koertge is wrong in thinking that it *does* matter that one follows 'rules'. Thinking only of part one, she cannot entertain the possibility that the history of science can be understood, let alone written, without reference to rules which ensure that the outcome of the enterprise is sound. True, the attempt to bring Zen into play is a very sophisticated advance over Bacon's recommendation that one ought to accumulate observations until they tell their own story. The wisdom of Zen and the folly of Baconian inductivism are tragically underlined by the story of the discovery of the molecular structure of DNA. While Rose Frank was following Bacon's rules and was getting nowhere, Crick and Watson were more relaxed and stumbled upon the great conjecture.[77]

The insistence that the story of theory-formation should show which rules have been followed and *that* rules have been followed derives directly from the failure to grasp that 'appraisal' is in part two. If part two is neglected or not recognised, then it would indeed be important to show that theory-formation has proceeded according to rules – for if no rules are followed, one could not distinguish between good and bad theories. And if no rules are followed, there is at least a demand that theories should be shown to have been induced from observation of the environment so that they can be seen as a rational response to the environment and distinguished from irrational responses to the environment.

The distinction between part one and part two was first clearly made by Darwin, for organic evolution – for this is, in essence, the meaning of 'natural selection' as distinct from artificial selection or breeding. It was later applied to the evolution of knowledge by Popper, where it is seen to operate as critical and conscious selection. Without the distinction, one must always fall back on the notion that theory-formation at least ought to pre-select what comes finally to be offered for rational appraisal and hence ask oneself what the rules for pre-selection are. For when there is no distinction, one could not tell the difference between good and bad theories unless one can see that some theories are formed according to certain rules and others are not. If, however, the vital distinction between formation and appraisal, random variation and natural selection (or, in the growth of knowledge, between wild invention and critical selection), is grasped, it becomes clear that there is not the slightest need for rules and not even for pre-selection on the theory-formation level.

More spectacular than attempts at establishing rules of discovery – attempts which are not basically different from Bacon's advice that one ought to proceed inductively and systematically and collect observations to make sure of the soundness of the results – are the efforts by Feyerabend and Lakatos. Feyerabend, taking part one for the whole, took one close and careful look at it and sized it up correctly. There are no rules in part one. Therefore, he recommended, there ought to be no rules. The logical hiatus between the 'is' and the 'ought' may be forgivable when one considers that part one is full of stories of how scientists made true discoveries – or rather, how they made discoveries and stumbled upon theories which later turned out to be true. Somehow or other, part one tells us, science gets there. We know, though Feyerabend neglects this, that science gets there because of the stories in part two. Feyerabend simply looks at part one. He sees that, among other things, by hook or by crook, by luck or by accident, some of the inventions in part one seem to be the right ones. And so he recommends that we simply allow anarchy to reign free. Part one contains inventions which eventually form part of knowledge because the events of part two tell how they came to be selected. Looking only at part one, Feyerabend thinks it is the whole story. Since part one must contain also inventions which turn out to be true, he suggests that there is no point in introducing rules for distinguishing between right inventions and wrong inventions. In chapter 18 of his *Against Method*,[78] he happily declares all boundaries between science and non-science are dissolved because in part one there are indeed no boundaries. Feyerabend reminds one of the infamous Inquisitor in the Albigensian Crusade at the beginning of the thirteenth century. When the King of France had surrounded one of the cities held by heretics, he asked the Inquisitor for advice as to what to do next. The Inquisitor advised that the king have all inhabitants killed indiscriminately: 'God,' he added, 'will recognise His own.' Similarly, Feyerabend advises that we should happily invent to our heart's content. Somehow or other, God will select the true inventions and consign the wrong ones to hell. With this advice, Feyerabend rejects not only Popperian falsificationism, but also Popperian selectionism.

Apart from the basic misunderstanding which consists in taking part one for the whole of the story, there is also a fundamental error of judgment in Feyerabend's advice. Alchemy, magic, witchcraft, astrology, Hermetism, Neoplatonism – all play a part in the story of part one. The reason why they do and why they have often proved so useful in the growth of knowledge is because, in part one, they are always open to criticism. The story of how they were criticised is, however, in part two. If one looks at part one only, one tends to forget that. Where astrology and magic, Neoplatonism and Hermetism occur, they mostly occur in a social context in which they are not only useless for the growth of knowledge, but directly contrary to it. For the most part, these systems of knowledge so-called occur in societies or communities which protect them artificially from criticism and error elimination. Acolytes and aspirants have to be 'initiated': they are usually sworn to silence and secrecy, made to promise obedience to authority, and are often kept in seclusion so that discussion and contact with alternative knowledge is minimised. In these places, these pieces of knowledge are accepted *dogmatically* and are, therefore, not really pieces of knowledge. Feyerabend, in wiping out the distinction between science and witchcraft, is neglecting the fact that what makes witchcraft so intolerable is not the witchery in itself, but the fact that in most cases it is practised dogmatically. When witchcraft or astrology or alchemy are espoused by men like Paracelsus, who lived in an environment in which all knowledge was sooner or later exposed to criticism, witchery and alchemy did not really matter: exposed to criticism, they eventually withered away. What matters in all these cases is the *mode* of knowledge, not the content of knowledge. There is no harm in trying a bit of alchemy if one is prepared to consider rational criticism of it. But if one disregards criticism, then even Newtonian Mechanics becomes non-knowledge. 'What does mark a man's beliefs as prejudices and superstitions,' Stephen Toulmin writes, 'is not their content, but the manner of holding them.'[79] Steven Weinberg begins his *The First*

Three Minutes[80] with some critical remarks about the *Edda* myth of origins. Gary Zukav intersperses his splendid popularisation of modern physics with comments on the similarity of physics to various Buddhist doctrines.[81] I think that both authors somehow miss the point. There remains always a very real difference between the *Edda* and Buddhism, on one side, and our modern knowledge, on the other. It does not matter whether the contents of these mythical stories are identical with the content of our modern knowledge or not. What does matter is that the myths are believed in dogmatically and are not exposed to criticism, whereas our modern knowledge is undogmatic and constantly exposed to criticism.

It is significant that Feyerabend, before rejecting Popperian falsificationism, did not stop to consider selectionism and Popper's Evolutionary Epistemology which led to the bipartite division of the scientific enterprise. His concentration on part one and the intellectual synecdoche by which he takes the part for the whole, result from his failure to appreciate the significance of Popper's evolutionism. This failure is inexcusable, for he wrote long after the appearance of Popper's works on Evolutionary Epistemology.

There is more than just a failure to take notice of Popper. Feyerabend takes care to barricade himself behind an assumption which makes it impossible for him to take evolution into account and consider its implications. As we have seen, evolution establishes hypothetical realism – for there has to be a real world which does the selecting. In knowledge, theories are selected or retained *after* clashes with that real world. If one does not consider evolution, the difficulties of establishing that there is such a real world are well-nigh insurmountable. In not considering evolution and in thus disregarding hypothetical realism, Feyerabend glories in the proclamation that there is no 'underlying substance',[82] that all we ever know is what theories tell us or what various styles of art depict – there is no opportunity to test theories or styles against an 'underlying substance' and thus distinguish the variety or verisimilitude of one from another. Had he taken evolution into account, he would have noticed that we could not be here, as the result of natural selection, had there not been an underlying substance to do the selecting. It is perfectly true, as he says, that we can have no knowledge of that underlying substance as such, or as it is in itself. But it is not true, as he concludes, that there is none. If there were none, the particular interaction which we describe as natural selection by the environment could not have taken place and Feyerabend would not be here to deny the interaction. His entire epistemological anarchy falls to the ground as soon as one takes evolution into account. It can sound faintly reasonable only if one believes that we were put here by God, created on the sixth day by a divine will. In this case, hypothetical realism would indeed be without foundation and one could not have confidence in the natural selection of organisms or the critical selection of verisimilitudinous theories. One would then be left with all sorts of pieces of knowledge about witchcraft and alchemy and Quantum Mechanics without a viable way of choosing between them. In such a situation, 'anything goes', as Feyerabend would have it. But one can only suppose that for a philosopher who believes that man was suddenly put on earth on the sixth day of creation, anything goes indeed!

A similar and similarly inexcusable disregard of Popper's evolutionism is to be found in Lakatos. Lakatos thus shared with Feyerabend the view that part one is the whole of the history of science. This view is common to Feyerabend and Lakatos, even though nothing else is. I understand that Feyerabend and Lakatos were planning to write a book on rationality together and that Lakatos was prevented by other commitments from carrying this plan out. When one considers the enormous differences between Feyerabend's and Lakatos's rejection of Popper's falsificationism, the mind boggles when one tries to imagine what that book might have been like.

More realistic than Feyerabend and less willing to put his trust in divine Providence 'to know His own', Lakatos reasoned in a diametrically opposite direction. Since knowledge has *grown* and since the history of inventions and experiments is all we have, there must have been internal controls built into these inventions and experiments. The falsification, Lakatos argues, can never take place *before* the emergence of a better theory.[83] But under most circumstances, a new theory would not emerge *before* the falsification of an old theory. Why indeed, in strict and narrow falsificationism, should it? With this sort of criticism, he put his finger on one of the weak aspects of Popper's initial, narrow falsificationism. As we have seen, narrow falsificationism does indeed present a real problem. Since all observations are theory-laden, there can be no single observation which one must take as falsification of a theory because such an observation would be dependent on a theory. If the theory it is dependent on is the theory to be falsified, one would have shown no more than that the theory in question had unforeseen consequences which turned out to be false. In that case, one is really forced to compare the theory in question with itself. If the theory the observation is dependent on is a different theory, one is rejecting the theory in question because one believes the other theory (the theory on which the crucial observation is dependent) preferable – so that one is comparing one theory with another theory. Stark falsification by the observation of a single falsifying instance is something which is very unlikely to occur. Whatever one is doing, one is comparing theories. This weakness of narrow falsificationism was spotted long before Lakatos, by Kuhn.[84] However, Lakatos poured out the baby with the bath water because he did not realise that these weaknesses had been eliminated by the broadening of falsificationism into selectionism and by evolutionism, which told the story of the controls of inventions in part two.

Lakatos argued that inventions come in, or follow from, discrete and discontinuous chunks – which are like quanta, we might add – but that, unlike quanta, these chunks can peter out gradually and fade away. Any such chunk is a research programme. A research programme can lead either to progressive or to degenerative problem shifts. These shifts are the controls. Looking at part one and its stories of inventions, Lakatos proposed that inventions result from particular research programmes, e.g. Cartesian metaphysics, that is, the mechanistic theory of the universe. Such programmes encourage certain theories and certain experiments and discourage others. As long as such a research programme shows a progressive problem shift, it will be continued. When it begins to show a regressive problem shift, it will be abandoned and a different programme will eventually take its place.[85] In this way, he thought that the mere story of inventions carries its own correctives in its wake. He sought to show that the history of science is at once descriptive (i.e. there have always been research programmes) and normative (i.e. these programmes produce their own controls in the form of problem shifts: if the shifts are degenerative, the programmes have always been abandoned). In this way, he avoided reliance on falsification as a controlling agent and as the mechanism which makes knowledge grow.

This argument has a strangely Hegelian ring to it. Hegel, too, sought to find the inbuilt controlling mechanisms of development.

Once there is development, Hegel was saying, it cannot go wrong because it follows inherent rules which compel it to be right. In Hegel's view, the development of thought is controlled by dialectical inferences which lead from thesis to antithesis to synthesis. Development and correct development are synonymous. For Lakatos, development consists in changes in research programmes and such development must lead to progress because we have an ability to distinguish between degenerative and progressive shifts in each research programme. Both Hegel and Lakatos tried to show that the weeding-out process is part of, or inside, the growth process. Lakatos was so confident that one can detect whether shifts are degenerative or not without further ado and without first writing a history of science, that he simply recommended that journals be closed to, and funds withheld from, scientists who pursue research inspired by programmes which show degenerative shifts.[86]

Kinship with Hegel may be a merit rather than a fault. The real *fault* of Lakatos's philosophy of knowledge is its failure to avoid historical circularity. We cannot know whether these shifts are degenerative or progressive unless we know what the history of science has been. If one embarks on research with a research programme in mind, one will soon see whether the problems are shifting in a degenerative or progressive direction. But one cannot establish the norm that one *ought* to have research programmes *because* history teaches us to; nor can we prove from historical observation that scientists in the past, unbeknown to themselves, have worked with research programmes and that, in so far as they have been successful, they have been successful because they worked in accordance with a research programme. This means we first have to write the history of science. Such writing cannot be done unless we first have a philosophy of science which helps us to select and link the separate events. Lakatos wanted to show that the existence of research programmes, with their built-in controls, is exhibited by history. We learn of them, he said, by studying history. Like Kuhn, he overlooked the fact that we cannot study history in order to find out which philosophy of science we ought to espouse. He tried to strengthen his argument by insisting that the history of science which would exhibit the role of research programmes was the so-called 'internal' history rather than the 'external' history. This distinction, as I argued above, is tenuous and not fruitful.[87] But even if it is maintained, not even internal history is sufficiently well established and known to dispense with an initial philosophy of science. Even an internal history of science will differ according to whether it is written from the standpoint of inductivism or conventionalism or research programmes or falsificationism. This conclusion implies that one has to decide upon the truth of the philosophy of science of research programmes *before* one writes history, even though this history is internal history only. Lakatos believed that the methodology of research programmes is an exception and that the philosophy they embody is revealed by a study of the history of science. In his calmer moments, he was quite aware of the intricacy of the whole problem he had created and explained that in order to evaluate rival logics of discovery, one has to evaluate the rival histories of science they lead to.[88] He did not even gloss over the fact that not even the internal history of science stands on its own feet: 'the history of science,' he admitted, 'is always richer than its rational reconstruction.'[89] But when the crunch came, in the end, he tried to lift himself up by his own bootstraps by claiming that rival methodologies can be evaluated by evaluating the rival histories of science to which they lead,[90] thus proving that he was not aware of the need to satisfy at least the 'Postulate of Sufficient Variety' discussed in chapter 2 above. He was oblivious of the fact that if that postulate is not satisfied, any effort to evaluate a methodology in terms of the history it leads to is a circular enterprise. Whichever way one is looking at him, he is running round in circles – an activity doubly regrettable because so unnecessary. One look at Popperian evolutionism rather than exclusive concentration on falsification and its problems, would have led Lakatos to grasp that the scientific enterprise is in two parts and that therefore his effort to introduce 'design' into part one is superfluous. Design, I repeat, results from the exposition of the events in part one to the events in part two. Design, in this lap of evolution, means progress towards truth.

A Lakatosian research programme is not a single theory enunciated by somebody at a certain time so that its presence is obvious, absolute and can be located. A research programme, on the contrary, is an over-arching set of assumptions which can only be detected if one studies a longish span of the history of science. One will then discover that certain scientific enterprises have been guided by a set of problems and assumptions called a research programme. The detection of the so-called Cartesian research programme is the result of historical study, not its presupposition. The mechanistic assumptions of this research programme – that the universe is a huge clockwork – was in competition with the Newtonian research programme. The Cartesian programme, unlike the Newtonian programme, discouraged research on action at a distance.[91] My point is that only historical knowledge can establish that this was so. But history has to be written before one can study it. The view that theory-formation is guided by research programmes presupposes the writing of history; the view that theory-formation about action at a distance was guided by the presence of a particular research programme presupposes a particular version of the history of science. Long before one can even start to assess whether a problem shift is progressive or degenerative, one has to have a history in order to know whether there was a research programme and, if there was, *what* the research programme was.

Let us look at examples. In most histories of science, we find that the Cartesian research programme exhibited generative problem shifts and was, for this reason, eventually abandoned in favour of the Newtonian programme which suggested research and theories about action at a distance. There is, however, nothing *absolute* about this particular history of science, even though it appears in a great many books. There was, in fact, a very good and plausible alternative to it. One could, for example, link Descartes's idea that things are shapes and that physics is part of geometry to Leibniz's idea that things are not only shapes but shapes and forces. This view leads to a new research programme in which one seeks to explain matter by a theory of space.[92] The degenerative shifts in that research programme were strong at first but have not led to a total eclipse. Eventually, the research programme of Leibniz came to be revived by Einstein's search for an overall theory of forces. This research programme, in which there was no room for theories about action at a distance, was enormously successful in its theory of gravitational fields in which it takes time for gravity to go from one place to another.[93] If one reads this version of history, neither changes nor eventual progress can be explained in terms of degenerative and progressive problem shifts. On strictly Lakatosian lines, Einstein's views on gravity, resulting from a research programme which had shown degenerative shifts for nearly two centuries, ought to have been kept out of journals and denied funds – which, to say the least, would have been a pity!

Or consider a different example. A few years ago, Brian Easlea published a book on the history of knowledge in the seventeenth century.[94] In this book, we find that magic was a research programme and that as the seventeenth century went by, it was abandoned because of degenerative problem shifts. However, and this is the crucial point, these problem shifts are not degenerative because they led to fewer and fewer problems and to less corroboration, but because there was a shift in psycho-metaphysical awareness. Magic as a research programme had been sustained and continued to show progressive shifts as long as people accepted a stance towards their environment which Easlea characterises as 'female submission'. When such submission gave way to 'male-oriented appropriation', the problem shifts in the programme became degenerative. Obviously, then, these problem shifts are not absolutely negative or absolutely progressive but they are so *relative* to a standard. In Easlea's history, the standard was whether people wanted to sever ties with Mother Earth in order to pursue a compulsive drive to prove their masculinity and virility by exploiting Mother Earth.[95] Anybody who has read his Jung and his Toynbee or his Alan Watts,[96] let alone his Freud, will recognise the viability of Easlea's meta-history. In reading the history which results from this meta-history, one can see that the criteria which enable us to decide whether problem shifts are degenerative or progressive depend on the history one has written, and are imported into it by the meta-history used. In some histories, the great competition was between the Descartes–Leibniz research programmes and the Newton research programme. In other histories, of which Easlea's is a good example, the competition was between the research programmes of magic and the Bacon–Descartes–Leibniz–Newton research programme. In the former, the criterion which determines whether a problem shift is degenerative or progressive was the question whether the attraction between bodies can be explained by the nature of bodies or not. In the latter, the criterion which determined whether shifts were degenerative or progressive was the question which vision of nature enabled masculine men to achieve power over Mother Nature and control her. In Easlea's history, once magic was going downhill, there was nothing much to choose between the Descartes–Leibniz programme and the Newton programme. The real competition was between programmes which promised power over nature; in this competition, the Baconian (non-mathematical) experimental philosophy, institutionalised in the 1660s in the Royal Society, was to win.[97] None of this helps us to pass judgment on any of these versions of history; but it does show firmly that our knowledge of research programmes and their degenerative and progressive problem shifts has to be derived from our knowledge of history. Like Kuhn and unlike Popper, Lakatos cannot make a contribution to our knowledge of the growth of knowledge.

In view of the inherent difficulties in the notion of falsification when it comes to the writing of the history of science, Lakatos's proposal that we consider the history of science as the history of research programmes has found wide support – even Popper himself has at times adopted the expression 'research programme'.[98] There have been several histories of science which have quite successfully described developments as degenerative and progressive shifts of research programmes. These histories seem to bear out Lakatos's contention that the dynamics of theory-change are determined not by falsification but by degenerative and progressive problem shifts in research programmes. Consider, for example, Peter Clark's paper on atomism versus thermodynamics.[99] Until around 1880, Clark shows, the succession of atomic–kinetic theories constituted a series of progressive problem shifts. But during the last part of the nineteenth century, Clark says, the progressive shifts ceased. Hence, the appearance of a new research programme – phenomenological thermodynamics – which started to show progressive problem shifts. Kuhn comments that this story sounds quite plausible, but that one could also write the history of the acceptance of the new research programme by telling how the old programme contained doubts all along and that the new programme emerged because of these doubts in the old programme – not because of the degenerative shifts in the old programme.[100] In other words, the detection of whether shifts are progressive or degenerative is only possible *after* one has written a history of the subject. And still on the history of thermodynamics, John Blackmore[101] has recently cast doubt on the idea that Boltzmann was engaged in a research programme which showed degenerative shifts and has suggested that these degenerative shifts are only apparent to historians who put 'too much stress on temporary and technical deficiencies which failed to bother people at the time.' Whatever the views of historians, it is clear that any judgment as to whether shifts are progressive or degenerative must always come after a history has been written, never before. As I argued above, it is not only the shifts in a research programme the detection and evaluation of which is consequent upon a history. Even the very presence of research programmes can only be ascertained after the history has been written. If one is looking at the debate between the caloric theory of heat and the vibration theory of heat, this will be clear. If one writes the history of the debate and the eventual triumph of the vibration theory in Lakatosian terms, one would say that the caloric theory began to show degenerative shifts and that therefore the vibration theory began to establish itself. However, one can also write the history of the debate without reference to research programmes. One can simply show that the vibration theory gained ground because it received open support from atomic theory, whereas the caloric theory did not. Here, we can see the dynamics of theories as the result of a coming together of two different theories which turned out to support each other.

Popperian philosophy of science, in connecting the growth of knowledge to organic evolution in general, offers in this way a new basis for the history of science. By encouraging us to divide it into two parts, it makes the whole task more manageable. True, the first part will remain difficult and untidy because it must contain reports about psychological vagaries and sociological conditions which have, in themselves, nothing to do with the story of science. But the second part, the part which deals with the selection of conjectures by error elimination, will become more tidy. Here, the subject-matter is circumscribed by rational and non-chance or anti-chance pressures. Using Popperian philosophy of science, the historian of science can, ideally, divide his task into two and make, at least on the second front, a positive and rationally intelligible contribution to the growth of knowledge. The first part cannot be left out. If it is, the story would cease to make sense. But by dividing the labour and by characterising clearly the differences between the two tasks, one can set about writing the history of science with a greater measure of certainty than the scene surveyed by Agassi would lead one to suspect.

Chapter 7

The Evolution of Evolution

The 'Tropic Principle'

The growth of scientific knowledge is only a special case of the growth of knowledge; and the growth of knowledge is a very special aspect of evolution. By evolution, I mean, here, not just the evolution of species or biological evolution, but the whole process of development which started with the Big Bang and has led, at the present moment, to the conditions of the universe in which we find ourselves. Little reflection is needed to understand that one can interpret the whole of evolution – physical, biological, cultural and scientific – as a growth of knowledge. There is always information transfer. Every evolutionary change – be it the emergence or fulguration of the heavy elements, be it the emergence of life, be it the growth of cultures or be it the growth of scientific knowledge – always consists in the growth of a system which grows by encoding information about its environment, i.e. the rest of the world or, in some cases, those parts of the world which are reasonably close to it. Every evolutionary change can be seen as a picture or coded statement about a system's environment. This picture is not a portrait or a mirror-image. Indeed, it bears no likeness to the object pictured at all, not even a structural likeness. It is more like a hologram than like a photograph, except that a hologram, when projected by the correct method, reproduces faithfully the scene it records. An evolutionary adaptation is like a hologram in that it does not contain any structural similarities with the scene recorded; it is unlike a hologram in that the information it contains rarely leads to a complete reconstruction of the scene it encodes. There is a lot of information about the air in every bird and in the gene pool of every bird species. But no amount of decoding will tell us everything about air.

For this reason, Popper's well-known epigram that evolution from the amoeba to Einstein is always the same has to be amended in two ways. First, it has to be amended because we have seen that from the amoeba to Einstein the path of evolution is by no means continuous, and that the discontinuities we have tracked down and described are not accidental interruptions but important detours. The negative sociology of knowledge tells us that the evolution of conscious knowledge is a rarity which is likely to take place only under very special social conditions when social bonding is either very loose or cognitively very neutral. Second, it has to be amended because when we see evolution as a growth of knowledge, it applies to pre-biotic and thus pre-amoebic times. The most general principle is that the environment always constrains the changes which can and will take place. The changes, read backwards, contain information about the environment. The presence of hydrogen, under certain conditions will yield helium; the presence and interaction of the two, given certain conditions of temperature and of the presence of the forces of nature (gravity, electro-magnetism, etc.), will yield other elements.

Throughout this kind of evolution there is at work a principle which we can call the 'Tropic Principle'. The environment always forces the changes which take place to take a certain 'turn' so that, given this 'turn', we can treat the changes as coded information about the environment. We can read back, from the presence and the nature of the heavier elements, what the universe must have been like before the heavier elements existed. From our galaxy or our solar system, we can trace back the conditions of the universe before our galaxy or our solar system existed. The 'Tropic Principle' is always at work and states that in all evolutionary change, there is a certain type of constraint between the environment and the results of evolution: the environment obliges changes to take a certain turn.

However, the nature of that constraint changes. We must distinguish: (1) pre-biotic evolution; (2) biotic or biological evolution; (3) cultural evolution; and (4) cognitive evolution or the evolution of knowledge.

In pre-biotic evolution, we get almost perfect constraint. Only such systems as are compatible with the environment evolve or are proposed. There is no 'trial-and-error' effort and one cannot say that the heavier elements have learnt to evolve. There are no conjectures and therefore no refutations. Only such proposals as are compatible with that kind of environment are made. The forces of nature together with the initial conditions do not make 'mistakes' which have to be weeded out; neither do they offer a variety of alternatives, some of which are more adaptive than others. This means that in this kind of evolution we get changes; but the changes are always *right* and there is no opportunity for selection. After every change, the resulting condition is therefore also a fairly accurate 'picture' or set of information about the earlier state or the environment.

With the advent of life, the pattern of change changes. We now get natural selection. Every time there is change, a variety of alternatives are proposed. These varieties compete with each other and those which are more adapted survive and the others die out, either immediately or after a span of time. The environment, here, selects, and the selection is always in favour of those organisms which encode more accurate information about the environment and against those organisms which encode less or no accurate information about the environment. The question of the accuracy of the information encoded in surviving organisms is extremely important. Most organisms which survive are underdetermined by their environment. They are only just compatible with it. This means that they contain accurate information about the environment, but that it is not accurate enough to enable an observer to reconstruct a complete picture of that environment from that information. Bearing in mind Uexküll's descriptions of the different worlds in which different organisms are living,[1] it is clear that each organism only encodes a sketchy description of its own environment. From its own point of view, it is accurate enough. One can think of progress in codification if one ranks those organisms which can infer information only about their own environment very low; and organisms which can derive information about the environment of other organisms very high. For example, *Homo sapiens* encodes information about man's environment as well as about the environment of the frog, but not the other way round.

With the emergence of consciousness, we get a further change in the nature of change. Conscious organisms can create falsehoods: they can lie and delude and deceive both themselves and others. Using deceits and falsehoods, they can construct artificial species which we call human societies and thus surround themselves with a wall of protection against the ravages of the environment. Hence, natural selection can be made to cease. In this way, cultures are created. The most elementary strategy used in the development of cultures is the artificial protection of knowledge from criticism. Certain pieces of knowledge, though obviously not all knowledge, are set aside and protected from critical appraisal. The thunder is identified with a god, the shadow of a man with his soul, and twins with cucumbers. Rational doubts are nipped in the bud by the mere absence of competing alternative proposals. Such protected knowledge can be used as a social bond. People who subscribe to it are members of a society; people who don't are outside that society. In this way, a lot of knowledge is syphoned off and used for non-cognitive purposes – that is, as a catechism. But such syphoning-off, though initially obviously counter-adaptive, is an oblique advantage. A society so constituted is larger than a group of people bonded by nothing but the web of kinship and is therefore capable of effective division of labour and co-operation. Thus, we get the astonishing spectacle of societies which cherish a mountain of false knowledge and which thrive for a long time not in spite of that false knowledge, but because of it. These cultures, though they are not coded information about the environment, have nevertheless enormous adaptive value. The information they encode is information about co-operation and division of labour as well as information about their relations, co-operative or hostile, with other societies, rather than information about their natural environment. Every culture makes division of labour and organised co-operation possible. This is an enormous advantage both for defence and for the provision of food and shelter. For this reason, cultures can survive by employing an oblique strategy, where natural selection – given the poverty of knowledge they harbour because of epistemic protectionism – would have made short shrift of them. The question of compatibility with the environment becomes relatively and, at times, totally irrelevant because division of labour and co-operation are more than ample substitutes for the environmental pressures which would have acted upon the gene pool of the population of any culture. In this sense, we now find a sort of evolutionary mercantilism or artificial protectionism. Mercantilism is the socio-economic strategy which made it possible for whole societies to provide for themselves the necessary food, shelter and defence in environments which were partially, or sometimes wholly, unsuitable. They achieved this by artificially protecting certain industries against competition so that they thrived where an open-market situation would have wiped them out. We can detect the same effects in cultural evolution and therefore speak of evolutionary mercantilism. As a result, the information encoded in any culture is only minimally relevant to the environment in which that culture manages to survive. That information is, for the most part, actually inaccurate and misleading. Culture employs an oblique strategy and, through consciousness, manages to invent institutions and habits which make up for the lack of accurate information.

The 'Tropic Principle' is nevertheless at work. One can learn very little about any environment by looking at any culture which exists in it. But one can learn a lot about the environment when one is looking at the consciousness and the nervous systems which make that mendacious culture possible. The information about the environment comes from the consciousness and the nervous systems of the people who have created the cultures.

Finally, under certain conditions of socio-cultural development, it becomes sometimes possible to release human knowledge from the job it had to be put to in cultural evolution. In cultural evolution, human knowledge was used to a large extent to act as a method of social bonding. Knowledge was in bondage to the need to create social bonds. In order to do the job of social bonding, it had to be protected from confrontation with the environment. As a social bond, false knowledge is as effective as, if not more effective than, correct knowledge. Cultures are built around entire systems of false knowledge, artificially protected from rational criticism. Such false knowledge can cover almost every field – from medicine to the belief in an immortal soul; from the belief that certain incantations will produce rain and certain rituals assure the fertility of the soil. They are doubly effective in promoting social behaviour because, not being exposed to rational criticism, they enshrine emotionally comforting and solidarity-producing attitudes. When it is possible – and there have been times and places where this has happened – to organise societies by methods other than grouping people around shared knowledge or shared beliefs, knowledge can be exposed to criticism and natural (i.e. critical) selection. Under these conditions, truthful knowledge can emerge in free and unlimited competition with false knowledge, and the accuracy and universality of such scientific knowledge can become very great. Such knowledge not only encodes information about the environment, but actually states information about the environment in a very explicit manner – by making use of concepts and language which can be written down so that it becomes an objective artefact or an artificial object.

In this last stage of evolution, the 'Tropic Principle' is at work because when knowledge is treated as knowledge, rational criticism will be completely selective and eliminate knowledge which is not compatible with the environment. The growth of knowledge will be subject to the 'Tropic Principle' by the mere fact of open competition. However, the process is here very complex, for the environment consists not only of nature, but also of cultures. Knowledge will be of both nature and cultures and also of those special cultures which have released knowledge from bondage to themselves and can, relying on different and non-cognitive bonds, afford free competition between theories and conjectures.

In the whole argument of the preceding chapter, evolution has been the key concept. We have argued that knowledge is historical, i.e. that it is an evolution. We have tried to show that the conditions which make the growth of science possible are governed by evolution and that the prevalence of societies in which science cannot grow is an evolutionary phenomenon. Similarly, we have seen that the most fertile philosophy of science is a philosophy which understands science as part of evolution and that the most intelligible way of writing the history of science is by using the evolutionary philosophy of science and an Evolutionary Epistemology which distinguishes between mutation and selection, or between the chance and the anti-chance factors. Again, by contrast, we have seen that all those philosophies of science which are non-evolutionary or anti-evolutionary in that they are based on the paradigm of closed systems which replace one another in a random, and non-evolutionary fashion, cannot do justice to the phenomenon of science.

Evolution as the key concept is quite specific. It does not mean, generally, that everything is in flux or that everything changes. It asserts very much more than that. It even asserts more than the minimum theory of progress. The conventional theory of progress asserts too much. It holds that we know of a goal and that we can align everything that has happened as a progression towards that goal. In this form, the theory of progress is clearly untenable, for we can have no knowledge of the goal which will withstand criticism. The minimum theory, however, asserts something perfectly plausible. It states that all change has been change away from a primitive condition. Evolution says a little bit more than this. It says that everything evolves in the sense that there is an incessant *selection* process of incessant mutations or inventions. This means that in evolutionary change some changes are favoured against others. At certain times, such selection is determined because no varieties or alternatives are proposed – as in the pre-biotic state. Nevertheless, on this level we can see that there are good reasons why the changes which have occurred were much more likely than those which have not occurred. At other times, selection is controlled by the environment in a ruthless and relentless manner – as when the environment selects for retention those changes which are more compatible with it than other changes. In this case, we speak of natural selection. We speak of artificial selection where conscious organisms invent oblique strategies for survival which, if left to natural selection, would be eliminated. In making division of labour and co-operation possible, these strategies compensate for any lack of 'fit' to the stark environment. And finally, in some rare cases, there is a conscious or critical selection (at a very fast rate) of theories which are directly informative about the environment. As a consequence, we detect evolution wherever we detect changes which were more likely than those which did not occur and wherever we find progressive selection of some changes and the elimination of others. Generally put, we speak of evolution wherever we see that the relation between change and the passage of time is not random. In every case of evolution, we have a response favoured or selected at the expense of another response. The selection is done by an independent system – a system which, however, may well be subject to evolutionary changes itself. The important point is that there is incessant interaction. On one side, there are the changes; and, on the other, the system which selects some changes rather than others. In the case of pre-biotic evolution, there is, of course, no real selection because all changes which take place are automatically correct changes which 'fit': the changes, here, are merely favoured.

Evolution has taken place whenever the result of change is compatible with the environment. The emphasis is on 'compatibility' and the leading question we have to ask is how this compatibility is achieved. When heavy atoms and molecules evolve, they are automatically compatible with the surrounding system of other atoms and molecules. Otherwise they would not have evolved. Incompatible changes do not take place in this part of the universe because all possible changes result from certain forces such as electro-magnetism, gravity, the weak force and the strong force, and alternatives which might have to compete for survival do not emerge. Hence, there is no selection because there is nothing to be selected from. One might say that this part of the universe is automatically self-selecting. When living organisms appear and divide or reproduce, the opportunity for error and novelty appears and, hence, there is a possibility of the appearance of systems which are incompatible with the environment or less compatible than others. Thus, there starts competition and, of course, selection. Some changes, unlike in that other part of the universe, are more compatible with the environment than others. The selection which now takes place is completely natural and both ruthless and relentless.

When organisms become conscious, they can shield themselves from the effects of the environment because they can build up artificial strategies to assure the survival of societies which are not very compatible with the environment. As a result of such artificial selection, 'non-fit' societies survive and flourish. They can become fit through the deviousness of their institutions. Division of labour, co-operation and solidarity resulting from adherence to a belief no matter how absurd, can hide multitudes of cognitive sins. There is selection; but the selection is not natural.

Next, we reach critical selection where conscious organisms propose a variety of consciously formulated theories about the environment and discard those which are not compatible with the environment. Here, the process of selection becomes again quite ruthless, though the consequences of making mistakes have to be evaluated critically rather than naturally. Here, it is very rare for the consequences of a failure in criticism to be experienced directly and fatally. The social system in which criticism can flourish is only cognitively neutral. Being a social system, it will nevertheless provide a lot of co-operative support and help protect its members from the fatal consequences of at least some errors.

Evolution and Historicism

Although the idea that everything is in constant change is very old, it received its teeth only during the last century with the emergence of a proper understanding of its procedure and of how that procedure can be described. The great breakthrough brought about first by Hutton and later by Lyell and Darwin was not the understanding that there is constant change, but the provision of a proper explanation of its procedure.

There is no need to tell again the story of how Hutton discovered uniformitarianism and opposed it to catastrophism; of how Lyell developed a proper methodology of change by pointing out that there are general laws which operate in the past as well as in the present, and how one can determine the nature of change by watching the way in which these laws transform initial conditions into something else; and of how Darwin absorbed the general methodology of Lyell during his long journey around the world. In modern times, this methodology was formally stated by Karl Popper in his account of 'causal explanation'. Popper argued as far back as 1934 (in his *The Logic of Scientific Discovery*) that a proper causal explanation consists in the deduction of a prognosis from an initial condition and a general law. This model of causal explanation has since been christened the 'Covering Law Model of Explanation', presumably because the two particular events – the initial condition and the prognosis – are brought into a causal relationship with each other by the help of the general law which could be said to 'cover' the two particular events which are, by themselves and without the general law, not connected with one another. The heart of this matter, from Hutton to Popper, is that one explains past effects in terms of presently acting causes. The real meaning of uniformitarianism is that one uses the same set of general laws to explain past events. If one does, one is a uniformitarian - even if and when such explanations result in the explanations of catastrophes rather than in explanations of uniformly gradual change. The debate about whether gradualism, saltationism or uniformism is true, is a debate about the substance of changes, not about their mode of operation and our method of describing them. When catastrophes or saltations occur, they are still capable of a uniformitarian explanation. Uniformitarianism can explain much more than mere gradual change.[2]

Unfortunately, in their enthusiastic espousal of evolution, most thinkers have made at least one of two fatal mistakes. Some believed that evolution by natural selection operates not only in biological evolution, but also in the history of mankind. An almost unbroken succession of thinkers – from Herbert Spencer to Konrad Lorenz and C.H. Waddington – has thus helped to bring the idea of evolution into disrepute. On the other side, there were thinkers who paid no attention to uniformitarianism and assumed, instead, that evolution is governed by a developmental law which determines human history. Here, we get a succession from Comte, Maine, and Morgan to Tylor and Frazer. These men were all historicists.[3]

Given these fundamental errors, it is not surprising that in our own century there has been a reaction against evolution outside the narrow field of biology. The discovery of anti-evolutionary functionalism and its explanatory potential in both anthropology and sociology helped to confirm the notion that all human societies are 'equidistant from God'. Such confirmation was aided by moral scruples about evolution. For if human societies evolve, some are more primitive than others; in our age of anti-colonialism, this implication of evolutionary thinking became ethically suspect. Finally, Karl Popper's famous attack on all forms of historicism did not help because it included a casual reference to Darwinism as a species of historicism.[4] For this reason, C.H. Waddington[5] believed that Popper had attacked Darwinism and rushed to a defence of historicism. Matters were not improved when Popper described Darwinism as a 'metaphysical' research programme and thus provoked Michael Ruse into a running battle against Popperian thought.[6] In reality, Popper himself has eventually formally withdrawn his earlier classification of Darwinism as historicism.[7] The matter can be put right if one recalls that Darwin's uniformitarian method, which explains past effects in terms of present causes, is impeccably Popperian and bears no likeness to any form of historicism. Moreover, Manfred Eigen has shown that 'fitness' can be understood without recourse to survival, so that the notion 'survival of the fittest' loses its tautological and therefore its metaphysical character.[8] Finally, the so-called Central Dogma of molecular biology has helped to make evolution by natural selection rather than by the inheritance of acquired characteristics a falsifiable, and therefore a non-metaphysical, theory.[9]

The Evolution of Evolutionary Mechanisms

The great obstacle to the reception of evolutionism is the difficulty one experiences in extending the principle of natural selection beyond the realm of biology. Darwin's theory of evolution was a theory about the origin of species and the descent of man. Darwin himself thought this evolution to be, at one end, continuous with the history of the earth and was, unfortunately, won over to see it as continuous at the other end by Herbert Spencer. But unlike Lyell, Spencer was not a good guide. Lyell's history of the earth was based on the sound methodology that one explains past effects in terms of presently acting causes; it made no reference to natural selection. Herbert Spencer, on the other side, made no reference to the sound methodology but transferred, instead, the principle of natural selection and the survival of the fittest to the history of societies and cultures. In order to disengage Darwin from Spencer, one has to find the common denominator in pre-biological, biological and cultural evolution.

This common denominator is the notion that, in all cases, the relationship between changes and the passage of time is not random and that therefore we can understand changes as a function of time. In other words, it is no accident that some events are earlier and others later. Apart from this common characteristic, biological and cultural evolution, though not pre-biological evolution, have a set of events in common. There is (1) mutation;[10] (2) the maintenance of invariance and (3) speciation. But in biological evolution, these three events are brought about by circumstances different from those by which they are brought about in cultural evolution. In culture, there are different mechanisms for mutation, invariance and speciation.

Finally, there is a difference between biological and cultural evolution. In biological evolution, changes and natural selection concern the individual organism but need the speciation of adaptive individuals to produce a large gene pool. If hybridisation occurs, especially if it occurs too rapidly, an adaptive mutation will be dispersed and lost too soon.[11]

In cultural evolution, the individual, though a biological organism, is almost completely subtracted from the process of biological evolution. The changes concern both individuals and collections of individuals (i.e. societies or cultures). It is therefore important to establish that in cultural evolution the unit to focus upon is not the species, but the pseudo-species.[12] If one thinks of cultural evolution and takes the biological species as the significant unit, one will be lost. Biologically, *Homo sapiens* is indeed a species. But culturally, *Homo sapiens* is a genus and the separate species are the innumerable societies formed by men. Indeed, human societies show very remarkable similarities to animal and plant species. To start with, human societies until quite recent times have erected artificial barriers to prohibit marriage between different societies so that, on the cultural level, the infertility which results from the mating of members of different biological species is reproduced artificially. Next, just as any species considers all other species as potential food, so any human society has always felt free to prey upon all other human societies. And finally, inside every human society great care is taken to protect and preserve the purity of the cultural strain by the nurture of a specific language, specific religion, specific rituals and traditions. This is the analogue of the biological fact that members of every species always reproduce like offspring. For these reasons, there is a real analogy between biological species and human societies, which one might consider therefore as quasi-species.

Evolution is subject to evolution. However it evolves, the relation between changes and the passage of time is not random. But the mechanisms which bring about this non-randomness of change and the units which evolved, are themselves evolving. Biologists have had no great difficulty in understanding that biological evolution has been subject to evolution, for there has been an evolution of sexual reproduction and of death. But beyond this, biologists themselves have shown the same resistance as everybody else. Biologists who have turned their attention to the history of man and culture, though admitting that education here takes the place of genetic inheritance, have proceeded as if natural selection and the survival of the fittest are still applicable. One only has to look at the last chapters of Konrad Lorenz's *Behind the Mirror* or at his famous *The Seven Deadly Sins of Mankind* (both of 1973) to see what happens when a biologist tries to extend evolution beyond biology. Lest it be thought that Lorenz is an exception, one will find the same shortcoming in Waddington's *The Ethical Animal* (1960) and in Bernard Rensch's *Biophilosophy* (1968). All in all, there is widespread resistance to the idea that evolution itself evolves.

When we speak of the evolution of evolution, we mean that there are, from time to time, thresholds beyond which, for certain parts of the universe, the mechanisms of evolution change. The general relation between the passage of time and change holds: it is not random.[13] But the absence of randomness results from different mechanisms in different parts of the universe.

On the pre-biotic or material level, evolution results quite simply from the operation of the forces of nature. One can reconstruct the evolution of the material universe with the help of the laws of gravity, electro-magnetism, the weak force, the strong force, the laws of thermodynamics, and so forth. One can reconstruct the evolution of the earth with the help of those laws and use, in addition, the laws about viscosity, friction, the action of water on rocks, and so forth.

With the emergence of life, the mechanisms of evolution change radically and drastically. We now get a completely different scenario. We get constant innovation through faults of reproduction. We get natural selection by the environment of those reproductions of living cells which are a better adaptation to the environment than others. Moreover, we get the formation of species because there has to be a gene pool which keeps to itself, lest the successfully adapted genes get too easily hybridised and diffused before they can reproduce at a fast rate among themselves. We get a maintenance of invariance through genetic copying to ensure that a given gene pool which is adapted survives.

With the emergence of consciousness we cross yet another threshold. It is impossible to locate this new threshold in time. We know that it is not to be linked to the appearance of *Homo sapiens* and we surmise that it might not be linked to any biological change at all, but that it might have taken place during the life-span of any of man's direct ancestors. We can, however, connect it to the emergence of consciousness and the formation of societies by ritual and myth or shared belief – of societies, in short, which were less volatile than troupes of non-human primates. Non-human primates are quite 'social'. But their sociability is a sociability which comes from the primary bond between mother and babies, and the pair bonds between male and female. These bonds are not lasting and rarely last for more than the life-time of the members. Moreover, they do not provide sufficient basis for organised division of labour and co-operation beyond the immediate tasks in hand, such as rearing the young, getting food and keeping watch for predators. The emergence of human or hominid societies represents a change in quality. These new societies emerge because they use an invention of a ritual or a myth or both in order to form a lasting social bond. People marry inside that bond and the next generation grows up inside that bond. Educated in the prevalent ritual and myth, the next generation continues to nurture that particular bond instead of drifting away. The mechanisms of evolution now change. Mutation is brought about by inventions. Invariance is maintained by education; and societies are formed because people group themselves around new inventions. Co-operation brings natural selection to a standstill. Mutations (i.e. inventions) are not adaptive because they fit the environment, but because they enable people to form a society. They are selected not by their degree of adaptiveness to nature and do not compete with other adaptive mutations, but because they perform a social function. In so far as they can be used as a social bond, they make division of labour and co-operation possible within a given circle. They are selected, usually naturally, for maintenance or retention because of this function, but not because they are a fit to the environment. We thus get the seemingly strange phenomenon that inventions which are not a fit to nature are nevertheless passed on by education. In fact, since 'fitting nature' is not the criterion of selection in this case, there is a sort of inverse proportion between being selected and being non-fitting. The more absurd an invention, the more likely its usefulness as a social bond. This seeming paradox is not hard to explain. The formation of society is supposed to be a brake on natural selection. It is a strategy to frustrate the survival of the fittest and to replace that survival by the survival of a group whose members co-operate with each other. Hence, the bond most likely to succeed in this purpose is the sort of knowledge which is the most absurd or the most false and which would, if held by a non-social organism, lead to almost certain distinction.

After this threshold is passed, we still recognise the operation of evolution. There is mutation, maintenance of invariance and, after the inventions, 'speciation' or formation of exclusive societies. However, knowledge is held in bondage and cannot grow because it must, for society's sake, be protected against criticism. Where knowledge is used as a social bond, people cannot afford the luxury of exposing it to criticism, lest their co-operation be endangered or cease.

In the modern world and only in very recent times and some parts of the world, men have crossed yet another threshold. They have managed to establish societies which are not dependent on the preservation of the purity of any given cultural strain and which are bonded by criteria other than the adherence to any particular belief system and its rituals. In the earlier primitive societies, membership had been defined by adherence to the catechism and everybody who was not explicitly included was excluded. In the modern, non-primitive societies, definition works the other way round. People who are excluded are specifically defined and all people who are not so defined are deemed to be included, regardless of the catechism, if any, to which they subscribe. Such a principle of residual inclusion of anybody no matter what his race, religion, belief or habits are, is a fairly neutral principle of inclusion. In those societies, evolution has taken yet a new turn. It has made the development of rational knowledge about the natural world and about human societies possible by subjecting any theory which is invented to radical, no-holds-barred, criticism. When, and only when, this threshold is crossed and where it is crossed, can we find the growth of knowledge. Its evolution is governed by critical discussion and its possibility depends on the presence of neutral social structures which are not damaged or eroded by the criticism of theories because the theories offered for radical criticism are released from the job which they used to perform on the pre-scientific level. Under these conditions of radical criticism, only very few theories are selected for retention; among those which are selected, there is further competition so that those which are more universal are selected at the expense of those which are less universal. Invariance is maintained over shortish periods by the practice of what Kuhn has called 'normal science'. This invariance depends on learning and teaching and on the presence of scientific institutions. The place of mutation is taken by inventions. Inventions are proposed in a manner which is random relative to the process of selection; but not altogether random relative to the cultural context in which the inventions are made. All this has been discussed more fully in earlier chapters. Here, it is merely recapitulated in order to show where rational criticism and scientific practice belong in the evolution of evolution.

The evolution of evolution is not a historicist idea. It is not claimed that there are stages in evolutionary mechanisms and that these stages have to take place in obedience to a developmental law which says that they have to take place. The stages can be distinguished because of the thresholds; and the thresholds, in turn, are crossed or brought about by the changes in the nature of the subject-matter. The emergence of living cells, the emergence of human societies, and the emergence of human societies sufficiently neutrally bonded to allow critical discussion of knowledge – these are the three most obvious thresholds. At each threshold, the mechanisms of evolution change in response to the changes in the evolving subject-matter. The resulting series – the evolution of evolution – can be explained, and its existence is not the result of a developmental law.

In every phase, we use the theory of evolution. For all phases, the theory that evolution has evolved can be used as a theory in terms of which particular events can be chosen and linked to each other to make a continuing series. This series, as was explained in chapter 2, is not identical with the time series. The theory of evolution and the theory of the evolution of evolution is a meta-history. It is a theory with the help of which one can compose historical series. The theory itself, however, cannot be inferred from watching history. It helps us to construct one *historia rerum gestarum*; but its truth cannot be established inductively from the study of *res gestae*.

The term 'meta-history' is comparatively new. It was first used by Hayden White, in 1973, in order to describe the non-historical ingredients in every historical narrative. In his *Metahistory*, Hayden White brought out the meta-historical elements in some major nineteenth-century historians. The idea that there always must be a meta-history in every history is, however, not new. Gibbon referred to it explicitly in his autobiography when he explained how his own experience in the Hampshire Grenadiers had proved useful for an understanding of Roman military institutions. F.M. Cornford laid bare, in 1907, the meta-historical elements in Thucydides which he had culled from Aeschylus and the tradition of Greek tragedy. In my *The Shapes of Time,* I have explained in general terms why it is impossible to compose a historical narrative or any historical sequence without a meta-history. One of the most detailed meta-histories we have is the biological theory of evolution, which enables biologists to narrate the actual history of biological organisms from the hyper-cycle and the primeval 'soup' to the emergence of *Homo sapiens*. There are, to be sure, many debates about the details of this meta-history. But as meta-histories go, we have here more consensus and more structured detail than in the meta-history for cultures. Above, I have attempted a brief sketch of a meta-history for narrating the evolution of cultures by indicating the changes we have to make to the meta-history of biological evolution if we want to use an evolutionary meta-history for the evolution of cultures. But this meta-history is still a wide-open field and will probably remain one for many years to come. When we come to the most recent part of the evolution of evolution – to the evolution of science – I have argued in chapter 6 that Popper's philosophy of science provides very sure ground for a meta-history of the history of science and the growth of knowledge.

The Adaptive Prostitution of Knowledge

Like our forebears in the plant and higher animal kingdoms, we humans store correct knowledge. In our pre-human forebears, this knowledge is stored in the gene pools of populations and is species-specific, so that each species has a different knowledge of the reality it lives in because each species is a temporarily successful adaptation to a specific environment. In human beings, this knowledge is partly stored in the gene pools and partly held collectively in the memories and traditions of each society. This knowledge is not the private opinions or convictions of individuals. Human beings know what to eat, what foods are poisonous, how to conceive babies, how to deliver them, how to rear them and how to hunt or gather food. Without such correct knowledge, handed down from generation to generation, human beings could not survive.

With the enlargement of the brain and the development of the neo-cortex, this knowledge became consciously held knowledge. There is an enormous evolutionary advantage in consciously held knowledge. When knowledge is held consciously, every individual can make experiments in thought and try out very quickly a large variety of possibilities and conjectures in order to decide which might be the most suitable conjecture. In such a situation, the process of selection ceases to be natural and becomes critical. The evolutionary advantage of conscious selection consists in the fact that there is a great saving in time, energy and risks. When knowledge is held consciously, its holders can learn by trial and error. They do not have to wait for their genes to be outnumbered and bred out of existence by genes which store more suitable knowledge. Organisms which hold knowledge consciously can provide an enormously fast turnover of knowledge. The extraordinary fact, however, is that this clearly advantageous energy-, time- and risk-saving strategy was rarely followed and, in most cases, after the acquisition of basic information about food and elementary conduct of life, not followed. Why?

There is no disagreement in regard to the presence of consciousness. But there is enormous disagreement as to the manner of its evolution. This disagreement is in part due to the vast areas of doubt surrounding the precise nature of the phenomenon of consciousness. There are philosophers who maintain that consciousness is simply another word for the operations of the nervous system. Other philosophers believe that consciousness is a mental state which interacts with the nervous system without being reducible to it. Some hold this interaction to be of a causal nature and that it consists therefore in a one-to-one relationship; others maintain that there is no one-to-one correspondence between mind and nervous system but that the two interact only tangentially and intermittently. The debate and the disagreements are very old and there is no sign that our recent enormous advances in neurology and neuro-science have shed any clear light on the matter. The disagreements are profound and the evidence inconclusive. One of the basic difficulties in the debate about consciousness is the difficulty – ought we to say impossibility? – of registering consciousness as anything other than consciousness or awareness. We can be aware of being aware and we can be aware of being aware of something that is happening at the same time. But we cannot be aware of something that is happening at the same time unless we are aware of that something. None of this proves that awareness does not have non-awareness correlates; but it does mean that by the nature of the case we cannot detect them if they are there. There is a lot to be said for the view that the problem is incapable of solution because we are really trying to use the human brain to make conjectures about itself. The hope of making a successful conjecture might be doomed because no system can completely refer to itself or understand itself in its own terms. By the nature of the case, there is no outside system, no external reference. As a result of this gap in our knowledge, it has been impossible to form a viable theory as to how consciousness emerged – for we do not really know what sort of emergence we are looking for.

However this may be and however mysterious the emergence of consciousness is, we have made some progress in determining the time at which it emerged. With the help of palaeontology and archaeology it has been possible to find clear evidence of the presence of consciousness in certain places and at certain times. The most striking evidence comes from the history of primitive flints. Many primates are known to use sticks and stones to find or hunt food. Early hominids followed this practice and there is no reason for assuming that one has to be conscious to make use of such simple tools. Unlike non-human primates, hominids appear to have chosen special stones for hunting. Obviously, some stones are more efficient than others. Trial and error will tell and one does not have to be *conscious* to learn to select the most suitable stones. Suitably shaped stones can be found lying around and when they are not lying around, other stones can be shaped to imitate those which have been found most useful. This, again, is an imitative process and does not require consciousness. The change *must* have come when hominids created stones rather than imitated existing shapes. The first flints made as artefacts rather than as imitations of existing stones can only have been created by a *conscious* mind, for to make an artefact one has to have an 'image' as to what one wants to make. One has to think before the actual making. To have an image presupposes some kind of language or linguistically formed and defined imagery. If one makes a copy, one follows precedent. This can be done without consciousness. But if one makes a *new* shape, a shape which is not a copy and which does not already exist, one has to be able to imagine. We know of teardrop hand-axes of the Acheulean industry which were made about one and a half million years ago and which are associated with *Homo erectus*. This *Homo erectus*, therefore, must have been capable or possessed some kind of consciousness.[14] The whole question is, of course, bedevilled by lack of further evidence. Conscious hominids may have evolved and then, because of lack of population density and absence of competition, subsided again.

Other important evidence comes from the discovery of symbols. When Neanderthal man performed ritual burials, he was doing something which is neither biologically nor economically necessary. He was doing something which, in terms of mere survival at that time, was superfluous. An unceremonial disposal of the body would have done equally well and possibly better because it would not have consumed rare commodities and precious time. Hence, we must conclude that when he performed a ritual burial, he was doing so in response to some kind of awareness. He must have been conscious of something. In the absence of actual evidence, we are also forced to speculate that consciousness must have emerged when people started to lie, to hallucinate, to have delusions, to simulate and to deceive either themselves or others. The creation of such 'alterity' – of images and of behaviour which is not a copy of what people actually find in their environment – is a creation of an artefact which requires consciousness. Many animals have learnt to simulate to protect themselves against predators. But such simulation is the result of natural selection. Those insects which did not look like sticks were found too easily by birds to survive. It would be absurd to postulate 'consciousness' in this kind of simulation. But a hominid who simulates a turn to the right when he means to turn left, or who hides his captured prey to avoid having to share it with his family, must be consciously intending to gain an advantage.

The emergence of consciousness, by whatever means, almost immediately produces a positive feedback and therefore increases itself in strength. The positive feedback can be imagined to work in the following way. Many animals are capable of some kind of memory and such memory becomes quite developed as evolution approaches the higher primates. With the emergence of consciousness, hominids become also conscious of memory. Consciousness of memory is bound to produce a startling result. When one is conscious of remembering, as distinct from just remembering, one is also conscious of being able to envisage events which are *no longer* present. As soon as one can do this, one can envisage the possibility of events which are *not yet* present and which one can choose to *make* happen. The ability to think of something which is other than what is in front of one's eyes is thus increased by one's ability to see events which are no longer in front of one's eyes. Consciousness of memory, therefore, enlarges and increases consciousness of alterity, of possibilities which have not yet been realised. One could almost say that the invention of alterities is a forward extension of memory – at least of the consciousness of memories.

There is, therefore, no doubt that consciousness emerged and no doubt that its emergence is a tremendous advantage. The amazing thing is that such consciousness was widely misused and not permitted straightway to operate in the purely biological sense of assisting the acquisition of knowledge. If one considers the speed and the saving of energy which would have resulted in the acquisition of knowledge if consciously held knowledge had been exposed to experiments and tests so that wrong conjectures could have been eliminated, it comes as an enormous surprise when one finds that, for over a million years after the acquisition of consciousness, human beings took no direct advantage of their consciousness. From the point of biological evolution, they proceeded almost immediately to put it mainly to the wrong use. For conscious knowledge to be used adaptively, it would have to be exposed to the environment so that natural selection could take place and scientific progress begin. Instead, we find that in all cases, apart from the exception of minor beginnings, progress was halted and conscious knowledge put to a *different* use. Being put to a different use, the coming of science was delayed and could easily have been prevented altogether.

In order to account for this curious fact, we have to take a closer look at the character of consciousness. Human beings had acquired, of course, basic information about their environment long before the emergence of consciousness. They knew how to get food and how to rear their babies. They would not have been there had they not 'known'. With the emergence of consciousness, they could have vastly increased their store of correct information very quickly. They did not do so because of the curious quality of consciousness. Consciousness is, among other things a sort of 'empty noetic experience', as J.N. Findlay once put it. It is an ineffable awareness of awareness. Had it been just that, it would have had very little evolutionary advantage and might never have appeared or been selected for retention when it did appear. But the strange fact is that this empty noetic experience is, to quote Findlay again,

> in no sense devoid of an analogue of sensory content: everything illustrated in sense is also capable of existing in and for the intellect . . . The precise pattern of an odd face, or the turns and twists of a melody, or anything else however dependent on sense for its full presentation, may live on intact as 'an abiding mood in the soul' (to use Lotze's telling phrase) long after its sensed or imagined presence has vanished. And there is, further, a necessary logical relation of sensuous to noetic presentation in the

> case of all things capable of being sensorily given at all: they could not be noetically given, if they were not also capable of being sensuously given, and we may add, vice versa.[15]

Whether consciousness first generates an uneasy and dimly perceived spiritual (noetic) awareness or whether this noetic awareness is a precondition or consequence of sensory awareness, does not really matter for our present case. The important thing is that since the noetic awareness is inevitably present but cannot be clearly apprehended or expressed, it gives rise to sensory images which, in turn, give rise to myths and rituals, to stories and performances which are biologically unnecessary but which bear witness to, or express, noetic awareness. It is thus this 'extra' element of consciousness which eventually leads to the formulation of a whole set of propositions and beliefs whose appearance and form are not distinguishable from propositions or instructions about how to hunt, how to educate children, how to build huts, what to eat, and so forth. Thus, we get speculation about life and death, about fertility and spirit, about power and health, which is formally indistinguishable from knowledge about the things which are necessary for physical survival.

If this 'extra' knowledge derived from, or generated by, the 'extra' element in consciousness had been exposed to natural selection, it would have disappeared almost immediately. But it was not exposed to natural selection because it clearly had an oblique usefulness. When turned into a catechism, it could be made to serve as a social bond. All people who shared a certain catechism were excluded from another catechism. In this way, the extra knowledge could become the social bond for a human society. Ordinary knowledge, acquired by trial and error and selected naturally for retention, could not have done this trick. It was shared by all humans and possibly by some animals and non-human primates. To form small groups distinct from other small groups of the same biological species – to form pseudo-species – it was necessary to use propositional knowledge which differed essentially from propositional knowledge similarly used by another group. Only 'false' knowledge can, in this sense, be sufficiently exclusive of beings which belong to the same biological species. 'Correct' knowledge would not have been able to provide a criterion of exclusion, for correct knowledge could be shared by members of other societies. Hence was born the famous maxim: *extra ecclesiam nulla salus*. This maxim would have lost its meaning and its usefulness had the definition of *ecclesia* consisted of correct knowledge. If it had, nothing would have been outside it; or, better, people who were outside would soon have come in and the maxim would have lost its point. With everybody in, it could not have distinguished those people who were supposed to divide labour co-operatively from those who were supposed not to divide labour but were available as prey. A single human being could, biologically, have survived if not alone – at least in membership of any human group at all. In order to make sure that he would stick with one group through thick and thin and keep away from all other groups, he had to be catechised. Through education, he had to share the given group's propositional beliefs about spirits and powers, about fertility, magic and immortality or reincarnation.

Such epistemological lunacy – for this was, from a purely biological point of view, genuine lunacy – had, however, an immediate enormous advantage. A group whose members are exclusively committed to one another provides solidarity and co-operation. It makes possible the division of labour and creates stable and enduring social structures across several generations – all things which even the most advanced non-human primates are completely unable to achieve. Such an achievement then becomes, in turn, biologically valuable because it improves the survival chances of a well-structured group. It does so, paradoxically, through this kind of epistemological lunacy. To make sure that knowledge remains false and that false knowledge is always available, knowledge has to be protected from natural selection. It has to be held dogmatically. The maintenance of dogma in large societies and in dispersed societies like the Catholic church is institutionally quite tricky and fraught with many difficulties. But in a small society, one simply has to insist that there be no marriage outside the small society, no social intercourse, no taking of meals together. A perfect isolation produces automatically perfect protection for the knowledge which is not treated as information about the environment but as a social bond. Knowledge is placed in bondage to society and societies which grow on the basis of the knowledge they hold in bondage are indeed well bonded. The pursuit of knowledge is diverted from its natural path. As long as there is good insulation, any individual member who has original ideas can conveniently be treated as a deviant. With the growing disappearance of perfect insulation, the definition of deviance becomes correspondingly difficult both to enforce and to justify intellectually.

In this way the evolution of consciousness does not, in the first instance, lead to an increase in genuine knowledge nor to a speeding-up of the growth of knowledge, but to an increase in *false* knowledge (if this contradiction in terms be permitted). Intellectual mercantilism or protectionism and epistemological lunacy are nevertheless evolutionary strategies which usher in, across the threshold from one set of evolutionary mechanisms to another, a new evolution of evolution. They yield an oblique reward – oblique, that is, when measured against the mechanisms of purely biological evolution by chance mutations and selective retention of those mutations which are a good 'fit' to the environment. In the new mechanism, the environment by itself tends to recede into the background. Societies form pseudo-species and manage to survive because they can, through the cultivation of false knowledge, provide social bonding. Moreover, inside the socially bonded area, there is a chance for a cognitive apparatus to develop. This cognitive apparatus develops best under intellectual protectionism. Its scope is enormous. It extends from the acquisition of reading and writing to the cultivation of quite complex intellectual discussion, even though such discussion remains in the grip of false knowledge. One can practise a large number of logical skills by discussing the implications of the proposition that God is omnipotent or that twins are cucumbers, even though one cannot afford to criticise the proposition itself.

In earlier chapters we have, from time to time, expressed serious criticism of the project conceived by the substantive sociology of knowledge which, in contrast to the negative sociology of knowledge, sought to devalue all knowledge by reducing it to a narcissistic reflection of society in the mirror of society. We now must face an even more serious criticism. Culture, we have argued, interferes with knowledge by protecting us from the consequences of falsehood and, in doing so, creates co-operation and solidarity which, in turn, have an adaptive advantage. The misuse of knowledge, in other words, can lead to an interference with the natural and critical selection of true theories and such interference can nevertheless have adaptive advantages.

This gives the lie to those sociologies of knowledge which assume that culture interferes with knowledge by creating bias, self-interest and class interest in order to serve communities or classes or dynasties. Jürgen Habermas suggests that we can seek to combat this kind of interference by focusing on an 'ideal-speech situation'. By this, he means that we can always imagine what we would have said in a given situation had we not been misguided or misled or seduced by partisan interest and then subtract it from culture-conditioned knowledge. What will be left, Habermas suggests, will be the truth. The so-called 'ideal-speech situation' is an idealised version of the absolute. It is certainly a version of something absolute; and since it is so unlikely a version, one must think of it as an 'idealised' version of the absolute, if such a thought is possible. The absolute is already something idealised; but Habermas's introduction of the absolute is nothing if not an idealised version of something idealised. This idealised version of the absolute assumes that culture's interference with knowledge is a straight distortion which one can isolate and diagnose in terms of a partisan interest, and that one can get the truth by subtracting what one has diagnosed from total knowledge. What one will be left with, Habermas says, will be the truth, i.e. what one would have said had one been in an 'ideal-speech situation'. However, as we have seen – gross and strident exceptions apart – the social interference with knowledge is not a matter of bias or self-interest; but results from the use of knowledge as a social bond. Such bonding is obliquely adaptive and therefore very different from the vulgar bias Habermas thinks it is subject to. Habermas sees in the cultural distortion of the truth nothing but self-interest and self-serving policies. He fails to recognise the oblique advantage of catechismic societies. On the other hand, societies which do not stand in need of this kind of social bonding, expose all knowledge automatically to criticism so that Habermas's strategy would appear redundant. Neutrally bonded societies can afford the luxury of the growth of knowledge by critical competition and do not have to resort to an idealised absolute like 'ideal-speech situation'. Habermas and many other advocates of the need for a sociology of knowledge appear to misunderstand the important role which captive or bonded knowledge has to play in cultural evolution.

The Conflict between Science and Religion: From Transcendental Idealism to Hypothetical Realism

Thus the stage was set for a problem of enormous importance which has proved intellectually challenging and very time consuming: the conflict between science and religion. Unless one has a proper philosophy of science, it is notoriously difficult to distinguish the vast amounts of false knowledge which have been pressed into the service of social bonding from genuine scientific knowledge – that is, from knowledge which is left standing when all conceivable criticisms have been temporarily exhausted. Obviously, as was indicated, the two had to exist side by side right from the beginnings of cultural evolution. Without a minimum of genuine knowledge, no society could have kept going. But the minimum was usually quite small and there was never a limit to the amount of false knowledge that was hitched to it. Both types of knowledge had to be withdrawn from the simple process of natural selection. If they had both been exposed, the false knowledge would not have been able to do its social job and since there was no way of distinguishing the one from the other and allow the one to be exposed and the other to be protected, both kinds of knowledge had to remain mixed up and equally protected. As mankind grew in numbers, more and more societies, each carrying its own set of beliefs, came to rub shoulders. There began, inevitably, a clash of different knowledge systems. From the sixth century BC onwards, we find a large number of attempts to cope with these clashes intellectually. Since there was no clear method in which the false could be distinguished from the true, there were really only three strategies available, each of which was employed at one time or another. The first strategy found its finest manifestation in Louis XII, the saintly thirteenth-century King of France who declared that when confronted with a 'heretic', he would run his sword through him rather than argue. Whatever one might think of this saint's morals, one has to concede that he had a firm grasp of the insuperable intellectual difficulties involved in the situation. When one cannot distinguish, on the basis of a proper philosophy of science, between science and non-science, all intellectual debate about who is right and who is wrong is really a non-debate. Hence, the royal saint's sword.

The second strategy was morally impeccable, but intellectually very cumbersome. It was started quite early, by the Prophet Isaiah in Israel and by the Ionian philosophers in Asia Minor. It consisted in the reinterpretation of old pieces of knowledge. When one has two propositions which are held in two different societies but which are incompatible with one another, one can try to resolve the conflict by arguing that they are *really* compatible provided one understands them in a new way or considers one to be a prefiguration of the other. Thus Isaiah claimed that circumcision should not be taken literally but should be seen to foreshadow the 'circumcision of the heart', i.e. an act of humility to God. The Ionian philosophers, right down to Hesiod himself, used ancient Babylonian and Hittite mythology and reinterpreted it to produce their own cosmogonies which had a much clearer air of verisimilitude about them. When the Christian Fathers of the Church came face to face with the science and philosophy of the ancient Greeks, they tried similar reinterpretations and reconciliations. Plato, they said, had been a sort of Moses of Attica; or the other way round. When confronted with the tribal lore of the Old Testament, they said that the passage of the children through the Red Sea had prefigured, dimly, the ritual of Christian baptism and that Abraham's sacrifice had prefigured the redemptive sacrifice of God's own Son on the cross.

The third strategy was also the most ambitious. It attempted to reconcile intellectually conflicting systems of knowledge. Its finest representative was St Thomas Aquinas. St Thomas sought to distinguish between rational knowledge and revealed knowledge and argued that there could be no real, though at times an apparent, conflict between the two because God had not only revealed certain propositions but had also created human reason. One would therefore have to assume that the knowledge yielded by one source would have to be compatible with and complementary to knowledge derived from the other. In the light of our modern hindsight, however, St Thomas's effort was nothing more than a valiant apologia for our inability to distinguish between the artificially protected, and hence false, knowledge and those few pieces of true knowledge which had to be available.

The conflict between science and religion began in earnest during the seventeenth century. There are many explanations why knowledge began to be exposed to the environment and why the protective mercantilism which had prevailed came, at that time, to an end. I would like to propose, without infringing on other views of this matter, that it came to an end because societies in Western Europe at that time began to find alternative social bonds and were therefore able to release knowledge from its social duties. In this way, scientists were able to test theories, propose alternatives, weigh them and compare them. The order of release was very slow in coming and many scientists in that century took great care to avoid too stark a confrontation with the traditional pieces of knowledge which, though they no longer performed the old job of social bonding, were often still *believed* to do so. Further, it is really impossible to say whether the growth of scientific knowledge and the sorting out of false knowledge from true knowledge at that time was the cause or the result of the coming of alternative social bonds. However this may be, the sorting out was started and grew rapidly. There remained a certain amount of cross-fertilisation, stretching from the influence of Kepler's solar mysticism on his determination to find the planetary orbits to Einstein's reason for objecting to the Copenhagen interpretation of Quantum Mechanics on the ground that 'God does not play dice.' Bit by bit, the religious knowledge about the soul, about immortality, about divine Providence and the design, about creation and the age of the earth, disappeared. It was found wanting and could not survive in the struggle for existence. Exposed to criticism, it failed to be selected for retention.

The growth of knowledge was accompanied by great emotional ravages. As the older knowledge had been protected from natural selection and not exposed to radical criticism, it is not surprising that in almost all cases it should have been fashioned in a way that was somehow comforting to the human condition. As it was free to grow without external control as long as it performed the useful function of social bonding, the framers of this knowledge took liberties to please themselves and their fellow-men. This knowledge contained comforts about immortality and rewards for good behaviour and contained information about a built-in purpose to promote confidence in an ultimate meaning of human life. Today, in the second half of the twentieth century, we have become so used to living without the comforts of religion that it is at times hard to imagine the emotional agonies, the soul-searching and soul-searing pain caused by the disappearance of the customary religious comforts. They are frequently described in nineteenth-century novels and it is sufficient to refer to George Eliot's *Middlemarch*, Jakobson's *Niels Lyne* and to the struggles of Ivan in Dostoievsky's *Brothers Karamasov*. Nietzsche always strikes one as the most heroic real-life victim. 'If there were a God,' he exclaimed, 'how could I bear not be Him?' There was no God and he could not bear it. There is no real evidence that his tragic illness was the direct result of his intellectual torment; but the two certainly run along parallel lines – a theme beautifully treated and elaborated by Thomas Mann in his Nietzsche novel, *Dr Faustus*.

The Enlightenment, of course, had to triumph. Here, we get a long line of theories to account for the millennia in which people had espoused religious knowledge and had been comforted. Voltaire argued that the delusions had been due to the cunning of priests. Marx suggested that the delusions had been invented and fostered by the exploiting classes to keep the exploited classes drugged with the comfort of opium. If one could distinguish between knowledge used for political suppression and economic exploitation and knowledge not so used, Marx said, one could separate science from religion. Unfortunately, most of his modern disciples refuse to make this distinction and tend to see even natural science as a strategy for the exploitation of the proletariat and the Third World. Freud maintained that these false beliefs were childhood projections of wish dreams, infantile neuroses of dreams of omnipotence and immortality. If one could help people to mature emotionally, he said, one could help them to distinguish genuine knowledge from neurotic fantasies. The last chapter in this Enlightenment saga was written by Jean-Paul Sartre and by Bertrand Russell, who came, independently, to very similar conclusions. Sartre described that contrary to traditional belief, this world consists of nothing but 'contingencies' and accidents; our realisation of this situation caused 'nausea'. His hero Roquentin is sitting in a park, gazing at a chestnut tree. Its blackness is

> like a bruise or a secretion, like an oozing – and something else,
> an odour, for example; it melted into the odour of wet earth,
> warm, moist wood, into a black odour that spread like varnish
> over this sensitive wood, in a flavour of chewed, sweet fibre.
> [Roquentin is] plunged into horrible ecstasy . . . I mean that one
> cannot define existence as necessity. To exist is simply *to be there.*[16]

Bertrand Russell in his celebrated essay 'A Free Man's Worship' (1902) described the whirling atoms which accidentally have produced human beings:

> Man is the product of causes that had no prevision of the end they were achieving; . . . his origin, his growth, his hopes and fears, his loves and beliefs, are but the outcome of accidental collisions of atoms . . . Only within the scaffolding of these truths, only on the firm foundations of unyielding despair, can the soul's habitation henceforth be safely built. How, in such an alien and inhuman world can so powerless a creature as Man preserve his aspirations untarnished? A strange mystery it is that Nature, omnipotent but blind, in the revolutions of her secular hurryings through the abysses of space, has brought forth a child, gifted with sight . . . with the capacity of judging all the works of his unthinking Mother.[17]

Both Sartre and Russell see man as an accidental and fortuitous intruder upon a scenario with which he has absolutely nothing to do – literally, he is like an alien from outer space, bringing thought and feeling, habits of meaning and necessity, into a world in which they have absolutely no place. The difference between Sartre and Russell is that where Sartre felt nausea at the realisation of the human condition, Russell claimed to experience some kind of elation.

The conflict between science and religion had to be decided in favour of science. The question we have to ask ourselves, however, is whether Sartre's nausea or Russell's elation was justified. The position of man's hopes and the question of the meaning of life appear more complex than either Sartre or Russell, let alone Freud or Marx, had envisaged.

Let us return for a moment to Darwin. Darwin had been very conscious of the enormity of his theory of evolution by natural selection and the well-known reaction of Bishop Wilberforce, to mention a dramatic instance, is proof that he was right in sensing the enormity of his theory. But Darwin had perceived – though in his own age there was no knowledge of chemistry, molecular biology or cosmology to support this perception – that while he had rejected the argument *from* design, he could not question the view that there *is* design brought about by natural selection. The argument from design had simply asserted that since there are so many 'fits' in the universe, God must have created and designed it. The theory of evolution by natural selection cannot possibly accept such reasoning. But it had become obvious to Darwin, and has since become more and more obvious to many other people, that natural selection produces design and that the Sartrean and Russellian views of contingencies and accidents are untenable – regardless of whether one treats them as an occasion for nausea or an occasion for elation.

The central figure in this story is Immanuel Kant. In order to solve the thorny question of how we can know the regularities of nature as presented in Newtonian Mechanics, Kant had proposed that we do not learn them from nature but that the human mind prescribes them to nature. Since all tests and all experiences conceivable for testing our knowledge of these regularities have to pass through the same human mind which imposes these regularities upon nature, there is no chance at all that we may one day discover, in making observation, that there are no such regularities. This volte-face of all thinking was described by Kant as a sort of Copernican Revolution.

There was a deep irony in his choice of Copernicus as an example for this volte-face. Copernicus, it is true, had proposed a volte-face too when he suggested that the sun rather than the earth is at the centre of the planetary system. We have become used to looking upon this Copernican change as the beginning of all those reorientations which have made man to be the result of accidents and which have placed him not in the centre, as the old story of divine Providence had had it, but on the very periphery, if that. After Copernicus, there had been other blows to human pride. There had been Darwin's rejection of teleology and his theory about our animal ancestors. Then there is Freud's demonstration that our will is not free to choose between good and evil but that, at best, we can struggle to acquire a certain amount of freedom through years of psychoanalysis. The irony in Kant's role in this story is that though he performed something like a Copernican Revolution, he really did his level best to make sure that man would remain at the centre. The thing in itself, to be sure, Kant had argued, is something we can never know. But the world as it appears to us, he had said, appears to us in a certain way because we *are* at the centre; or better, where we are, there must be a sort of centre. Kant had thus reinforced the belief in the centrality of man's mind. The one great question which he never asked, though the matter must have been a bit of a mystery to him, was how it had come about that the mind was able to prescribe regularities to nature. The world of appearances, according to him, is a closed world and we are, as knowing subjects, entirely confined in it. But it must have been a mystery to him why the human mind of all minds or of all things, for that matter, should be in that peculiar position. Whichever way one looks at it, we should really say that Kant performed something more like a Copernican Counter-revolution. The consequence of this counter-revolution was that Kant placed a sort of philosophical iron curtain in front of the world as it is in itself and introduced a complete dichotomy: on one side, there was the world as it appeared to us and as we know it, in parts; on the other side, there was the world as it *really* is, but totally unknowable. There was no bridge between these two worlds other than in non-cognitive action. In acting autonomously, the self, Kant pointed out, participates in the noumenal world.

Looking back after a century of evolutionary thought, we are able to clear up the mystery which Kant had left.[18] The human mind, with its categories and forms of perception, must be the product of evolution. It could never have survived and been selectively retained had it not been formed in such a way as to be able to pick up precisely the fact that there *are* regularities in the real world. The reason why the mind can have some genuine knowledge of the real world is because it is a product of that world – a product, that is, in the sense of evolution. We can understand the world not because the world is understandable, but because the mind is worldly. With evolution, the absolute distinction between the noumenal world and the phenomenal world breaks down.

How exactly should one envisage the Kantian categories in evolutionary terms? If one thinks of the human organism as an evolved system, the categories – be they purely mental or be they neutral structures – must be fairly adaptive. An organism with non-adaptive categories of perception and understanding could not have evolved. The notion that there is a totally other 'thing in itself' to which the categories do not apply must be abandoned. However, since the human organism is also separate from the environment it can live in and since it is a self-regulating system, these categories may well have a bit of a will of their own in that they must have suffered from the feedback of the system of which they are a part. They are, in other words, not only adaptive to the environment in which the organism is living; but also adaptive to the organism of which they are a part. For this reason, Kant was right in supposing that the categories are not just part of the environment or are mirroring the thing in itself with complete accuracy. Being apart from the environment, they help us to prescribe laws to it; but having been selectively retained by evolution, they help us to prescribe laws which are not arbitrary and which contain adequate information about the environment.

With this amendment, Kant's transcendental idealism is transformed into hypothetical realism. Kant had argued in the Preface to the second edition of the *Critique of Pure Reason* that there must be a world of things in themselves of which the world we know is an appearance. If it were otherwise, he had written, we would be committed to the irrational conclusion that there is no world the world of appearance is an appearance of. This argument is the crux of his transcendental idealism. It was an idealism which differed from vulgar idealism in that it asserted that there *is* a real world and that our inability to know it is the result of mental methodology.

It is quite easy now to transform this transcendental idealism into hypothetical realism.[19] If we say that the human mind is the product of evolution and that it has been selected for retention because it is a 'fit' to reality, we can change the argument. We must now say that the world we experience is the product of a mind which has been selected. But it would be a contradiction in terms if we did not also add that if the mind has been selected, there must have been something there to do the selecting. This argument is the crux of hypothetical realism. We do not quite know what the real world really is like; but we must think that it is there and that it has interacted with the nervous system for millions of years to produce, by natural selection, the sort of nervous system which can pick up at least some correct information about that real world. If we trace the possibility of this transformation of transcendental idealism into hypothetical realism back to Kant, we can also see that the so-called 'Anthropic Principle' which is beginning to loom so large in modern cosmology and philosophy is to be traced back to Kant.

The 'Anthropic Principle' says that since man is the product of natural selection, we can learn a lot about the world which has done the selecting by looking at man. If the world from the Big Bang onwards had been significantly different, we would not be sitting here today to think about it.[20] The 'Anthropic Principle' is really only a special instance of the 'Tropic Principle' which, we argued at the beginning of this chapter, accounts for the fact that there has always been interaction in evolution. Whatever evolves has been constrained to evolve in a certain way rather than in another:[21]

> The space through which we are travelling with our solar system has acquired a new appearance. It is no longer the cold empty space, hostile to life in which we happen to exist as the result of an irrelevant accident. It is *our* space. It has produced us and maintains our lives. We are its creatures. This idea might give us confidence even though nobody can tell us the goal of the journey.[22]

With this insight we can see the conflict between religious knowledge and science in a new light. The initial conflict, as we have sketched it from Voltaire to Sartre and Russell, had led to nausea or to elation. Man, philosophers had concluded, is the accidental outcome of non-designed, undetermined happenings. We now see, through Kant and with the help of the 'Anthropic Principle' that this conclusion is not really correct. Man is anything but the outcome of innumerable accidents. There was no design at the beginning. But thanks to the 'Tropic Principle' in general and to the 'Anthropic Principle' in particular, all through evolution, design has been produced. It is no accident that we are sitting here today and are capable of contemplating the whole process.

Amor Temporis Fugacis

The great and persistent obstacle to an acceptance of evolution has been man's hostile attitude to time. When we are here speaking of 'time', we are not thinking of the problems which have plagued our thought from Zeno's paradoxes about time right down to the General Theory of Relativity, to Minkowski's Space–Time, and to the Arrow of Time of Thermodynamics. We are thinking here of something more simple and yet more difficult to deal with because its roots are in the human mind rather than in physical nature, however constituted.

When we are thinking of space and the growth or extension of space, we are always quite pleased because the extension of space is an enrichment. As things grow in space, that growth is increased extension of anything at the same time. When we notice an increase in differences at one and the same time, we speak of creation or an extension of spatial dimension. Such an extension is a growth, an enrichment. We feel happy when we notice it. As a result of such growth, there is something where there had been nothing.

Our attitude to time is quite different. When we look at any one point in space and begin to notice differences, we say that time is passing. As it is passing, qualities or attributes of the point we are watching are wiped out. They disappear or appear to have disappeared. Whichever, we notice that something has gone and feel impoverished. For this reason, we have a positive attitude to the extension of space, and a negative attitude to the extension of time. The more time passes, the more we are impoverished. The passage of time is an experience of loss. At one moment, we had something; the next moment, we are without it. There may be something 'new' at that next moment. But it is unfamiliar, we are not used to it, the chances are it will disappear again and, therefore, at the best of times, the new moment is not really an adequate compensation for the moment we have lost.

As a result of this asymmetry between our experience of space and our experience of time, we have developed a hostile attitude to the passage of time. We are afraid of the passing of time and, by all manner of subterfuges, we have tried to convince ourselves that time does not *really* pass. We have used elaborate rituals to convince ourselves that the changes we know to have taken place are ephemeral and that the condition which prevailed at the beginning of the world – arch-time, as Mirca Eliade calls it – is still with us. We have developed complicated philosophical arguments to show that the passing of time is a delusion and that, deep down, behind the appearance of changes, time stands still and changes do not happen. Much of the cosmology and theology of the higher religions is devoted to the doctrine that the passage of time is unreal and that the deity or the non-deity is a timeless condition of eternity without changes. The practitioners of almost any religion one cares to think about are promised, as the highest reward for faithful and punctilious observances of works or faith, that in the end they will be united with that eternal deity or absorbed into a state of Nirvana and cease to be reborn. Escape from change, avoidance of change, fear of change, proclamation that change is unreal or illusory – such is the main burden of religious thought and practice. On the more vulgar level, this theme is pursued by embalming corpses, by the pretence that death is the entry into eternity and an escape from change, or by the burial of corpses in funerary monuments of gigantic proportions as if to say: Here is our ultimate protest against the passage of time. The corpse may wither away and decay and we are not so sure about the 'spirit' either. But we can, at least, make sure that the stone monument we have erected on top of the ashes will remain. From the desire for fame to the belief that we have a soul which will survive the body, not to mention the idea that bodies will be resurrected, man's grand religious aspirations and efforts are dedicated to the denial of change and the belief that time is not for real.

Philosophers who have endeavoured, from Plato to Marx, to improve the lot of mankind, have always thought that the greatest contribution they could make is to devise ways to arrest change. Plato thought he might stop change in one fell swoop by setting up the regime of his philosopher kings. Marx thought that he had discovered that the changes which had taken place would lead, before long (provided we make one last great effort), to one last and final revolutionary change after which there would be no further changes. In between, there were countless theologians like St Augustine who had persuaded themselves that the changes which were taking place were willy-nilly destined to lead to the cessation of change. There were political thinkers who thought that it was the task of political thought to find out how change can be stopped. Some, like Machiavelli, believed that they had plumbed the secret of how change can be stopped. If one surveys this vast and almost universal conspiracy against time and change, one is less impressed by the differences in the visions of ultimate stability as by the fact that everybody equated happiness with absence of change and considered change, even change for the better, to be intolerable. If at all, change was held to be tolerable because and when it presaged cessation of change.

As long as men are preoccupied with that fear of time and as long as they devote their efforts to sustaining the belief that time is an illusion and, at best, confined to the ephemeral world of our experiences, the theory of evolution is impossible to accept. For the theory of evolution implicitly or explicitly presupposes a very different view of time. Since the changes which are selected for retention are the results of time and since the connection between changes and the passage of time is not random, all evolutionary thinking requires a positive evaluation of the passage of time. The more, the merrier! The evolutionist, we are almost tempted to think, not only welcomes the passage of time but must wish that it could be speeded up. Evolutionary thinking considers the passing of time as an enrichment. Only the passing of time produces new fulgurations – to use the term invented by Konrad Lorenz. Even if old inventions and old species pass away, the continuation of the process which was responsible for their fulguration is to be welcomed as an enrichment, not as a loss. Sometimes, I suspect that the spontaneous and deeply ingrained hostility to evolution was not due to the fear that man might have something in common with animals, nor to the worry that revealed religion might not be true. It had, most probably, a lot to do with the realisation that if evolution has taken place, the passage of time must have been real and all attempts to recapture or re-enact arch-time – the still moment at the centre of the turning wheel – must have been useless and perverse. Compared with that anxiety about time, Wilberforce's fear that his grandfather might have been an ape would indeed appear to be a minor worry.

The man who cleared the ground for an acceptance of evolution by suggesting that we alter our attitude to change was Nietzsche. Nietzsche has many claims to fame – as a precursor of Freud, as the man who inspired Thomas Mann's masterpiece *Dr Faustus*, and as the man who challenged not only the fond hopes entertained by Christians, but also exposed the hypocrisy of Christian love. The truths of religion and especially of the Christian religion had been questioned long before Nietzsche; but Nietzsche mounted an original attack in that he did not worry much about whether the historicity of the Christian revelation was true. He challenged the wisdom and honesty of the content of Christian teaching and by-passed the question as to whether that content was revealed as claimed or not. There is one doctrine which he considered central to his teaching. This is the doctrine of eternal recurrence. This doctrine is recognised by all Nietzsche readers, but rarely understood. It is often considered as some kind of embarrassment. Nietzsche considered it crucial. He kept a special record of the moment in which the idea first crossed his mind: 'August 1881, "beyond man and time", near Surlei.'[23]

On the face of it, the notion that everything will and must happen again and again is essentially absurd and untenable and one keeps wondering why Nietzsche considered such a mystical vision (compared with which most ideas he attacked as rank superstition were plain common sense) not only crucially important, but referred to it as 'scientific' – only to add immediately that the doctrine should not be taken literally and would, in any case, not stand up to logical analysis. The truth is that the vocabulary at his disposal was inadequate and not equal to the task. He couched his revaluation of time in the form of a declaration of eternal recurrence. This doctrine, as it stands and on the face of it, reads like a vulgar prophecy. One has to allow for the traditional vocabulary of cyclical time and place it into the context of Nietzsche's thought. What he meant was that we should act in such a way that we could wish for the consequences of our action to occur again and again.[24] Do not live, he said, as if the passage of time was to be feared, but as if it was to be welcomed. He considered this revaluation of time more fundamental than any of his other revaluations and believed that all the other revaluations would follow from his revaluation of time. We should try to understand what he meant. 'I, the last disciple of the philosopher Dionysus,' he wrote,[25] 'I, the teacher of the eternal recurrence.' Nietzsche sought to show that time is not to be feared and that change is to be welcomed. Therefore he created the image of his superman Zarathustra, who dances time away and does not present, as deities are wont to do, a static image of eternity. Eternal recurrence, to Nietzsche, meant openness to the future. When he wrote in one of his poems that all joy demands eternity, he did not mean to say that all joy demands to last for ever, but that we should appreciate that, in one form or another, it will recur time and again. In short, Nietzsche's ultimate message, his ultimate transformation of all values, consisted in the invitation that we change our attitude to time. Instead of abhorring and fearing the passage of time, he said, we should welcome it. Nietzsche's superman is a man who has conquered the fear of time and rejoices in the future. Nietzsche, to the best of my knowledge, was the first philosopher who taught us to enjoy the passage of time and who wanted us to realise that the passing of time, far from depriving and impoverishing us as all people had thought, is enriching. It produces more species and, on the level of consciousness, it can generate more truths. At least this is what he would have added had he thought in evolutionary terms. He also expressed the joy he took in the passage of time by his rejection of teleology. Time, he wrote in his famous 'Sils Maria' poem of 1881, was without goal. By the 'Tropic Principle', the more time passes, the greater the number of systems which will show in their workings the constraints exercised upon them by other systems. This self-generation of designs on all levels – cosmological, biological, cultural and scientific – is very different from the pre-ordained creation of one single Design. Its self-display and its fulgurations depend on the passing of time. An understanding of evolution should move us closer to Nietzsche; and, conversely, an appreciation of Nietzsche, should pave the way for an acceptance of evolution. We ought to abandon the fear of time and replace it by *amor temporis fugacis*:

> Here I sat waiting – not for anything –
> Beyond Good and Evil, fancying
>
> Now light, now shadows, all a game,
> All lake, all noon, all time without all aim.
>
> Then suddenly, friend, one turned into two –
> And Zarathustra walked into my view.

Notes

Introduction

1 *Relativity,* 15th edn, London, 1960, p. 22.

2 The term was coined by H. Putnam, 'What Theories Are Not', in E. Nagel *et al.*, eds, *Logic Methodology and Philosophy of Science,* Stanford, 1962. For modification of the 'Received View' and its link to Positivism, see Frederick Suppe, 'Introduction', in F. Suppe, ed., *The Structure of Scientific Theories,* Urbana, 1977.

3 For documentation of these doubts and uncertainties, see Peter Munz, 'The Unity of Science and the Dubious Credentials of Positivism', *Proceedings of the XIIth International Conference on the Unity of the Sciences, 1983,* N.Y., 1984.

4 Cp. M. Bunge, *Foundations of Physics,* New York, 1967.

5 Cp. G. Buchdahl, *The Image of Newton and Locke in the Age of Reason,* London, 1961, p. 13.

6 I am using the term here in the sense in which it was, to my knowledge, first used by Donald T. Campbell, 'Methodological Suggestions from a Comparative Psychology of Knowledge Processes', *Inquiry,* 2, 1959, pp. 152–82.

7 See Norman Malcolm, *Ludwig Wittgenstein: A Memoir,* London, 1958, p. 69.

8 *Philosophical Investigations,* para. 202.

9 In a more humanistic tradition, the same strain is presented by Niklas Luhmann, *Gesellschaftsstruktur und Semantik,* Frankfurt, 1980.

10 Donald Campbell's single most important contribution in which he described Popper's theory of knowledge as 'evolutionary' is his 'Evolutionary Epistemology', in P.A. Schilpp, ed., *The Philosophy of Karl Popper,* La Salle, 1974.

11 Popper himself has stated that the real link between his thought and Darwin is provided by the work of Niels Jerne and Macfarlane Burnet on antibody formation. 'The Rationality of Scientific Revolutions', in R. Harré, ed., *Problems of Scientific Revolution,* London, 1975, p. 80. With uncanny precision, Wittgenstein placed himself at the opposite end of the philosophical spectrum: 'The Darwinian theory has no more to do with philosophy,' he wrote in his *Tractatus,* 4.1122, 'than has any other hypothesis of natural science.' Though he rejected the *Tractatus,* he always retained his view of the irrelevance of Darwin. Cp. Ernest Gellner, *The Devil in Modern Philosophy,* London, 1974, p. 201.

12 See Ernst Mayr, *The Growth of Biological Thought,* Cambridge, Mass., 1982, p. 589. The target of selection is not considered to be the mutated gene. Selection is determined by the interaction between the external environment and the physiological processes of the organism as a whole. See e.g. R. Riedl, *Order in Living Organisms,* English trans., Chichester, NY, 1973, as an example of post-neo-Darwinism.

13 Ernst Mayr, *op cit.*, pp. 585–600.

14 Cp. e.g. F.J. Ayala, 'The Mechanisms of Evolution', *Scientific American,* 239, 1978, pp. 48–69.

15 See Sewall Wright, 'Comments on the Preliminary Working Papers of Eden and Waddington', in P.S. Moorhead and M.M. Kaplan, eds, *Mathematical Challenge to the Neo-Darwinian Interpretation of Evolution,* Philadelphia, 1967, p. 117.

16 *Karl Popper,* London, 1980.

Chapter 1 The Historicity of Knowledge

1 See Donald T. Campbell, 'Pattern Matching as an Essential in Distal Knowing', in K.R. Hammond, ed., *The Psychology of Egon Brunswik,* NY, 1966; H. v. Ditfurth, *Der Geist fiel nicht vom Himmel,* Hamburg, 1976, p. 162.

2 *Philosophy of the Physical Sciences,* Cambridge, 1939, pp. 56–7.

3 Konrad Lorenz, *Studies in Animal and Human Behaviour,* English trans., London, 1971, vol. 2, p. 293.

4 Konrad Lorenz, *Behind the Mirror,* English trans., London, 1977, p. 54. Cp. also Peter Marler, 'Perception and Innate Knowledge',

in H. Heidcamp, ed., *The Nature of Life,* Baltimore, 1978, pp. 115 ff. and the literature cited.

5 Konrad Lorenz, *Studies in Animal and Human Behaviour,* vol. 2, pp. 293.

6 My presentation of Aristotle's position is derived from M.J. Adler, *The Difference of Man and the Difference it Makes,* NY, 1967, pp. 220 ff.

7 A.N. Whitehead, *Science in the Modern World,* Cambridge, 1946, chapter 1.

8 J. Needham, *The Grand Titration,* London, 1969, p. 308.

9 *Intellectual and Manual Labour: A Critique of Epistemology,* English trans., London, 1978.

10 E. Gans, *The Origins of Language,* Berkeley, 1981.

11 There is a growing literature on this subject. See Donald T. Campbell, *op. cit.,* p. 85; Konrad Lorenz, *Die acht Todsünden der zivilisierten Menschheit,* Munich, 1973, p. 74; C. Blakemore, *The Mechanics of the Mind,* Cambridge, 1977, p. 130; Konrad Lorenz, *Behind the Mirror,* English trans., London, 1977, pp. 114, 118, 162; E. Schrödinger, *Mind and Matter,* Cambridge, 1958, p. 5; B. Rensch, 'Laws of Evolution', in *Philosophia Naturalis,* 1960, vol. 6, p. 311; J.M. Cullen, 'Ritualisation of Behaviour in Animals and Man', *Philosophical Transactions of the Royal Society of London,* series B, vol. 251, 1966; Robin Fox, 'Introduction' to Robin Fox, ed., *Biosocial Anthropology,* London, 1975, p. 7; W.H. Thorpe, *Purpose in a World of Chance,* London, 1978, p. 29; F.J. Ayala, 'The Concept of Biological Progress', in F.J. Ayala and T. Dobzhansky, eds, *Studies in the Philosophy of Biology,* London, 1974, p. 350; H. Mohr, *Biologische Erkenntnis,* Stuttgart, 1981, p. 35; Richard L. Gregory, *Mind in Science,* London, 1981, p. 335; G. Vollmer, *Evolutionäre Erkenntnistheorie,* 3rd edn, Stuttgart, 1981, p. 56. Cp. note 18, chapter 7, below.

12 Konrad Lorenz, *Behind the Mirror,* p. 118.

13 Quoted by J. Bernstein, *Einstein,* London, 1973, p. 139.

14 I.B. Cohen, *The Newtonian Revolution,* Cambridge, 1980, p. 99.

15 *Ibid.*, p. xii.

16 F.E. Manuel, *A Portrait of Isaac Newton,* Cambridge, Mass., 1968, pp. 83–4.

17 *Objective Knowledge*, Oxford, 1972, p. 202.

18 Cp. G. Radnitzky, 'Progress and Rationality in Research', in M.D. Grmek, R.S. Cohen and G. Cimono, eds, *On Scientific*

Discovery, Dordrecht, 1980, p. 57. On the relation between molecular genetics and Mendelian genetics, see M. Ruse, *The Philosophy of Biology*, London, 1973. Progress does not mean that one can deduce Mendelian genetics from molecular genetics. It means that the *phenomena* explained by Mendelian genetics can be explained by molecular genetics.

19 I owe this example to my colleague George Hughes.

20 F. Jacob, *The Possible and the Actual*, NY, 1982, p. 36.

21 *Progress in Art*, London, 1976.

22 London, 1960.

23 Oxford, 1982.

24 Once one is in the business of setting up heteronomous goals, one could also look at Anton Ehrenzweig, *The Hidden Order of Art*, London, 1967, who takes the history of art as the story of the endeavour to depict the serial rhythms of the unconscious. By this reckoning, neither the naturalism of Andy Warhol nor the abstractions of Sol LeWitt turn up trumps; but the highest level of progress is reached by Brigid Riley and by Boulez's music.

25 *Principles of Art History*, 1st edn, Munich, 1915.

26 'Purity and Danger Revisited', *Times Literary Supplement*, September 1980, pp. 1045 ff.

27 W.H. Newton-Smith, *The Rationality of Science*, London, 1981, p. 3.

28 K.R. Popper, *Conjectures and Refutations*, London, 1963, p. 216.

29 See W.W. Bartley III, 'The Philosophy of Karl Popper, III', *Philosophia*, vol. II, 1982, and the same author's 'Rationality', in G. Radnitzky and H. Seiffert, eds, *Handlexikon zur Wissenschaftstheorie*, Munich, 1980.

30 In order to stress that in spite of the absence of predictive power, Freud's psychology is 'knowledge', Walter Kaufmann has described Freud's psychology as 'poetic science' (*Discovering the Mind*, NY, 1980, vol. 3, chapter 1).

31 Bartley's pancritical rationalism, as he calls it, is well charted in his *The Retreat to Commitment*, La Salle, 1984; see also W.W. Bartley III, 'The Alleged Refutation of Pancritical Rationalism', *Proceedings of the XIth International Conference on the Unity of the Sciences, 1982*, NY, 1983, vol. 2, pp. 1139–79; also his 'Rationality'; *Flucht ins Engagement*, 2nd rev. edn, Tübingen, 1982, Appendix; 'The Philosophy of Karl Popper III', *Philosophia*, vol. 11, 1982, pp. 157 ff. Cp. G. Radnitzky, 'The Science of Man', in V.

Cappelletti *et al.*, eds, *Saggi di Storia del Pensiero Scientifico,* Rome, 1983, p. 385.

32 In all his writings cited above, Bartley insists, correctly, I think, that ultimately total criticisability is a question of attitude more than of mere logic. It is therefore irrelevant whether the statement 'all statements are criticisable' is itself open to criticism and could conceivably be false. If that statement were criticised successfully, one would have to reconsider the matter. Willingness to reconsider is the heart of the matter.

33 This is not to be confused with Feyerabend's dictum: 'The only rule is that there should be no rule.' On the contrary, we are saying: 'The only rule is that everything must be exposed to criticism and that the limits of criticism must remain infinite.'

34 G. Vollmer, *Evolutionäre Erkenntnistheorie,* 3rd rev. edn, Stuttgart, 1981, p. 213.

35 See Peter Munz, 'DNA, Falsificationism and Dogmatism: Continuities and Discontinuities in Popper's Evolutionism', in P. Levinson, ed., *New Directions in Evolutionary Epistemology,* forthcoming.

36 Princeton, 1979.

37 Typescript of William James Lectures, p. 2.

38 New York, 1968.

39 London, 1981.

40 English trans., NY, 1976.

41 London, 1978.

42 Frederick Suppe, ed., 2nd edn, Urbana, 1977.

43 *Op. cit.*, p. 12.

44 C.C. Gillispie, 'Intellectual Factors in the Background of Analysis by Probabilities', in A.C. Crombie, ed., *Scientific Change,* London, 1963, esp. p. 449.

45 W.V. Quine, 'A Postscript on Metaphor', in Sheldon Sacks, ed., *On Metaphor,* Chicago, 1978, p. 159.

46 'From Form to Function', *Daedalus,* summer 1977, p. 148.

47 *Op. cit.*, p. 250.

48 To my knowledge, the first to draw attention to the functional dependence of living organisms on the size of atoms was E. Schrödinger, *What is Life,* Cambridge, 1945.

49 Heinz R. Pagels, *The Cosmic Code,* NY, 1982, p. 90.

50 W. Heisenberg, *Physics and Philosophy,* NY, 1958, p. 168.

51 *Reliable Knowledge,* Cambridge, 1978, p. 53. See also C.F.v.

Weizsäcker, *Die Einheit der Natur,* Munich, 1971, p. 65; R. Feynman, *The Character of Physical Law,* London, 1965, pp. 55–6; and I. Prigogine and Isabelle Stengers, *Dialog mit der Natur,* Munich, 1981, p. 243.

52 I owe this intriguing turn of thought to my friend Jagdish Hattiangadi.

53 Cp. Gerhard Vollmer, *Evolutionäre Erkenntnistheorie,* 3rd rev. edn, pp. 161 ff.

54 The crucial question is whether the pricking or nicking or perturbations which we observe are performed by sub-atomic particles or by our eyes. The world can refer itself to our eyes (which are part of the world) or to sub-atomic particles (which are also part of the world).

55 'Das is ja ganz schön,' I believe he is supposed to have said, 'aber der alte Jakob ist das noch nicht!'

56 R.K. Merton, *Social Theory and Social Structure,* Chicago, 1949, pp. 516, 558. This approach is based on K. Mannheim, *Ideology and Utopia,* English trans., London, 1936, p. 267.

57 Guy E. Swanson, *Religion and Regime,* Ann Arbor, 1967.

58 R.K. Merton, 'Science, Technology and Society in Seventeenth Century England', *Osiris,* 4, 1938.

59 B.M. Hessen, *The Social and Economic Roots of Newton's 'Principia',* English trans., NY, 1971.

60 P. Forman, 'Weimar Culture, Causality and Quantum Theory, 1918–1927: Adaptation of German Physicists and Mathematicians to a Hostile Intellectual Environment', *Historical Studies in the Physical Sciences,* 3, 1971.

61 Margaret Jacob, *The Newtonians and the English Revolution,* Ithaca, 1976.

62 This example is taken from a Tübingen seminar conducted by Bloch himself. I was privileged to attend.

63 Mary Douglas, *Natural Symbols,* London, 1970.

64 Peter L. Berger and Thomas Luckmann, *The Social Construction of Reality,* N.Y., 1966.

65 M. Mulkay, *Science and the Sociology of Knowledge,* London, 1979, p. 3.

66 *Ibid.*, p. 21.

67 *Knowledge and Social Imagery,* London, 1976, pp. 9 ff.

68 E. Evans-Pritchard, *A History of Anthropological Thought,* NY, 1981, p. 123.

69 *Science and Civilisation in China,* Cambridge, 1954, vol. 3, p. 166. The view I am proposing is similar to the view of R. Horton, 'African Traditional Thought and Western Science', *Africa,* 37, 1967. See also R. Horton, 'Tradition and Modernity Revisited', in M. Hollis and S. Lukes, eds, *Rationality and Relativism,* Oxford, 1982.

70 See, for example, Peter Munz, 'The Problem of the Renaissance', *Parergon,* April 1975.

71 'Men first think in *tropes,*' *Essai sur l'origine des langues,* London, 1783, p. 565.

72 *The Foundations of Primitive Thought,* Oxford, 1979.

73 'Two Dogmas of Empiricism', in *From a Logical Point of View,* Cambridge, Mass., 1953.

74 For Foucault's 'politics of truth', see Larry Shiner, 'Reading Foucault', *History and Theory,* 21, 1982.

Chapter 2 The Conditions of Historical Knowledge

1 For a fuller discussion, see Peter Munz, *The Shapes of Time,* Middletown, Conn., 1977.

2 Edinburgh, 1795, vol. 1, p. 373.

3 For a more detailed discussion of the soundness of the historical methodology used by Hutton, Lyell and Darwin, see Peter Munz, 'Finches, Fossils and Foscarini', *New Zealand Journal of History,* 14, 1980, p. 137.

4 See Peter Munz, *The Shapes of Time,* chapter 4.

5 This history is not only governed by the fact that our knowledge of the laws which cause changes is growing; but also by the fact that there are more 'configurational causes' than Lyell had allowed for. Lyell allowed that the change in the position of the land masses would affect climate. See D. Ospovat, 'Lyell's Theory of Climate', *Journal of the History of Biology,* 10, 1977. There are, however, a great many more different constellations than changes in land masses. See G.G. Simpson, 'Uniformitarianism, etc.', in M.J. Hecht and W.C. Steere, eds, *Essays in Evolution and Genetics,* NY, 1970, pp. 43–96.

6 Cp. Thomas S. Kuhn, *The Structure of Scientific Revolutions,* 2nd edn., Chicago, 1970, p. 138.

7 See G. Radnitzky, 'Popperian Philosophy of Science as an Antidote Against Relativism', in R.S. Cohen *et al.*, eds, *Essays in Memory of Imre Lakatos,* Dordrecht, 1976, pp. 517–8.

8 B. Hoffmann, *Einstein,* London, 1975, p. 84.
9 Hilary Putnam in Frederick Suppe, ed., *The Structure of Scientific Theories,* 2nd edn, Urbana, 1977, p. 361.
10 Cambridge, 1980.
11 *Ibid.*, p. 4.
12 *Ibid.*, pp. 141, 219.
13 *Ibid.*, p. 130.
14 *Ibid.*, pp. xii–xiii, 15–16, 51, 56, 99–100, 278.
15 *Ibid.*, p. 100.
16 *Ibid.*, p. 13.
17 *Ibid.*, pp. 16, 51 and esp. pp. 99 ff.
18 'On the Origins of the Special Theory of Relativity', *American Journal of Physics,* 28, 1960, p. 636.
19 Cp. the evidence in Adolf Grünbaum, 'The Special Theory of Relativity as a Case Study of the Importance of the Philosophy of Science for the History of Science', in B. Baumrin, ed., *Philosophy of Science,* NY, 1963, vol. 2, p. 185.
20 Erik H. Erikson, *Young Man Luther,* NY, 1958. For further examples, see Peter Munz, *The Shapes of Time,* p. 187.
21 *History and Theory,* Beiheft 2, 1963.
22 Popper himself had sketched snippets of the history of science based on his falsificationism in his *Logic of Scientific Discovery,* first published in German in 1934.
23 R.C. Buck and R.S. Cohen, eds, *Boston Studies in the Philosophy of Science,* 1971, vol. 8, pp. 91 ff.
24 See also the list provided by Robert J. Richards, 'Natural Selection and other Models in the Historiography of Science', in Marylinn B. Brewer and B.E. Collins, eds, *Scientific Inquiry and the Social Sciences,* San Francisco, 1981.

Chapter 3 Historical Circularity

1 Chicago, 1962.
2 It is, for example, symptomatic that W. Stegmüller, *The Structure and Dynamics of Theories,* New York, 1976, should have confined his doubts and misgivings about Kuhn entirely to the degree of 'irrationality' alleged to be contained in the view that theories are often comparatively immune from falsification. This kind of irrationality, if it is indeed an irrationality, Kuhn shares with almost every philosopher of science of the post-Positivism era. Stegmüller is silent about the real irrationality contained in the

circularity by which Kuhn sustains his particular philosophy of science.

3 *The Logical Structure of Mathematical Physics,* Dordrecht, 1971, p. 288.

4 Quotations will be from the Harvard University Press paperback, 9th printing, Cambridge, Mass., 1977.

5 *Op. cit.*, pp. 143–4.

6 *Ibid.*, p. 227.

7 *Ibid.*, p. 182.

8 *Ibid.*, p. 182.

9 First published in London, 1959.

10 Pelican edn, London, 1968, pp. 327–8.

11 *Ibid.*, pp. 185 ff.

12 New York, 1961.

13 London, 1924.

14 Princeton, 1960, p. 24.

15 *Op. cit.*, p. 144.

16 *Op. cit.*, Harper Torchbooks, NY, p. 169.

17 'Die Beziehung zwischen Wissenschaftsgeschichte und Wissenschaftstheorie', in L. Krüger, ed., *Die Entstehung des Neuen,* Frankfurt, 1977, p. 68.

18 *Paradigms and Revolutions,* Notre Dame, 1980.

19 See his 'Die Beziehung zwischen Wissenschaftsgeschichte und Wissenschaftstheorie', pp. 61-2.

20 *Ibid.*, pp. 66–7.

21 *Ibid.*, p. 69.

22 Cp. Peter Munz, *The Shapes of Time,* Middletown, Conn., 1977, pp. 44 ff., for an explanation of how these meaningful structures are created with the help of general laws.

23 See W.H. Walsh, *An Introduction to Philosophy of History,* London, 1951, pp. 59 ff.

24 Michael Oakeshott, *On Human Conduct,* Oxford, 1975, p. 106. A similar argument occurs in A.R. Louch, *Explanation and Human Action,* Oxford, 1966, p. 93.

25 For the wide popularity of Kuhn among historians and social scientists, see David A. Hollinger, 'T.S. Kuhn's Theory of Science and its Implications for History', *American Historical Review,* 78, 1973, pp. 370–93.

26 R.C. Buck and R.S. Cohen, eds, *Boston Studies in the Philosophy of Science,* 1971, vol. 8, p. 91.

27 *Ibid.*, p. 109.
28 *Ibid.*, p. 118.

Chapter 4 Closed Circles

1 The failure to recognise that Kuhn's own paradigm is old wine in new bottles is well-nigh universal. See, for example, D.A. Hollinger, 'T.S. Kuhn's Theory of Science and its Implications for History', *American Historical Review,* 78, 1973.
2 Cp. Peter Munz, 'Finches, Fossils and Foscarini', *New Zealand Journal of History,* 14, 1980, p. 137.
3 The similarity between Malinowski and Wittgenstein is most probably quite accidental. It is remarked upon by Ernest Gellner, 'The New Idealism', in I. Lakatos and A. Musgrave, eds, *Problems in the Philosophy of Science,* Amsterdam, 1968, p. 399, and by Edmund Leach, 'Malinowski Malapropos', *Times Literary Supplement,* July 1974, p. 759. For Wittgenstein's use of the closed-circle model see Karl-Otto Apel, *Towards a Transformation of Philosophy,* London, 1980: Wittgenstein's later philosophy is the 'hitherto most radical presentation of *conventionalism* known in the history of philosophy'; and G. Radnitzky, '*Philosophie und Wissenschaftstheorie zwischen Wittgenstein und Popper*', in J. Marek *et al.*, eds, *Österreichische Philosophen und ihr Einfluss auf die analytische Philosophie der Gegenwart,* Innsbruck, 1977, vol. 1, pp. 273, 276.
4 In fairness to Wittgenstein one has to add that he advanced subtle considerations to support his contention that there can be no private language. He argued, for example, that in isolation we cannot trust our memory of the meaning we assign to an expression and that we need other people to whom we are tied by rule-following conventions to shore up our memories. There is no denying that Wittgenstein was wrestling with genuine difficulties and problems. My criticism concerns his facile solutions, not the reality of the problem or the sincerity of his efforts.
5 London, 1958.
6 Cp. the penetrating observations on this spell by W.W. Bartley III, 'Wittgenstein and Homosexuality', *Salmagundi,* 58–9, 1982–3.
7 Quoted by L. Kolakowski, *Religion,* London, 1982, p. 61. Kolakowski does not give the source of the quotation, but Wittgenstein made identical and similar remarks all the time. For example: 'Do not say "one cannot" but say instead: "it

doesn't exist in this game". Not: "one can't castle in draughts" but "there is no castling in draughts"; and instead of "I can't exhibit my sensation" – "in the use of the word 'sensation' there is no such thing as exhibiting what one has got"' (*Zettel*, para. 134).

8 Paris, 1966.

9 I agree therefore with W.H. Newton-Smith, *The Rationality of Science,* London, 1981, chapter 7, that one must distinguish types and degrees of incommensurability and that there are at least three degrees of meaning-invariance. However, even Newton-Smith's third degree, 'radical meaning-invariance', is, as I will argue, not as absolute as its proponents think. My own case rests on the consideration forced upon us by evolution. Though all organisms are adapted to different parts of the environment, those parts must be compatible with one another; and statements about them must be commensurable.

10 *Ontological Relativity,* NY, 1969, p. 48.

11 *Progress and its Problems*, Berkeley, 1977, pp. 143–4.

12 *Against Method,* London, 1975, p. 230.

13 G. Radnitzky attributes all relativism of this kind to 'the failure of the justificationist approach, including probabilistic justificationism after Hume's criticism of induction' ('The Science of Man', in V. Cappelletti *et al.* eds, *Saggi di Storia del Pensiero Scientifico,* Rome, 1983, p. 382).

14 I know I am not literally 'fair' in classing Kuhn with other arbitrary relativists like Rorty, Feyerabend and Mary Douglas. For Kuhn does maintain that we are restricted in the choice of a new paradigm by the consideration that the new paradigm has to solve the anomalies that have arisen in the old paradigm. However, in making this the only constraint on the choice of a new paradigm and in neglecting to state that the choice of a new paradigm must *also* be governed by the requirement that it explains more, Kuhn extends a very generous invitation to a wide variety of paradigms of equal value when he expects from the new paradigm no more than the solution of old anomalies. His largesse may not be wholly arbitrary, and in that sense he is more restrained than the real relativists and historists; but in broad perspective his rejection of the all-important restraint imposed by the requirement that any new paradigm ought to have greater explanatory power than the old paradigm, is more significant than the minor restraint he imposes on one's freedom

of choice. If one wrote a book about Kuhn, one would have to stress the difference between Kuhn and the relativists proper. But in writing about the major divisions in the modern philosophy of knowledge, that difference, though real, becomes negligible.

15 For the use of the closed-circle model by deconstructionists, see e.g. T.K. Seung, *Structuralism and Hermeneutics,* NY, 1982. Cp. Rorty's own essay on deconstruction in his *Consequences of Pragmatism,* Brighton, 1982.

16 Much Marxist historical study is concerned with explanations of why absolutism in Prussia was later or earlier than absolutism in Russia, or the other way round. The historicist succession of stages is accepted unquestioningly as the fundamental law of development and the only thing left to be explained are the apparent deviations or retardations which occur. See e.g. P. Anderson, *Lineages of the Absolutist State,* London, 1974; and his *Passages from Antiquity to Feudalism,* London, 1974.

17 See Mary Douglas and A. Wildavsky, *Risk and Culture,* Berkeley, 1982. Cp. also Mary Douglas, 'Purity and Danger Revisited', *Times Literary Supplement,* 19 September 1980, p. 1045.

18 R.G. Collingwood, 'Oswald Spengler and the Theory of Historical Cycles', *Antiquity,* 1 1927.

19 Oxford, 1946, p. 117.

20 Hegel's non-historicist historical theory about changes in thought systems makes him highly relevant as an alternative to the closed-circle methodology and its anti-historical bias.

21 See Peter Munz, *The Shapes of Time,* Middletown, Conn., 1977, p. 301.

22 A similar travesty of Darwin and neo-Darwinism is to be found in A. Koestler, *Janus,* Picador edn, London, 1979, p. 197.

23 'Popperian Philosophy of Science as an Antidote against Relativism', R.S. Cohen *et al.*, eds, *Essays in Memory of Imre Lakatos,* Dordrecht, 1976, p. 506.

Chapter 5 The Defence of Closed Circles

1 *The Order of Things,* English trans., London, 1970, p. xxiv.

2 Princeton, 1979.

3 *Archeology of Knowledge,* English trans., NY, 1972, p. 231.

4 *Zettel,* para. 320.

5 We must note that Rorty's use of the term 'historicism' is eccentric. 'Historicism' is the view that human history is determined by developmental laws, whatever they may be. What Rorty has in mind is more properly labelled 'historism', that is, the view that everything that happens is relative to a closed circle and that every closed circle is a law unto itself and 'equidistant from God', as L.von Ranke put it.

6 English trans., London, 1977.

7 *Ibid.*, p. 8.

8 That is to say, Wittgenstein frequently referred, often critically, to his *Tractatus* in the *Philosophical Investigations,* first published in 1953. But these references and criticisms concern points of detail and specific opinions. There is no discussion of the central theme of the *Tractatus,* let alone a criticism of that theme. To judge from the references to the *Tractatus* in the *Philosophical Investigations,* one might conclude that the *Tractatus* had no theme.

9 Wittgenstein either set in motion or countenanced the wide philosophical movement in which language-skill competence, 'know-how', is taken as primary, ultimate and self-explanatory.

10 Wittgenstein's position was shared, it seems, by Hannah Arendt. In the chapter on 'Thinking' in Mary McCarthy, ed., *The Life of the Mind,* NY, 1978, she stated that thinking is objectless and self-referential and that thinking's 'result' is meaning or a meaningful story. Hannah Arendt, however, did not derive this idea from Wittgenstein, but from Heidegger. To find meaning, Heidegger always said, one must adopt an attitude to the whole universe. When one is merely seeking knowledge, one is engaged in an attempt to possess only part of the universe. Knowledge is therefore transient and unimportant because too easily testable and nothing more than a prejudice of our intoxication with science. One must wonder why Wittgenstein came so close to Heidegger.

11 Quoted by K. Blackwell, 'Early Wittgenstein and Middle Russell', in I. Block, ed., *Perspectives on the Philosophy of Wittgenstein,* Oxford, 1981, p. 8.

12 For a more detailed discussion, see Peter Munz, 'Philosophy and the Mirror of Rorty', *Journal of the Philosophy of the Social Sciences,* July 1984.

13 The circumstances of Heidegger's Nazism are discussed in Walter Kaufmann, *Discovering the Mind,* NY, 1980, vol. 2, pp.

235 ff.; those of Wittgenstein's homosexuality by W.W. Bartley III, 'Wittgenstein and Homosexuality', *Salmagundi*, 58–9, 1982–3.

14 *Ontological Relativity*, NY, 1969, p. 87.

15 One way or another, we have come a long way from the time when Freud, asked by Jung whether he considered Dadaism a form of insanity, could say with complete self-assurance: 'Nonsense, it is far too mad to be a proper kind of insanity.'

16 *The Myth of Mental Illness*, NY, 1962.

17 *The Divided Self*, London, 1960.

18 See H.v. Ditfurth, *Der Geist fiel nicht vom Himmel*, Hamburg, 1976, pp. 169–71.

19 Gerhard Vollmer, 'Mesocosm and Objective Knowledge', in F.M. Wuketits, ed., *Concepts and Approaches in Evolutionary Epistemology*, Dordrecht, 1982.

20 Donald T. Campbell, 'Pattern Matching as an Essential in Distal Knowing', in K.R. Hammond, ed., *The Psychology of Egon Brunswik*, NY, 1966. Also E.H. Gombrich, *Art and Illusion*, London, 1960, pp. 24 and 62 and the literature cited on p. 24.

21 pp. 209 ff. See also H.v. Ditfurth, *op. cit.*, p. 127.

22 2nd edn, NY, 1973.

23 E. von Holst, *The Behavioural Physiology of Animals and Man*, English trans., London, 1973, vol. 1, chapter 7.

24 Ditfurth, *op. cit.*, pp. 244 and 312.

25 *Ibid.*, p. 162.

26 *Ibid.*, p. 301.

27 Rorty's discussion of this matter has not really gone beyond the sort of arguments advanced in the seventeenth and eighteenth centuries. For examples, see Keith Thomas, *Man and the Natural World*, London, 1983, p. 39. If we are to be reduced to making philosophical decisions dependent upon who is to be admitted to an epistemic community, we ought to start with Darwin's classic *The Expression of the Emotions in Man and Animals*, London, 1872, and then proceed to Konrad Lorenz's paper of 1950, 'Part and Parcel in Animal and Human Societies', in his *Studies in Animal and Human Behaviour*, English trans., London, 1971, vol. 2, and esp. the diagram on p. 155 which shows schematically the differences between lovable and non-lovable features.

28 English trans., London, 1977.

29 Konrad Lorenz, *op. cit.*, pp. 54, 118–19.

30 Ditfurth, *op. cit.*, pp. 34–5, 80, 253, 284.

31 Modern biologists no longer see the acquisition of knowledge as a simple linear process by which organisms propose themselves to the environment and are selected for survival. There is no linear causality but an enlargement of this linear causality into a functional causality. Through the network of the whole system, all effects have feedback and can influence their own causes. Thus, one can see the relationship between organisms and their environment as a feedback process and understand it cybernetically. In principle, nothing can detract from the fact that the cognitive relationship between organisms and their environment is fundamental, even though biologists no longer see this relationship as a simple one-way process in which the organism proposes and the environment selects. These ideas are clearly formulated by R. Riedl, *Order in Living Organisms,* English trans., Chichester, NY, 1978.

Chapter 6 Evolutionary Epistemology

1 *The Logic of Scientific Discovery,* English trans., London, 1959, p. 108.
2 Gerald Holton, *Thematic Origins of Scientific Thought,* Cambridge, Mass., 1973, chapter 9. Even if Einstein had known the Michelson–Morley experiment it would still have been open to him to regard it either as an experiment which measured the optics of ether drift or as an experiment which measured the rigidity of the rods used.
3 Cp. J. Ziman, *Reliable Knowledge,* Cambridge, 1978, p. 35; C.F. von Weizsäcker, *Die Einheit der Natur,* Munich, 1971, p. 125.
4 Thus, for example, S.B. Barnes, *Scientific Knowledge and Sociological Theory,* London, 1974, p.31.
5 S. Toulmin, 'From Form to Function', *Daedalus,* summer 1977, p. 153.
6 Oxford, 1972.
7 Konrad Lorenz, *Behind the Mirror,* English trans., London, 1977, p. 54.
8 'Creative Self-Criticism', *Encounter,* 314, 1979, p. 10.
9 Oxford, 1972, p. 322.
10 Cp. Ernst Gellner, *Spectacles and Predicaments,* Cambridge, 1979, p. 141, and Gerard Radnitzky, 'Analytic Philosophy as the

Confrontation between Popper and Wittgenstein', in J. Agassi and R.S. Cohen, eds, *Scientific Philosophy Today,* Dordrecht, 1981, pp. 252 ff. *Pace* Popper, Tarski provides cold comfort in the search for genuine realism. Cp. the appropriate remarks of G. Radnitzky, 'Progress and Rationality in Research', in M.D. Grmek, R.S. Cohen and G. Cimino, eds, *On Scientific Discovery,* Dordrecht, 1980, p. 64, last para.

11 Cp. for example, J.W.N. Watkins, 'The Unity of Popper's Thought', in P.A. Schilpp, ed., *The Philosophy of Karl Popper,* La Salle, Illinois, 1974, vol. 1 p. 404.

12 Cp. Gerard Radnitzky, 'Theorienpluralismus – Theorienmonismus', in A. Diemer, ed., *Der Methoden- und Theorienpluralismus in den Wissenschaften,* Meisenheim am Glan, 1971, pp. 166–7.

13 *The Roots of Reference,* La Salle, Illinois, 1973, p. 138. Quine's 'slight preference' for observation as a source of knowledge seems more reasonable than Ayer's dogmatic preference in his *Language, Truth and Logic,* London, 1946, p. 48. Ayer's dogmatism is symptomatic and is shared by countless people who consider it no more and no less than the dictate of good sense.

14 *From a Logical Point of View,* 2nd edn., NY, 1963, p. 44.

15 Cp. chapter 1, note 74, above.

16 Heisenberg insisted that a theory need not contain more than the observations. Cp. L.N. Cooper, *An Introduction to the Meaning and Structure of Physics,* NY, 1968, p. 510. Cp. also W. Heisenberg, 'Zur Geschichte der physikalischen Naturerklärung', in *Wandlungen in den Grundlagen der Naturwissenschaften,* 6th edn, Leipzig, 1945, p. 36: 'that is to say, any picture of the atom that our imagination is able to invent is . . . defective.'

17 In such situations, Aristotle's naive good sense that universals are spiritual or immaterial or mental because they transcend physical particulars brings genuine relief. Cp. the beautiful summary of Aristotle by Mortimer J. Adler, *The Difference of Man and the Difference it Makes,* NY, 1967, pp. 220 ff.

18 Donald T. Campbell, 'Evolutionary Epistemology', in P.A. Schilpp, ed., *The Philosophy of Karl Popper,* La Salle, Illinois, 1974.

19 *Against Method,* London, 1975, p. 20.

20 One could find lots of examples. Lyell, for example, framed his 'uniformitarian' methodology because he had a 'presentist' ontology. Descartes had a mathematical ontology and framed his deductivist and axiomatic methodology accordingly. For these

examples, see L. Laudan, *Progress and its Problems,* Berkeley, 1977, pp. 80–1.

21 *Realism and the Progress of Science,* Cambridge, 1981.

22 I must confess that Smith does not refer to black holes but to simpler entities of which he can establish 'predications' more readily. The black holes are supposed to underline the seeming improbability of establishing a realist ontology on our mere ability to make predications.

23 Brighton, 1978.

24 *Ibid.*, p. 36.

25 *Ibid.*, pp. 65, 74.

26 *Ibid.*, p. 65.

27 *Ibid.*, pp. 79, 221.

28 *Ibid.*, p. 98.

29 *Ibid.*, p. 78.

30 *Ibid.*, pp. 64–5.

31 *Knowledge,* Oxford, 1974.

32 *Ibid.*, p. 248.

33 I owe this information to a personal communication by Gerard Radnitzky of 24 June 1983.

34 The 'Anthropic Principle' is by now well known. I am using it here in the sense in which it is used by Gerhard Vollmer, 'Kann es von einmaligen Ereignissen eine Wissenschaft geben?', in F.W. Korff, ed., *Redliches Denken,* Stuttgart, 1981, p. 191. Vollmer refers to B.J. Carr and M.J. Rees, 'The Anthropic Principle and the Structure of the Physical World', *Nature,* 278, 1979, pp. 605–12; and to J.A.Wheeler, 'The Universe as a Home for Man', *American Scientist,* 62, 1974, pp. 683–91.

35 Hypothetical Realism is derived in part from the Anthropic Principle which states that if the universe were significantly different from the way it is, neither the earth nor man would have evolved. All biological systems are, in this sense, carriers of information about the reality of the cosmic order: *cogito, ergo mundus talis est,* to quote the incisive formulation by B. Kanitscheider, *Kosmologie,* Stuttgart, 1984, p. 273. For a slightly different version of the Anthropic Principle see I. Prigogine and I. Stengers, *Dialog mit der Natur,* Munich, 1980, p. 290. Cf. also R. Breuer, *Das anthropische Prinzip,* Munich, 1981; and P.C.W. Davies, *Space and Time in the Modern Universe,* Cambridge, 1977, 7.3, and his *The Runaway Universe,* New York, 1978, Ch. 11.

36 'The Rationality of Scientific Revolutions', in R. Harré, ed., *Problems of Scientific Revolution,* Oxford, 1975.
37 François Jacob, *The Possible and the Actual,* New York, 1982, p. 35.
38 *The Logic of Life,* English trans., NY, 1976, p. 296.
39 *Language, Truth and Logic,* London, 1946, p. 48.
40 One of the pioneering attempts in this matter was Abner Shimony's paper, 'Perception from an Evolutionary Point of View', *Journal of Philosopy,* 68, 1971, pp. 571–83. However, Shimony seems to me to be mistaken in the conclusions he draws from the evolutionary point of view. He argues that the 'evolutionary point of view supports the causal theory of perception' (p. 575) and thus supports Carnap's preference for perception and, by implication, the view that knowledge is induced or caused by the world. With this view, one is close to the idea that knowledge is knowledge if and only if it can be verified. A correct appreciation of evolution leads to the opposite view. Organisms are or make proposals and conjectures. As a result of pattern matching, in Donald Campbell's sense, the environment makes selections from these conjectures and retains those that are a 'fit'. Hence, adaptation of the surviving organisms or conjectures. Shimony thinks that evolution lends support to the priority of observation and to the generalisation of observations by induction. In my view, evolution lends support to Popper's theory that knowledge is the result of problem-solving and that problem-solving progresses by conjectures and refutations; and to Donald Campbell's view that knowledge acquisition comes from chance mutations and selective retentions.
41 Cp. R. Riedl, *Biologie der Erkenntnis,* Hamburg, 1979, p. 43.
42 Konrad Lorenz, 'Die angeborenen Formen möglicher Erfahrung', *Zeitschrift für Tierpsychologie,* 5, 1943.
43 Imperfect adaptation is sufficient for survival. 'The rule probably is that most species most of the time are not fully adapted to their environments, but are just a little better than their competitors for the time being'. P.J. Darlington, 'The Cost of Evolution and the Imprecision of Adaptation', *Proceedings of the National Academy of Science, USA,* 74, 1977, p. 1647.
44 The Central Dogma of molecular biology states that the relationship between DNA and proteins is asymmetrical and that proteins cannot pass messages to DNA.
45 See Peter Munz', 'DNA, Falsification and Dogmatism: Con-

tinuities and Discontinuities in Popper's Evolutionism', in P. Levinson, ed., *New Directions in Evolutionary Epistemology,* forthcoming.

46 J.v. Uexküll, *Umwelt und Innenwelt der Tiere*, Berlin, 1920.

47 See Gerhard Vollmer, *Evolutionäre Erkenntnistheorie,* 3rd edn, Stuttgart, 1981, p. 44.

48 *Behind the Mirror,* English trans., London, 1977, p. 19.

49 In a very real sense, Hegel anticipated some arguments used in Evolutionary Epistemology. His critique of Kant's notion of the 'thing in itself' is very similar to the idea of hypothetical realism that our understanding *must* refer to something real. Cp. Walter Kaufmann, *Hegel,* NY, 1965, pp. 193 and 197; and Stanley Rosen, *G.W.F. Hegel,* New Haven, 1974, p. 62. Hegel's critique of Kant's absolute dichotomy is well known. But it is both helpful and instructive to compare it with Lorenz. 'Can an organ [the human cognitive apparatus] that has evolved in the process of a continuous coping with the laws of nature have remained so uninfluenced that the theory of appearances can be pursued independently of the existence of the thing-in-itself, as if the two were totally independent of each other?' (Konrad Lorenz, 'Kant's Doctrine of the *A Priori* in the Light of Contemporary Biology', English trans., *General Systems Yearbook,* 7, 1962, p. 23.) Hegel did not put it in biological terms, but his description of the process of perception shows that he knew that the 'subject', by scanning, picks out some regularities in the 'object' and computes them into what we call perception of the object so that we can be confident that this kind of interaction results in knowing rather more than an appearance of the object. See *Phenomenology of the Spirit,* A.V. Miller, trans., Oxford, 1977, paras 244–5, and the comments by R. Norman, *Hegel's Phenomenology,* London, 1976, pp. 37–8, and compare it to section 7.2 in Konrad Lorenz, *Behind the Mirror*. Allowing for the differences in terminology, the passages are strikingly similar.

50 *Unended Quest,* London, 1976, p. 85.

51 'Creative Self-Criticism', *Encounter,* 314, 1979, p. 10.

52 'Reflections on my Critics', in I. Lakatos and A. Musgrave, eds, *Criticism and the Growth of Knowledge,* Cambridge, 1970, p. 266.

53 Nor are we in the business, in seeking knowledge, of reading or deciphering the book of nature. 'Explanation' consists, in all cases and without exception, in the subsumption of a particular

event under a statement of regularities. This applies to causes of events as well as to reasons for events. I entirely agree with Donald Davidson, *Essays on Actions and Events,* Oxford, 1980, p. 3.

54 Cp. G. Radnitzky, 'Philosophie und Wissenschaftstheorie zwischen Wittgenstein und Popper', in J. Marek, ed., *Österreichische Philosophen und ihr Einfluss auf die analytische Philosophie der Gegenwart,* Insbruck, 1972, vol. 1, p. 270.

55 See J. Powers, *Philosophy and the New Physics,* London, 1982, p. 191. Powers ought to have added the name of Eccles to those of Medawar and Bondi.

56 'On the Improvement of the Sciences and the Arts and the Possible Identity of the Two', in R.S. Cohen and M. Wartofsky, eds, *Boston Studies in the Philosophy of Science,* 1967, vol. 3, pp. 386 ff.

57 In R.H. Stuewer, ed., *Historical and Philosophical Perspectives of Science,* Minneapolis, 1970.

58 See Mary Hesse, *Revolutions and Reconstructions in the Philosophy of Science,* Brighton, 1980, pp. 29 ff.; and Thomas S. Kuhn, 'History of Science', *International Encyclopaedia of Social Science,* 1968, vol. 14, pp. 76 ff.

59 'History of Science and its Rational Reconstruction', in R.C. Buck and R.S. Cohen, eds, *Boston Studies in the Philosophy of Science,* 1971, vol. 8, quoted hereafter as HSRR.

60 E. Garin, *Science and Civilisation in the Italian Renaissance,* English trans., NY, 1969.

61 F.E. Manuel, *A Portrait of Isaac Newton,* Cambridge, Mass., 1968, pp. 83–4.

62 C.C. Gillispie, 'Intellectual Factors in the Background of Analysis by Probabilities', in A.C. Crombie, ed., *Scientific Change,* London, 1963, p. 449.

63 See Peter Munz, 'The Problems of the Renaissance', *Parergon,* 1975, p. 12.

64 L.S. Feuer, *Einstein and the Generations of Science,* NY, 1974.

65 Brighton, 1980, p. 29.

66 P.M. Heimann, 'The Scientific Revolution', in P. Burke, ed., *The New Cambridge History,* Cambridge, 1979, vol. 13, pp. 260–1.

67 J. Cairns *et al.*, eds, *Phage and the Origins of Molecular Biology,* Cold Spring Harbor, 1966.

68 *The Logic of Scientific Discovery,* English trans., new edn, NY, 1965, p. 31.

69 *Thematic Origins of Scientific Thought,* Cambridge, Mass., 1973, p. 389.
70 J. Bernard Cohen, 'History and the Philosopher of Science', in Frederick Suppe, ed., *The Structure of Scientific Theories,* Urbana, 1977, p. 324.
71 Gerald Holton, *op cit.*, p. 82, and E.A. Burtt, *The Metaphysical Foundations of Modern Science,* London, 1924.
72 HSRR, p. 113.
73 Typescript of William James Lectures, p. 12.
74 Cp. G. Radnitzky, 'Progress and Rationality in Research', in M.D. Grmek, R.S. Cohen and G. Cimino, eds, *On Scientific Discovery,* Dordrecht, 1980, pp. 46–7.
75 Cp., for example, Noretta Koertge, 'Ansätze zu einer neuen Theorie der wissenschaftlichen Forschung', in G. Radnitzky und Gunnar Andersson, eds, *Fortschritt und Rationalität der Wissenschaft,* Tübingen, 1980, pp. 247 ff.
76 Quoted by J. Bernstein, *Einstein,* London, 1973, p. 139.
77 A. Sayre, *Rosalind Franklin and DNA,* NY, 1975.
78 London, 1975.
79 *Human Understanding,* Princeton, 1972, vol. 1, p. 257.
80 New York, 1977.
81 *The Dancing Wu Li Masters,* London, 1979.
82 *Against Method,* London, 1975, p. 242.
83 I. Lakatos, 'Methodology of Scientific Research Programmes', in Imre Lakatos and Alan Musgrave, eds, *Criticism and the Growth of Knowledge,* Cambridge, 1970, p. 119.
84 *The Structure of Scientific Revolutions,* 2nd edn, Chicago, 1970, p. 77.
85 HSRR, pp. 105 ff.
86 See P. Feyerabend, 'Ein Versuch die Vernunft zu retten', in N. Stehr and R. König, eds, *Wissenschaftssoziologie,* Westdeutscher Verlag, Opladen, 1975, p. 490.
87 Cp. Robert Young, 'Man's Place in Nature', in M. Teich and R. Young, eds, *Changing Perspectives in the History of Science,* London, 1973, p. 436; M. Teich, 'From "Enchyme" to "Cyto-Skeleton"', in *ibid.*, p. 441.
88 HSRR, p. 133.
89 *Ibid.*, p. 105.
90 *Ibid.*, p. 109.
91 'The Methodology of Scientific Research Programmes', in I. Lakatos and A. Musgrave, eds, Cambridge, 1970, p. 133.

92 Joseph Agassi, *The Continuing Revolution,* NY, 1968, p. 156.
93 *Ibid.*, p. 228.
94 *Witch-Hunting, Magic and the New Philosophy,* Brighton, 1980.
95 *Ibid.*, p. 65.
96 The topic occurs in all later works by Jung. For Toynbee, see his *Mankind and Mother Earth,* London, 1976, and for Watts, his *Nature, Man and Woman,* London, 1958 – though if Easlea's mottos are anything to go by, he has taken his inspiration from Herbert Marcuse.
97 B. Easlea, *op. cit.*, p. 195.
98 *Unended Quest,* Fontana paperback, London, 1976, no. 37.
99 'Atomism vs. Thermodynamics', in C. Howson, ed., *Method and Appraisal in the Physical Sciences,* Cambridge, 1976.
100 See Kuhn's review, 'The Halt and the Blind', *British Journal for the Philosophy of Science,* 31, 1980.
101 In an unpublished paper, 'On Boltzmann's Alleged "Degenerating Research Programme"'.

Chapter 7 The Evolution of Evolution

1 J.v. Uexküll, *Umwelt und Innenwelt der Tiere,* Berlin, 1920; see Konrad Lorenz, 'Methods of Approach to the Problems of Behaviour', in *Studies in Animal and Human Behaviour,* English trans., London, 1971, vol. 2, pp. 273–7.
2 The term 'uniformitarian' covers a variety of assumptions and methods. See Ernst Mayr, *The Growth of Biological Thought,* Cambridge, Mass., 1982, pp. 376–9. It is used here in only one of its many senses. It means here what Mayr calls 'actualism', i.e. the idea expressed in Lyell's subtitle of the *Principles*: the former changes of the earth's surface can be explained by reference to causes now in operation.
3 Hegel, Marx and Toynbee are usually also classed as historicists. A close scrutiny of their methods would show, however, that they practised uniformitarian methods more frequently than they are given credit for.
4 *The Poverty of Historicism,* London, 1957, p. 60.
5 *The Ethical Animal,* London, 1960, pp. 66 ff.
6 *Is Science Sexist?*, Dordrecht, 1981, chapter 3, pp. 65–84.
7 *Objective Knowledge,* Oxford, 1972, p. 241.
8 See G. Vollmer, 'On Supposed Circularities in an Empirically

Oriented Epistemology', *Proceedings of the XIth International Conference on the Unity of the Sciences, 1982,* NY, 1983, vol. 2, p. 826. See also Ernst Mayr, *The Growth of Biological Thought,* p. 519: 'survival of the fittest is not a tautology'; and I. Prigogine and I. Stengers, *Dialog mit der Natur,* Munich, 1981, p. 184; see also the literature cited in E. Mayr, *op. cit.*

9 See note 45, chapter 6.

10 'Mutation' here is used in the sense of 'emergence of something new'. Biologists differ in their view of the precise nature of biological mutation and ascribe evolutionary change now to events other than mutation. See Ernst Mayr, *The Growth of Biological Thought*, p. 589.

11 See Ernst Mayr, *Evolution and the Diversity of Life,* Cambridge, Mass., 1976, chapter 2, esp. pp. 19–20. Cp. also M.T. Ghiselin, *The Triumph of the Darwinian Method,* Berkeley, 1969, pp. 146–7, and Thomas Dobzhansky, *Genetics and the Origin of Species,* 2nd rev. edn, Cambridge, 1939, p. 366.

12 See Richard Sennett, *The Fall of Public Man,* Cambridge, 1976, p. 308. The term 'pseudo-species' was first used by E.H. Erikson, 'Ritualisation', *Philosophical Transactions of the Royal Society of London,* series B, 251, London, 1966, p. 340.

13 Cp. B. Carter, 'Large Number Coincidence, etc.' in M.S. Longair, ed., *Confrontations of Cosmological Theories,* Dordrecht, 1974, pp. 291–8; C.B. Collins and S.W. Hawking, 'Why is the Universe Isotropic?', *Astrophysics Journal,* 180, 1973, pp. 317–34; R.H. Dicke, 'Dirac's Cosmology and Mach's Principle', *Nature,* 192, 1961, pp. 440–1. If there is to be a habitable planet, gravity, for example, has to vary with time and so do the number of particles in the universe.

14 I am aware of the ingenious hypothesis of Julian Jaynes (*The Origin of Consciousness in the Breakdown of the Bicameral Mind,* Boston, 1977) but consider it untenable because of the chronology involved.

15 *The Transcendence of the Cave,* London, 1967, pp. 125–6.

16 *The Diary of Antoine Roquentin,* L. Alexander, trans., London, 1949, p. 176.

17 Reprinted in *Mysticism and Logic,* London, 1918, pp. 47–8.

18 By all standards, Kant was a conventionalist. Our knowledge, he said, is a convention. But in saying that the convention is *not arbitrary* but absolutely common to all human beings, he stood on

the threshold of Evolutionary Epistemology. He could not take the next step without Darwinism, but *we* can take the next step and thus transform Kant's transcendental idealism into hypothetical realism. Konrad Lorenz, 'Kants Lehre vom apriorischen im Lichte der gegenwärtigen Biologie', *Blätter für deutsche Philosophie,* 15, 1941, pp. 94–125 (translated as 'Kant's Doctrine of the *A Priori* in the Light of Contemporary Biology', *General Systems Yearbook,* 7, 1962, pp. 23–35) proposed that the Kantian knowledge *a priori* may be knowledge which was, thousands or millions of years ago, first acquired *a posteriori* and that it became later genetically fixed by natural selection. See also Konrad Lorenz, *Behind the Mirror,* English trans., London, 1977, p. 9; Gerhard Vollmer, *Evolutionäre Erkenntnistheorie,* 3rd rev. edn, Stuttgart, 1981, pp. 120–1; H. Mohr, *Biologische Erkenntnis,* Stuttgart, 1981, pp. 36–7; H.v. Ditfurth, *Der Geist fiel nicht vom Himmel,* Hamburg, 1979, pp. 221–2; Donald T. Campbell, 'Evolutionary Epistemology', in P.A. Schlipp, ed., *The Philosophy of Karl Popper,* La Salle, Illinois, 1966. As this view is finding wider acceptance now, it is important to stress that the notion of an early phylogenetically *a posteriori* acquisition is misleading. As each species evolved, so did its *a priori* knowledge, i.e. by invention and by the selective retention of that particular *a priori* knowledge which happened to be a fit to the environment. We must not think that any individual learnt from experience. Those individuals which had proposed wrong expectations, i.e. wrong *a priori* knowledge, were eliminated. In this way, the species becomes adapted to its environment. There is no inductive learning involved in this process at any stage and it is therefore, strictly speaking, wrong to call such knowledge 'phylogenetically *a posteriori*'.

19 Hegel anticipated this argument against Kant's absolute dichotomy between the phenomenal world and the thing in itself. See chapter 6, note 49, above.

20 For literature on the 'Anthropic Principle', see chapter 6, note 35, above.

21 It seems inexplicable that Feyerabend, in his solemn declaration 'that the world we want to explore is a largely unknown entity', (*Against Method,* London, 1975, p. 20), should have forgotten about the 'Anthropic Principle'. With the 'Anthropic Principle', Feyerabend's headlong rush into intellectual anarchy becomes pointless.

22 H.v. Ditfurth, *Kinder des Weltalls,* Hamburg, 1970, last para. My translation.

23 *Ecce Homo,* 'Also sprach Zarathustra', I.

24 I owe this interpretation of Nietzsche to a long conversation with Jörg Salaquarda. See also B. Magnus, *Nietzsche's Existential Imperative,* Bloomington, 1978. The myth of eternal recurrence is a counter-myth against Plato's myth of the cave. Plato said: becoming is bad; Nietzsche says: becoming is good. The Nietzschean imperative is supposed to challenge Kant's imperative. Nietzsche says: act in such a way that you can wish to return again and again.

25 *Beyond Good and Evil,* 295.

Name Index

Subject Index